HUMAN ANATOMY

HELEN L. DAWSON, PH.D.
Associate Professor of Anatomy
and Histology, College of Med-
icine, University of Iowa.

APPLETON — CENTURY — CROFTS
Division of Meredith Publishing Company
NEW YORK

PRINTED IN THE UNITED STATES OF AMERICA

M-25755

To My Teacher

DR. ROBERT J. TERRY

whose interest and enthusiasm in the pursuit of
scientific truths, whose personal integrity and firm
adherence to the principles of professional ethics
have been a source of continuing inspiration

PREFACE

This book is written for the beginning student of Human Anatomy, whether he has elected to take the course in order to satisfy his own curiosity about the structure of the human body or whether he finds he must take the course to fulfill a curriculum requirement for certification or degree. I have attempted to present the great mass of anatomical material in a condensed version organized to include the basic, essential points in a clear, concise, and graphic manner. It is my hope that this book will catch the interest and arouse the curiosity of this captive audience, providing a stimulus which will serve to drive the student to read more widely in this and related fields.

Aware of the pressure of time on most students, I have organized the text in such a manner that the essential material is available in a readily comprehensible form. The book starts with a discussion of Man and his place in the Animal Kingdom. Next is discussed the cell and the organization of cells into tissues, tissues into organs, and the grouping of organs to form systems—all of which make up the structure of the living individual. Along with the discussion of the structure of the body will be included brief, general statements of function, since structure and function are inseparable. Knowing how a thing is built without knowing what it is built to do leaves an intolerable void in our understanding of the structure examined.

It is hoped that the student will be encouraged by the use of simple, diagrammatic illustrations placed in close approximation to the pertinent text material to fortify and clarify, by visual means, the understanding gained through the written text.

It should be recognized that the author of a textbook derives his material in great part from the work and contributions of innumerable predecessors and from his contemporaries. Suggestions and criticisms during the preparation of the manuscript by my colleagues in the Department of Anatomy at the University of Iowa have been most helpful.

I also wish to express my thanks to Miss Kathryn Smith and Miss Helen Reich, two friends, who made very real contributions in the composition, proofreading, and typing of the manuscript.

HELEN L. DAWSON

CONTENTS

Contents

INTRODUCTION

Since we are starting the study of Human Anatomy, we should know something about Man, the organism, serving as the object of our investigation. Man is a member of the Animal Kingdom. If we were to look him up in a taxonomist's *Who's Who Among Animals,* we should find him listed as follows:

> *MAN.* Age: precise age unknown, but estimated to be about a million years. Place of origin: unknown. Membership in various fraternal groups: kingdom: Animalia; subphylum; Vertebrata; class: Mammalia; subclass: Eutheria; order: Primates; suborder: Anthropoidea; family: Hominidae; genus: *Homo;* species: *sapiens.*

What was the basis for the election of Man to each of these particular groups? Being an animated organism capable of moving from place to place admits Man to the Animal Kingdom rather than to the Plant or Mineral kingdoms. The fact that he possesses a string of bony vertebrae forming a dorsally placed vertebral column serves to admit him to the Vertebrata subphylum along with a multitude of other animals so diversified in appearance and differing from Man in so many characteristics as to belie any close relationship.

Admission to the Mammalian class requires that the applicant have mammary glands and suckle its young, and also have hair. Man qualifies on both counts. Other members of this class, however, include such creatures as the whale, bat, cow, dog, and many others that, except for mammary glands and hair, have very little in common with one another or with Man. The subclasses of the Mammalia are the Protheria, Metatheria, and Eutheria. The Protheria suckle their young but lay eggs. The Metatheria are the marsupials or pouched mammals. These animals give birth to undeveloped (fetal) young that must finish their development in the pouch of the female. Therefore, Man must be assigned to the remaining subclass, the Eutheria. In this group the young develop in the uterus to which they are attached by a placenta. The members of this group have deciduous (milk) teeth which are replaced by a permanent set.

The Eutheria are subdivided into nine orders: Cetacea, Sirenia, Edentata, Ungalata, Carnivora, Rodentia, Cheiroptera, Insectivora, and Primates. Members of the first two orders are aquatic. The Edentata have vestigial teeth without enamel or no teeth at all. The Ungulata are four-footed, hoofed animals. The Carnivora are meat eaters, four-footed, with claws that can be extended or retracted, and they have long, canine teeth. The Rodentia are characterized by long chisel-shaped incisor teeth, claws, and furry covering. The Cheiroptera are winged, night flying mammals, the bats. The Insectivora are nocturnal insect eaters. The ninth and final order is the Primates. The members of the Primate order have prehensile hands and feet, flat nails on the distal ends of the fingers and toes in place of claws, and relatively large brains with the front part of the forebrain folded on itself and convoluted. Man qualifies as a member of this order.

The Primates is subdivided into three suborders: Lemuroidea, Tarsioidea, and Anthropoidea. Members of the Lemuroidea have laterally directed eyes with separate vision for each eye. In Man the eyes are directed forward, and the visual fields overlap to give stereoscopic vision. The Lemuroidea progress on all fours, or some of them hop on their hind legs. They live in trees, are nocturnal, reproduce by multiple births, and have two pairs of breasts—one pair pectoral in position and the second pair located in the groin. The Tarsioidea are small in size (about as big as a rat), nocturnal, and are found only on the Malay Peninsula and in the East Indies. This leaves only the suborder, Anthropoidea, containing such diverse animals as the New and Old World monkeys, the great apes, and Man.

The Anthropoidea are subdivided into five family groups: the Hapalidae, the Cebidae, the Cercopithecidae, the Simiidae, and the Hominidae. The Hapalidae and Cebidae include the New World monkeys. Members of these two families vary in size, and some of them are quite small. They live in trees, have litters of young, and have tails. Those belonging to the Cebidae have prehensile tails which are so modified and specialized as to serve as a grasping organ. To belong to the family Cercopithecidae, each member must have a tail and ischial tuberosities (calloused, hairless areas on the buttocks). Only the Old World monkeys meet these morphological requirements. Members of the Simiidae family include the great apes: the gibbon, gorilla, orang-utan, and the chimpanzee; they have no tails and no cheek pouches. Their brains are relatively large, their upper extremities are long in comparison to their lower extremities and they progress, when on the ground, in a semi-erect position, using their upper extremities for balancing rather than for weightbearing, and they are completely covered with hair. Even if we tried, we could not assign Man to this group, but we shall have to admit that he more nearly resembles and has more characteristics in common with this group than with any other group we have examined so far.

There is one family group remaining, the Hominidae. It is a ground dwelling group, and its members walk on their hind legs in an upright position. Their heads are covered by hair and there is a variable amount of hair scattered over their bodies. Their brains are large, and the front part is convoluted. The skull is balanced on the upper end of the vertebral column, and the face does not project beyond the cranial portion of the skull. Man's characteristics fit into this group, and he is the sole member of this family.

In attempting to subdivide the family Hominidae into living species groupings, as can be done in other family groups among animals, we are confronted by an interesting, and for some people, disturbing fact. In the crossing between varieties of any species, the hybrid offspring are sterile. This is not true with crossing between varieties of Man. There is no single group of people in the world today that cannot crossbreed with any other "racial" group and produce fertile hybrids or offspring. This is one test of the closeness of relationship among members of the Animal kingdom, and we shall, therefore, be forced to admit to the close relationship among all of the peoples on this planet. There are, without any question, varieties of Man in the world today—the White, the Black, the Red, the Yellow, the Pygmies of Africa, and the tall northern European—but these differences involve for the most part characteristics that may well be explained on the basis of natural selection and environmental factors rather than on the more basic morphological and genetic factors.

In determining Man's place in the Animal kingdom, we have used criteria based on certain specific structural or morphological characteristics, very general at first, but becoming more selective and specific with each succeeding group until finally the species grouping contains only Man and his immediate ancestors. By now the importance of morphology (anatomy) should be obvious. It is one of the broadest and most basic of the sciences, and its application is practically limitless. The botanist is concerned with the anatomy of plants, the chemist struggles to determine the structural formulae (anatomy) of chemical compounds, the geologist studies the structure of rocks, and the zoologist and the professional anatomist are concerned with the structure (anatomy) of animals.

BASIC HUMAN ANATOMY

1

THE CELL AND FUNDAMENTAL TISSUES

It may be rather difficult for the beginning student in the biological sciences to realize that the bodies of all animals are made up of microscopic living units called cells and nonliving extracellular components, ground substance (matrix) and fibers, which form the supportive tissue framework. There are literally hundreds of billions of these cells in the human body, and they are amazingly complex, both morphologically and physiologically (functionally). Many of them are mobile, but we are not aware of their movements.

Cells are composed of a material called *protoplasm* which exhibits the important dynamic properties of *growth, metabolism, irritability, contractility,* and *reproduction.* The chemical composition of protoplasm is complex. Its physical structure places it in a class of substances called *colloids*.

Because of the importance of protoplasm, we should take a look at this material which is made up of the following fundamental substances:

Water
Proteins
Carbohydrates (sugars and
   glycogen)
Lipids (fats and fat-like
   substances)
Enzymes (biological catalysts)
Salts

Electrolytes (substances, e.g.,
   salts, that will conduct an
   electric current when put
   into solution)
Hormones (substances regulating
   body functions, secreted by
   endocrine glands)
Vitamins (organic compounds
   that are essential trace
   nutrients)
Trace Minerals

Water makes up the greater part of protoplasm. It has been estimated that it contributes from 85 to 92 per cent of the weight of the cell. Not all of the water of the cell is in a *free,* readily extractable form. Much of this water is *bound* to other cellular components. The water component of the cell is vitally important since physiologic processes in the cell can take place only in a fluid medium; significant loss of water (dehydration) kills the cell.

Protein is also abundant and is a most important component, since it is essential for building more protoplasm. This indicates the need for adequate protein in the diet, particularly for children, who are growing and whose cells are multiplying rapidly, and sick people,

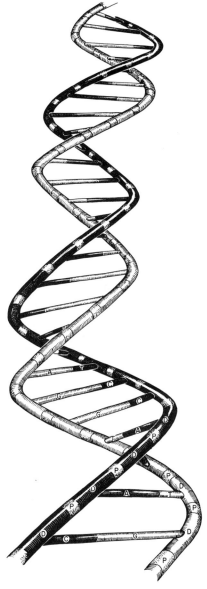

Schematic representation of the double helix of a portion of the DNA molecule. A, adenine; G, guanine; C, cytosine; T, thymine; D, deoxyribose; P, phosphate. (From Elliott and Ray. *Biology,* 2nd ed., Appleton-Century-Crofts. Based on a model by Crick.)

1

Round

Squamous

Cuboidal

Columnar

Fusiform

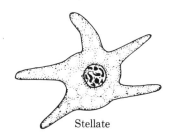

Pyramidal

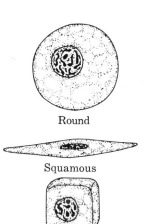

Stellate

Fig. 1.   Drawing of cells to show their varied shapes.

whose damaged and wornout cells must be replaced. Protein can also substitute for carbohydrates and fats as an energy source.

Carbohydrates and fats are the energy fuels of the cells.

The enzymes are vitally important in the metabolism of cells since they serve as catalysts in metabolic reactions. They induce and speed up chemical reactions in other substances without actually entering into the chemical reactions themselves. All of the enzymes are protein, and most contain a vitamin as a prosthetic group. Each cell contains numerous enzymes; each enzyme is specific and will act on only one substance or class of substance to effect a reaction. However, the enzymes are eventually used up and have to be replaced. They must be synthesized (created) by the cells themselves; their vitamin components may be synthesized or they may be obtained from foods taken into the body and distributed to the cells.

Salts are defined as that group of compounds formed from the reactions between acids and bases. Within the cell, the inorganic and mineral components are usually in the form of salts, and some of them are essential if the cells are to function properly. The inorganic compounds in the cell usually serve to maintain the acid-base equilibrium of the cell and to regulate osmotic pressure.

Electrolytes are compounds which, when dissolved in water, are disassociated and can conduct a current of electricity.

The hormones are substances secreted by the cells of endocrine glands. These secretions enter the blood stream and are transported throughout the body. They affect specific cells of certain organs of the body, often at some distance from the gland that produced the hormones.

The vitamins are essential to the metabolism of cells. Often, they form prosthetic groups which, together with certain proteins, make up enzymes.

Trace minerals are essential inorganic substances found in extremely small quantities in the cell.

The following are physiological properties of protoplasm which every student of the biological sciences should know:

Respiration	Irritability
Contractility	Conductivity
Absorption and Assimilation	Secretion and Excretion
Reproduction and Growth	

THE CELL

DEFINITION.   A cell may be defined as the smallest bit of living matter (protoplasm) that can live independently and reproduce its own kind; a cell can also be defined as the structural and functional unit of the body.

ORIGIN.   Cells are derived from the primary germ layers of the developing fertilized ovum (egg). There are three primary germ layers—*ectoderm, endoderm,* and *mesoderm,* and they give rise to all of the cells of the entire body.

COMPOSITION.   All cells are composed of protoplasm.

NUMBER.   It has been estimated that there are roughly 25 quadrillion cells in the adult body.

SIZE.   The cells of the body vary markedly in size from the smallest cells with a diameter of 4 micra (a micron is one thousandth

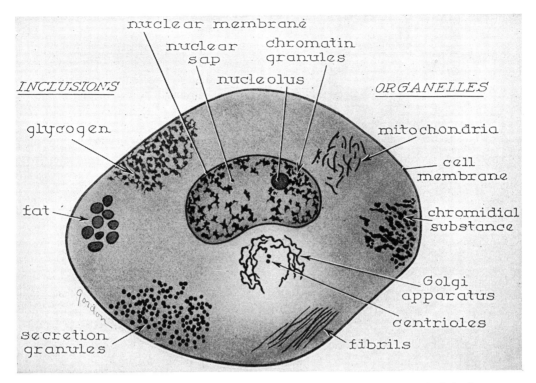

Fig. 2. Diagrammatic drawing of a composite cell designed to show in one cell all the important components of nucleus and cytoplasm that can be demonstrated by different staining technics and seen by light microscopy. Cytoplasmic inclusions are shown on the left and cytoplasmic organelles on the right. (From Ham and Leeson. *Histology*, 4th ed., J. B. Lippincott Co.)

of a millimeter) to the largest cell (the ovum) measuring about 120 micra.

SHAPE. The shapes of cells are also variable. Free cells tend to be round or oval. In tissues, and particularly in organs, the shapes of cells are influenced by the pressure of adjacent cells. From observations made on dead, fixed tissues, cells are described as round, oval, squamous, cuboidal, columnar, fusiform, pyramidal, and stellate (Fig. 1).

STRUCTURE. A cell consists of two parts—the *nucleus* and the *cytoplasm*. The mass of protoplasm forming the cell is differentiated into a more or less centrally located *nucleus* enclosed in a nuclear membrane, and the surrounding protoplasm, called the *cytoplasm,* which is enclosed by the cell membrane (Fig. 2).

THE NUCLEUS. The shape of the nucleus varies somewhat but, in general, tends to match that of the cell. In round or cuboidal cells the nucleus is usually spherical (round); in columnar cells the nucleus is oval, and the taller columnar cells have more elongated oval nuclei than the shorter columnar cells. In certain types of cells (white blood cells), the nucleus may be oval, horseshoe shaped, or in the form of lobes connected by thin strands of chromatin material.

While most cells of the body contain only one nucleus, there are certain kinds of cells that have two (binucleated cells) or more nuclei (multinucleated cells).

Components. The nucleus has several components—the nuclear membrane, nuclear sap, chromatin material, linin fibers, and nucleoli.

1. The nuclear membrane—a relatively thin, but tough, structure which encloses the nuclear protoplasm (nucleoplasm).

2. Nuclear sap—a homogeneous, viscid protoplasmic substance which fills the nucleus and forms the matrix or ground substance.

3. Chromatin material—masses of deeply staining basophilic material concerned with cell division or mitosis.

4. Linin fibers—a network of delicate, pale-staining fibers within the nuclear sap. The chromatin material is arranged along the linin fibers.

5. Nucleoli—most nuclei contain one or more nucleoli. These are sharply demarcated structures which usually occupy an eccentric position in the nucleus. There are two kinds of nucleoli: (a) *true nucleoli,* called *plasmosomes,* which are associated with secretory activity of the cell, and (b) *false nucleoli,* called *karyosomes,* which are related to mitosis or cell division.

Function. The nucleus is responsible for (1) the transmission of hereditary characteristics from generation to generation, and (2) the increase in or the maintenance of the cell population of the organism through cell division.

THE CYTOPLASM. Surrounding the nucleus is the cytoplasm, a most important part of any functional cell. It appears as a homogeneous, clear, viscid, structureless, ground substance. Embedded within the cytoplasm is a variety of "formed bodies" that are classed either as *organelles* or as *inclusions.*

Organelles. These are living, protoplasmic structures that have a definite form and participate in the functional activities of the cell. Included as organoids are: the cell center, Golgi body, mitochondria, chromophilic substance, and fibrils.

1. The cell center—a cytoplasmic organoid consisting of a small spherical granule called the *centriole,* surrounded by a clear, dense zone of protoplasm called the *centrosome.* It is considered to be the dynamic center for mitotic cell division.

2. Golgi body (Golgi net or apparatus)—appears as a fibrillar network located in the vicinity of the nucleus. It is thought to be related to the secretory activity of the cell.

3. Mitochondria—appear as fine rod-like or granular structures within the cytoplasm. These structures are associated with the metabolic activities of the cells.

4. Chromophilic substance—blue-staining granules of RNA (ribonucleic acid) of the cytoplasm, involved in protein synthesis of the cell.

5. Fibrils—threadlike structures within the cytoplasm of certain types of cells, for example, the neurofibrils found in nerve cells or the myofibrils found in muscle cells.

Inclusions. These are non-protoplasmic, non-living, usually only temporary structures found in cells. The more common inclusions are: stored food, pigments, and secretion granules.

Function of cytoplasm. The cytoplasm carries out most of the work the cell is called upon to perform.

DIFFERENTIATION OF CELLS. From a single, fertilized, human ovum, through a tremendous and prolonged proliferation of cells, the complex, multicellular human organism is produced.

In the beginning, the cells formed by repeated divisions of the germ cell appear to be all alike. However, as the cell mass continues

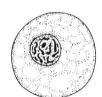

Round

Squamous

Cuboidal

Columnar

to enlarge, with some cells on the surface of the embryo and some buried deeply within the cell mass, it seems only natural that there should develop the need for a division of labor among the cell population. This means that groups of cells would have to become specialized in order to carry out a particular function, to better serve the whole organism (cell population). This phenomenon is called differentiation and, at least in the beginning, was dependent to a large extent on the environmental factors that affected certain groups of cells and determined the direction their specialization would take.

Differentiation affects both the *morphology* of the cell and its *physiological capabilities*. These changes are so marked that a trained histologist can recognize specific types of cells by their microscopic appearance and predict in a very general way what their function might be.

Once cells become fully differentiated, when they undergo cell division, they continue to reproduce only their own specialized kind of cell. Even in the adult body, scattered among the fully differentiated cells, there remain some undifferentiated cells that are multipotential and are capable of differentiating into one of several cell types if the need should arise. Differentiation and specialization lead to loss of potentiality and adaptability in cells, thus limiting what cells are able to do.

CELL DIVISION. Increase in number of cells (proliferation) occurs by means of cell division. This is a process by which a single cell divides into two roughly equal halves, each half containing an equal amount of the cytoplasm and the nuclear material of the parent cell. Each of these "daughter" cells, after a period of growth, repeats the process. Through a continuation of this process of cell division, growth and an increase in the cell mass takes place. Through differentiation of the cells, the various kinds of body tissues are formed and are organized into the organs and systems of the body.

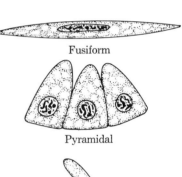

Fusiform

Pyramidal

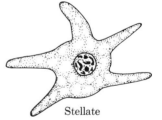

Stellate

Even after the adult form is reached and growth has stopped, cell division still takes place on a limited scale to replace wornout or damaged cells of the body.

There are two types of cell division:

1. Direct cell division or amitosis.
2. Indirect cell division, including mitosis and meiosis.

In *amitosis* or direct cell division, the cell that is to divide elongates a bit and a constriction of the cell occurs which splits the nucleus and the cytoplasm of the cell in half, forming two new cells. This process, called binary fission, is the method by which simple organisms, such as the ameba, multiply. Each of the new daughter cells contains one half of both the nuclear material and the cytoplasm of the parent cell.

In *mitosis* the process is more complicated. The nuclear chromatin material undergoes a series of changes which results in the formation of two daughter cells, each containing the same number of chromosomes as the parent cell. In *meiosis,* or reduction division, such as occurs during the maturation of the ovum or the spermatozoon, the newly formed cells each contain one-half (haploid number) the chromosomes characteristic of the species. The other half of the chromosomes is introduced at the time of fertilization. More detailed descriptions of mitosis and miosis are available in medical textbooks of histology.

FUNDAMENTAL TISSUES

DEFINITION. A tissue may be defined as a group of *like cells* and their *extracellular products* that form a definite structure capable of carrying out a particular function.

KINDS. In the entire body there are only four basic (fundamental) tissues, from which are derived all of the organs and structures that make up a human body.

Epithelial tissues   Connective tissues
Muscle tissues   Nerve tissues

EPITHELIAL TISSUES. *Components.* An epithelium consists only of *cells* and a *cement substance* to hold them together.

Derivation. The epithelial cells are derived from ectoderm and endoderm of the embryo; epithelioid cells look like but are not identical to epithelial cells and are derived from mesoderm.

Location. An epithelium is found covering the surface of the body and lining the ducts or structures that connect either directly or indirectly with the surface.

Function. Epithelial cells provide protection, as in epidermis of skin; effect absorption, as in the epithelium lining the digestive tract; and secrete substances important to body function, as in the glandular epithelium.

Kinds. There are a number of kinds of epithelium. An architect designing a frame building uses several kinds of wood, cut into massive beams or thin strips depending on where it is to be used and how strong it must be. Similarly, epithelial tissues vary in the size and shape of the cells and the thickness of the layers, depending on their location and function.

Classification. Classification of an epithelium will depend on two criteria—the *shape* and the *arrangement of cells.*

1. The shape of the cells may be squamous, cuboidal, or columnar.

2. If the cells are arranged so as to form a thin sheet only one cell thick, it is called a simple epithelium (Fig. 3A). If the cells are arranged in layers two or more cells thick, it is called a stratified epithelium (Fig. 3B). In identifying the shape of the cells forming a stratified epithelium, the surface cells are used, since they are least affected by the pressure exerted by adjacent cells.

There is one exception to this general classification that should be mentioned, namely, *pseudostratified columnar epithelium* (false stratified columnar) (Fig. 3C). It is really a simple epithelium that at first glance looks like a stratified epithelium.

General Characteristics of Epithelial Tissues. 1. These tissues are avascular. Since not even the capillaries enter an epithelial layer of cells, nutrient materials and oxygen for these cells must reach them by diffusion from nearby capillaries, or from tissue fluid of the connective tissue to which they are attached.

2. Epithelium can regenerate. If an epithelial layer of cells is injured, it can be repaired by neighboring epithelial cells dividing to form new cells which move into the damaged area.

3. Epithelial cells must be kept moist or they will die. The epithelial cells lining the mouth or the stomach are kept moist by the secretions of glandular epithelial cells, e.g., the mucus-secreting

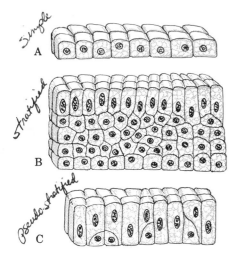

Fig. 3. Drawings of epithelial membranes to illustrate classification based on arrangement of cells.

cells of the stomach. On a comparatively dry surface, such as the skin, the outer cells become *keratinized,* i.e., they form a relatively insoluble albuminoid material which protects the underlying cells, preventing their dehydration and death.

CONNECTIVE TISSUES. *Derivation.* The cells of this type of tissue are derived from mesoderm.

Components. A connective tissue consists of *cells* and *fibers,* embedded in a *matrix* or *ground substance.* The cells produce both the fibers and the matrix. Three kinds of fibers are produced—collagenous, elastic, and reticular. The matrix varies in consistency and chemical composition in the various classes of connective tissue.

Distribution. Connective tissues are found in all parts of the body.

Function. Connective tissue forms the supporting framework of all the organs, gives shape and support (skeletal system) to the body, and one kind of connective tissue, blood, plays an important part in the transport of oxygen and nutrient materials to the cells, and the removal of soluble waste products of cellular metabolism.

Classification. After birth, the mature connective tissues are classified according to *kinds of fibers predominating* (collagenous, elastic, or reticular fibers); *arrangement of fibers* (in parallel, interwoven, or forming branching networks); and *character of the matrix* (fluid as in fibrous connective tissue and blood, semisolid as in cartilage, or solid as in bone).

On the basis of the above criteria, we can separate connective tissues into the following classes.

Fibrous Connective Tissues. These are tissues in which the fibers predominate—chiefly tendons, ligaments, and areolar and reticular tissues.

Tendons (Fig. 4A) consist primarily of dense, collagenous fiber bundles arranged in parallel. The matrix is fluid and the cell type is the fibrocyte. Tendons have great tensile strength and do not stretch. They serve to attach muscle to bone, cartilage, or other muscle.

Ligaments (Fig. 4B) are predominantly elastic fibers arranged in parallel. As in tendons, the matrix is fluid and the cell type is the fibrocyte. Ligaments allow for a certain amount of stretch, and will return to their original length when they are released. They are associated with the formation of joint capsules.

Areolar tissue is mixed, collagenous fiber bundles with some elastic fibers, interwoven in all directions. The matrix is fluid, and the cell type is the fibrocyte. If the fibers are closely woven, it is called dense areolar tissue, as in the dermis of the skin (Fig. 4C). If the fibers are very loosely interwoven, it is called loose areolar tissue. In loose areolar tissue there are a number of cells present besides the fibrocytes, such as multipotential stem cells, macrophages, mast cells, plasma cells, white blood cells, and fat cells. The potential spaces between the fibers and fiber bundles may become filled in by fat cells. When great numbers of fat cells crowd in, it becomes known as adipose tissue (Fig. 4D).

Reticular tissue occurs as a meshwork formed by the interwoven, fine, branching, reticular fibers. It forms the supporting framework of all lymphoid organs, such as lymph nodes and tonsils. The parenchymal cells (in this case the lymphocytes) are caught in and supported by the reticular tissue framework.

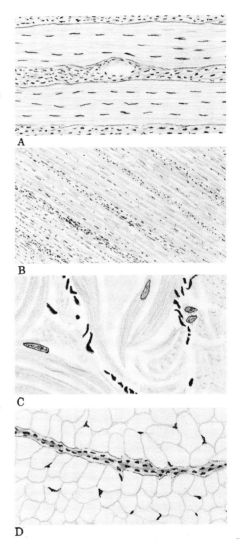

A

B

C

D

Fig. 4. Drawings of collagenous and elastic fibrous connective tissues.

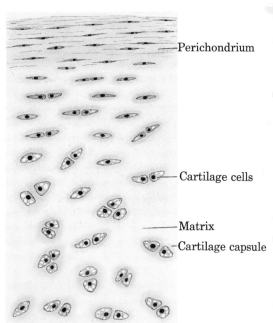

Fig. 5.   Drawing of a section of hyaline cartilage. From adult costal cartilage.

Perichondrium

Cartilage cells

Matrix

Cartilage capsule

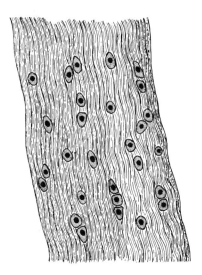

Fig. 6.   Drawing of a section of fibrous cartilage. From an intervertebral disc of a child.

Cartilage.   Three criteria characterize cartilage—the semisolid consistency of the matrix, its avascularity, and the presence of lacunae. The cells of cartilage, the chondrocytes, lie in small spaces called lacunae, within the semisolid matrix. Since cartilage is avascular, all nutrient materials must reach the cells by diffusion through the matrix.

There are three kinds of cartilage, classified according to the fibers present in the matrix: hyaline, fibrous, and elastic.

Hyaline cartilage (Fig. 5)—characterized by a semisolid matrix that appears relatively homogeneous, and obscures the fibers embedded in it. The cells are called chondrocytes, and one, two, or four cells may lie in one lacuna. This cartilage is commonly known as "gristle."

Fibrous cartilage (Fig. 6)—characterized by bundles of collagenous fibers arranged in parallel, with chondrocytes in lacunae between the fiber bundles. This tissue forms the intervertebral discs of the spinal column.

Elastic cartilage (Fig. 7)—characterized by elastic fibers interwoven throughout the semisolid matrix, around and between the lacunae containing the chondrocytes. This cartilage forms the framework of the external ear. Its shape can be distorted by pulling or twisting, but because of the elasticity of the cartilage, it will resume its original shape when released.

Bone (Fig. 8).   In this tissue the matrix is solid and the bone cells (osteocytes) lie in small lacunae within the matrix. Bone is a vascular tissue and the blood vessels are contained in canals of varying sizes that extend throughout the bone and transport nutrients to the osteocytes in the lacunae. This strong, supportive tissue forms the bones of the skeletal system.

Blood.   Blood is classed as a connective tissue because it contains cells and a fluid matrix and, on clotting, fibers are formed in the fluid matrix converting it into a more or less solid mass (clot).

MUSCLE TISSUE.   *Derivation.*   Muscle is derived from mesoderm.

Components.   Muscle tissue consists of cells that are so modified in form that they actually resemble fibers rather than cells. These cells are "harnessed" by means of connective tissue to form a functionally effective tissue.

Kinds.   There are three kinds of muscle.

1. Striated muscle (Fig. 9), which represents the bulk of the musculature of the body. It forms the "muscles" that are controlled voluntarily and by their contraction make movement possible.

2. Smooth muscle (Fig. 10), which forms the muscular walls of all visceral organs and the erector pili muscle of the hair follicle. Smooth muscle is involuntary muscle, and we cannot consciously control its function.

3. Cardiac muscle (Fig. 11) which forms the muscular wall of the heart (myocardium). Although its cells are striated, it is an involuntary muscle.

Function.   *Contraction* is the only function of muscle. It results in a shortening of the fiber along the long axis. The lengthening of a muscle fiber is a passive action, due either to the inhibition of the original impulse causing contraction, or to its being stretched by an opposing group of muscles that are contracting.

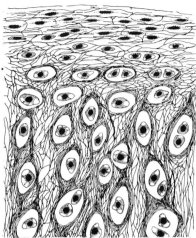

Fig. 7. Drawing of a section of elastic cartilage stained with an elastic tissue stain. Elastic fibers appear as fine black lines. From the cartilaginous plate of the ear.

Lacunae   Volkmann's canal

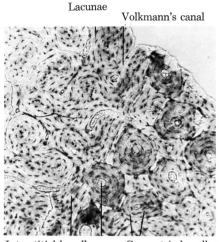

Interstitial lamella   Concentric lamellae
Haversian canal

Fig. 8. Cross section of compact bone (not decalcified). Photomicrograph.

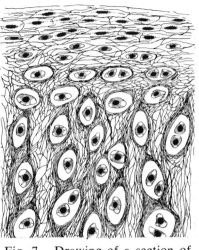

Fig. 9. Longitudinal and cross sections of striated muscle.

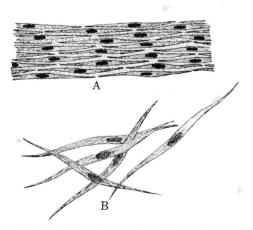

A

B

Fig. 10. Smooth muscle and teased smooth muscle fibers.

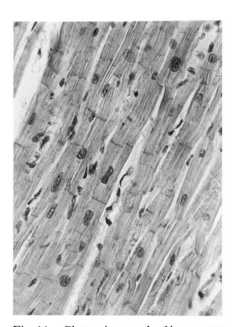

Fig. 11. Photomicrograph of human cardiac muscle. Longitudinal section.

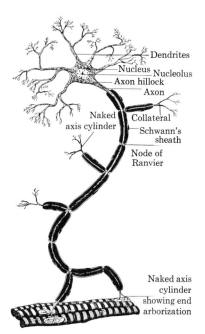

Dendrites
Nucleus
Nucleolus
Axon hillock
Axon
Naked
axis cylinder
Collateral
Schwann's
sheath
Node of
Ranvier
Naked axis
cylinder
showing end
arborization

Fig. 12A. Diagram of a neuron.

NERVE TISSUE (SEE CHAPTER 8, PAGE 152). *Derivation.* Nerve tissue is derived from ectoderm.

Components. The nerve cells or neurons (Fig. 12A) and a special form of supportive tissue called neuroglia make up nerve tissue (Fig. 12B).

Distribution. Nerve tissue is found throughout the body, but it is concentrated along the dorsal midline portion of the body and in the skull where it forms the spinal cord and brain, referred to as the central nervous system (CNS).

Function. Neurons conduct impulses; neuroglia are supportive.

It is from the four fundamental tissues—epithelial, connective, muscle, and nerve—that the body and all of its organs are constructed. Now that we know what the structural material consists of, it is time to examine the finished structure and begin the study of Gross Anatomy.

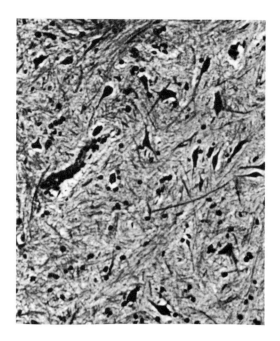

Fig. 12B. Photomicrograph of nerve tissue. (Photo taken by Dr. Noel Owers.)

2

ANATOMICAL TERMINOLOGY

The beginning student of anatomy must acquire a new and concise vocabulary of terms. He must know the exact meaning of words and be able to define terms precisely. In the scientific field, particularly, it is most important to use words correctly in order to meaningfully express knowledge and ideas in communicating with others.

What does the word "anatomy" mean, and what does the study of anatomy include? From a good medical dictionary, one learns that "anatomy" is derived from two Greek words: *ana,* meaning up, and *tome,* a cutting. Therefore, anatomy is a cutting up or dissection, and refers to the knowledge of the structure (morphology) of an animal or plant gained through dissecting it. We can define anatomy, then, in its broadest sense as: the study of the structure (morphology or architecture) of an organism (plant or animal).

Anatomy is subdivided into a number of more specific and limited areas. For instance, Human Anatomy restricts the study to the structure of the human organism. Gross Anatomy refers to the study of the gross (large) structures of an organism that can be seen with the eye, unaided by magnifying devices. Originally, anatomy was limited to the study of the gross structures, but man's curiosity was not satisfied with this. The microscope was developed, and with it was born Microscopic Anatomy (Histology), which deals with the minute structure of the body—the cells, tissues, and their organization into organs.

Another broad division of anatomy is Developmental Anatomy, or Embryology, as it is often called. This subject is concerned with the structure of a developing organism from the time of the fertilization of the egg to the birth of the offspring. In the field of gross anatomy a subdivision, Neuroanatomy, has become separated and represents a large, complicated mass of information that deals with the structure (morphology) of the nervous system.

The study of gross human anatomy with which this text is primarily concerned, deals with the structure of the human body and may be approached in one of two ways: by the study of *systems* of the body or by *regions* of the body. The regional method is the approach most often used in conjunction with dissection of the body. The body is divided into gross areas or regions such as the upper extremity, lower extremity, head and neck, thorax, abdomen, back, and perineum. Each region is dissected and associated structures such as muscles, arteries, nerves, and organs are studied, with particular attention given to their relationships.

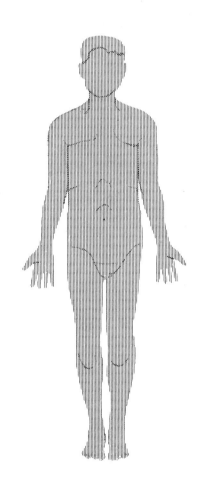

Fig. 13. Drawing of the body in the anatomical position.

11

The systemic method involves the study of all the organs belonging to a functional system, and includes the following:

1. Skeletal system
2. Joints and ligaments
3. Muscular system
4. Respiratory system
5. Digestive system
6. Reproductive system: male and female
7. Urinary system
8. Nervous system
9. Circulatory system
10. Endocrine system
11. Integumentary system (skin and appendages)
12. Organs of special sense

Since without the benefit of dissection, the systemic method better maintains a continuity of structure, it will be used in presenting the material in this text.

For descriptive purposes and to avoid confusion, it is necessary to have as a reference point a standard body position that remains constant regardless of the position in which a body is placed for examination or dissection. The anatomical position is such a constant and must be kept in mind by the student at all times. The *anatomical position* is the position in which the body is standing erect, facing the observer, with the feet together and parallel, the arms at the sides with the palms directed forward (Fig. 13, p. 11).

Anatomical Terms in Common Usage

Planes: The body or various organs are frequently cut and these cuts originally are made in reference to specific planes (Fig. 14A and B).

1. Median plane—a vertical plane that would divide the body into right and left halves.

2. Sagittal plane—a vertical plane, parallel to the median plane, that would cut the body into longitudinal slices of any thickness, but it must parallel the median plane.

3. Frontal or coronal plane—a vertical plane, at right angles to the median plane. It cuts the body into anterior (front) and posterior (back) portions. These are not referred to as halves.

4. Transverse plane—a horizontal plane, at right angles to both the median and frontal planes, that would cut the body into superior (upper) and inferior (lower) portions.

Terms of Position

1. Anterior—front or belly side. Ventral is a comparable term applied to pronograde animals (animals that go on four legs).

2. Posterior—back side. Dorsal is a comparable term applied to pronograde animals.

3. Superior—nearer the head end.
4. Inferior—farther from the head end.
5. Superficial—nearer the surface.
6. Deep—farther from the surface.
7. Medial—nearer the midline of the body.

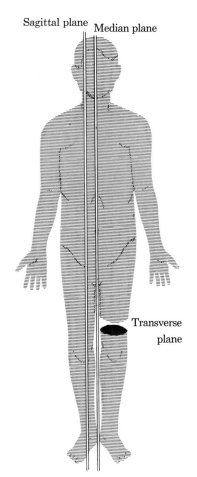

Fig. 14A.   A body cut to illustrate the sagittal, median, and transverse planes.

Sagittal plane Median plane

Transverse plane

8. Lateral—farther from the midline of the body.

9. Proximal—used in reference to the extremities and meaning nearer the attached end (to the body).

10. Distal—opposite of the above term and meaning farther from the attached end.

The last eight terms are relative terms. To illustrate, think of the terms superior and inferior in connection with the three segments of the lower extremity—the thigh, the leg, and the ankle. The thigh is superior to the leg, and the leg is inferior to the thigh, but superior to the ankle.

Similar relationships hold in regard to the terms superficial and deep. In the thigh, the skin is superficial to all other structures of the area, but if we dissect off the skin, then what was deep to the skin becomes superficial with the skin removed, and so on.

Terms of Movement

1. Flexion—to bend or decrease the angle between two parts, as the action taking place at an articulation or joint.

2. Extension—to straighten or increase the angle between two parts of the body.

3. Abduction—to move laterally, away from the midline of the body.

4. Adduction—to move medially, toward the midline of the body.

5. Circumduction—the free swinging circular motion of an extended extremity.

6. Rotation—a term applied to movement of a body around its long axis, as in rotation of an extremity. To illustrate, imagine a long rod (axis) extending through the upper extremity, from the head of the humerus straight down through the middle finger. If the extremity is turned on this axis, it is rotated. If the rotation turns the thumb toward the body, it is *medial rotation;* if the extremity is turned in the opposite direction so that the thumb is turned away from the body, it is called *lateral rotation.*

7. Supination—a term restricted to the upper extremities. With the arms flexed, in supination the palms of the hands are turned upwards. The opposite of this term is pronation.

8. Pronation—with the arms flexed, the palms of the hands are turned downward in pronation.

9. Inversion—a term restricted to the lower extremities. The foot is turned so that the sole is directed toward and parallel with the median plane. Its opposite is eversion.

10. Eversion—the movement where the foot is turned so that the sole is directed laterally.

Regions of the Body and Their Subdivisions

Head, divided into cranium and face
Neck
Trunk, divided into thorax, abdomen, and pelvis
Upper Extremity, divided into arm, forearm, wrist, and hand
Lower Extremity, divided into thigh, leg, ankle, and foot

Coronal plane

Fig. 14B.   A body cut to illustrate the coronal plane.

Surface Areas of the Abdomen (Fig. 15)

Right and left hypochondriac	roughly the upper ⅓
Epigastric	of the abdomen
Right and left lumbar	roughly the middle ⅓
Umbilical	of the abdomen
Right and left iliac	roughly the lower ⅓
Hypogastric	of the abdomen

Students should learn these terms and begin using them as soon as possible. These terms make up an important part of the new anatomical vocabulary.

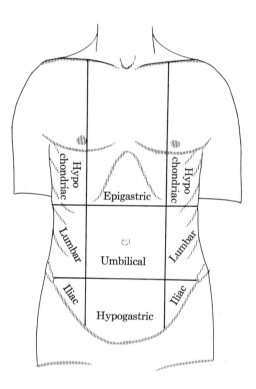

Fig. 15.   Surface areas of the abdomen.

3

OSTEOLOGY

This chapter will be devoted to osteology, the study of bones. We shall consider bone as connective tissue, and bones as organs and as part of the skeletal system.

BONE AS A TYPE OF CONNECTIVE TISSUE

DEFINITION. Bone (osseous tissue) is a hard, rigid type of connective tissue that serves as the principal supportive tissue of the body.

DERIVATION. Like all other types of connective tissue, bone is derived from mesoderm.

COMPONENTS OF BONE. Bone is made up of *cells, fibers,* and a relatively abundant, solid *matrix.*

CELLS. There are three types of bone cells: osteoblasts, osteocytes, and osteoclasts.

Osteoblasts (Fig. 16) are derived from connective tissue cells (mesenchymal cells). Under appropriate stimulation (either during growth or after injury), the primitive connective tissue cells increase in size and become somewhat cuboidal in shape. These cells arrange themselves in a single layer along the surface of the matrix and begin to form the precursor of bone called *osteoid* or preosteal tissue, which is later converted to real bone through the process of ossification.

Osteocytes (Fig. 16) are osteoblasts that have surrounded themselves with osteoid. These cells lie in small spaces (lacunae) within the osteoid, and later between the layers (lamellae) of bone.

Osteoclasts (Fig. 16) are large, multinucleated cells found along margins of bone where resorption of the bone is occurring. They are considered to be bone-destroying cells.

FIBERS. Collagenous fibers are present in the matrix, but cannot be seen because of the denseness of the matrix.

MATRIX. The matrix of bone is the obviously dominant component. It appears as a dense, more or less homogeneous material.

FORMATION OF BONE. The formation of bone always occurs in relation to either embryonic or adult type of connective tissue. Some bones form within the membranous tissue at the site of their ultimate location, and because of this are known as *membrane bones,* e.g., the flat bones of the cranium and the bones of the face. The process by which these bones are formed is known as *intramembranous bone formation.*

The second type of bone formation is called *endochondral bone formation.* In this type the original membranous matrix is converted to

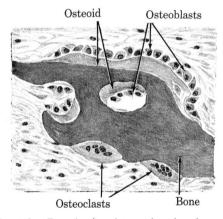

Fig. 16. Developing bone showing bone cells, osteoid, and bone.

15

cartilage and the cartilaginous "skeleton" is then gradually removed and replaced by bone. The coordination and timing of this replacement is so delicately balanced that normally there is no weakening of the supportive function of the skeletal framework during the process.

Regardless of whether bone is formed directly from membrane or indirectly through replacement of cartilage, the end product, bone, is the same histologically.

(Note: For more details concerning the precise methods of bone formation, the student should consult a textbook of Histology.)

PHYSICAL CHARACTERISTICS. Bone contains both *organic* and *inorganic* (mineral) constituents. The most abundant of the inorganic components are calcium phosphate and calcium carbonate. Calcium fluoride and magnesium chloride are present in small quantities.

The organic elements give bone flexibility and elasticity, and account for about one third of the weight of a mature bone.

The inorganic constituents give the bone hardness and rigidity and account for the remaining two thirds of the weight of the bone.

The organic and inorganic constituents of bone are bound in an intimate chemical relationship during the process of ossification. The distribution and qualities of the organic and inorganic components of bone can be demonstrated by the following simple experiment. If one of the long bones is placed in a relatively weak acid solution for a sufficient length of time, the inorganic salts will be dissolved out leaving only the organic constituents. When this process, called *decalcification,* is complete, the bone retains its original shape, size, and characteristic markings, but is no longer hard and rigid; it can be bent and twisted. On the other hand, if a bone is subjected to intense heat for a period of time, the general form and size of the bone remains as before, but it appears chalky and crumbles when handled. The bones of young children have a greater proportion of organic matter and are, therefore, less brittle and resist breaking better than the bones of an older person. In case of a fracture, the long bone of a child usually breaks as a green stick would break, without a cleancut severance of the broken ends of the bone. This type of break is actually referred to as a "green-stick" fracture. The bones of old people, on the other hand, have less organic and more inorganic matter and, therefore, become brittle and more subject to fracture. In these old people a bone breaks as an old dried stick would, clear through, leaving jagged, sharp edges that are often splintered.

BONES AS ORGANS

All osseous tissue (bone) is organized to form specific organs, the bones. These are classified by shape into four groups.

CLASSIFICATION OF BONES.

LONG BONES. As the name implies, these bones are long in relation to their width. Each long bone has a shaft and two extremities, e.g., the tibia. Small, long bones would include the metacarpals (bones of the palm of the hand), and the metatarsals (comparable bones of the foot), and the phalanges (bones of the fingers and toes). These long bones serve as levers that, when pulled by contracting muscles, make movement of the body possible.

SHORT BONES. These are blocky, often somewhat cube-shaped bones that are found in areas where compactness and only limited

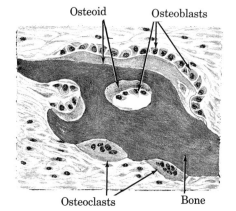

Osteoid   Osteoblasts

Osteoclasts   Bone

Developing bone.

motion are required, e.g., bones of the wrist (carpus) and ankle (tarsus).

FLAT BONES.   Generally, flat bones consist of two more or less parallel, plate-like layers of hard, compact bone separated by a thin layer of cancellous (spongy) bone. Bones of the skull and the scapula (shoulder blade) belong in this group. Their shapes afford large areas for muscle attachment; the bones of the skull also form a protective encasement for the brain.

IRREGULAR BONES.   This group includes the bones that cannot be placed in the first three classes because of peculiarities in their shape. Because the shape of these bones is often complex, they must be described individually. Examples of irregular bones are: the vertebrae, bones of the face, and the pelvic bones.

GROSS STRUCTURE OF A BONE (FIG. 17)

Examination of a typical long bone that has been split longitudinally shows a cylindrical collar of hard, *compact bone* forming the *shaft* (diaphysis) of the bone and enclosing a hollow space, called the *marrow cavity* (medullary cavity), which contains yellow *bone marrow*. At either end of the shaft where it expands to form the *extremities,* the compact bone of the shaft becomes thinner, and covers an inner anastomosing network of fine bone spicules and trabeculae which form the *cancellous* or *spongy bone*. Cancellous bone is also found in the bodies of vertebrae and between the inner and outer bony plates of flat bones. If the flat bone happens to be one of the bones of the cranium, the cancellous tissue is referred to specifically as *diploë*. Red marrow fills the spaces in cancellous bone. Careful examination of the pattern formed by the spicules and trabeculae of cancellous bone will show that they are not arranged in a "hit and miss" manner, but that they show a pattern of arrangement adapted to resist the stress and pressures the particular bone will be required to withstand. Since these stresses and pressures vary throughout the life of an individual, it is readily understandable that the pattern in cancellous bone is subject to change and remodelling throughout life. Except for their articular surfaces, the outer surfaces of bone are not "bare" but are covered by a membrane of fibrous connective tissue called the *periosteum*. This tissue will be discussed in more detail later. (See page 18). On the inner surface of the bone, bordering the marrow cavities is another, thinner layer of connective tissue called the *endosteum*.

MARROW SPACES AND THE MARROW CAVITY.   There are two types of marrow spaces formed during the development of bone.

1. *Primary marrow spaces* which are the first marrow spaces to form during bone formation.

2. *Secondary marrow spaces* which result from the resorption of bone between primary marrow spaces and the fusion of two or more primary marrow spaces. The marrow cavity of any long bone is actually the terminal secondary marrow cavity resulting from the continued erosion of the junctions between primary marrow cavities. This cavity contains the bone marrow. The smaller marrow spaces which are found in cancellous bone also contain bone marrow.

BONE MARROW.   Bone marrow consists of a *recticular tissue meshwork,* developing *blood cells,* and/or *fat*. In the adult two kinds of bone marrow can be found, red and yellow marrow.

1. *Red marrow* (myeloid tissue, hemopoietic tissue) is actively engaged in the production of blood cells. It is called "red" marrow

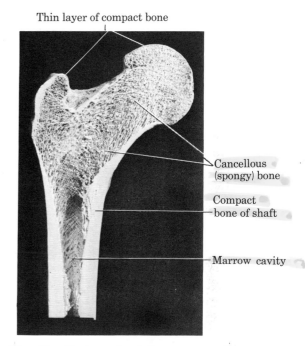

Thin layer of compact bone

Cancellous (spongy) bone

Compact bone of shaft

Marrow cavity

Fig. 17.   Photograph of the upper portion of a right femur cut longitudinally.

because of the red color imparted by the numerous red blood cells that it is producing. Red marrow occurs in most of the bones of the fetus, but in the adult it is restricted to the following areas: in the ends of long bones, in some of the short bones, the bodies of vertebrae, in the sternum and ribs, and in the diploë of the flat bones of the cranium.

2. *Yellow marrow* is not actively engaged in producing blood cells. It is called "yellow" marrow because of its color, which is due to the large number of fat cells it contains. It does have the potential for blood cell production, and if the need ever arose, could produce them. If this occurred, it could be recognized by the change of color from yellow of the inactive to the red color of the blood cell forming red marrow.

PERIOSTEUM.   With the exception of the articular surfaces, which are covered by a thin layer of hyaline cartilage, the outer surface of bone is covered by a fibrous connective tissue called the periosteum. The periosteum is essential for the maintenance of normal, viable bone since it contains numerous blood vessels which are distributed to the bone and nourish it. The periosteum is predominantly collagenous tissue with some elastic fibers intermingled with the collagenous fiber bundles. The periosteum is arranged in two layers: an outer *fibrous layer* and an inner *osteogenic layer* which is closely applied to the bone. Under certain conditions, the cells of the osteogenic layer are capable of producing more bone. In the adult, the cells of the osteogenic layer are inactive unless the bone is damaged to such a degree that new bone formation is required. The osteogenic cells then enlarge and become typical osteoblasts, capable of producing new bone.

ENDOSTEUM.   A similar type of fibrous membrane called the endosteum, lines the inner surface of bone, adjacent to the marrow cavities.

MICROSCOPIC STRUCTURE OF BONE.   At first glance, the compact bone of the shaft of a long bone appears to be a dense, solid mass of tissue. However, microscopic examination of a paper-thin section of this tissue, using low power magnification reveals numerous "holes" in a cross section, or long, narrow canals in a longitudinal section (Fig. left). **These are the *Haversian canals*, which run longitudinally** (parallel to the long axis of the bone) in the compact bone of the shaft. They contain blood and lymph vessels, nerves, and some loose connective tissue.

The solid part of bone consists of thin layers of bone called *lamellae* (singular, lamella), which are bound together by a cement substance reinforced in some places by bundles of fibrous connective tissue called *Sharpey's fibers.*

Between the lamellae there are small, almond-shaped spaces called *lacunae* (singular, lacuna) which contain the *bone cells* or *osteocytes*. Tiny canals, the *canaliculae,* extend between adjacent lacunae and connect them with the central Haversian canal.

Canals, called *Volkmann's canals,* extend transversely through compact bone. They connect Haversian canals with each other and with the surface of bone and the marrow cavity. Blood vessels from the periosteum enter the bone by way of Volkmann's canals. These canals are similar in size to the Haversian canals, but are easily differentiated from them since they have no encircling concentric bony lamellae.

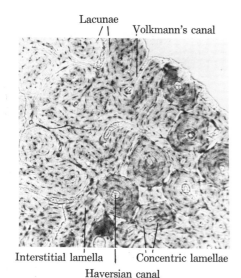

Lacunae / \ Volkmann's canal

Interstitial lamella | Concentric lamellae
Haversian canal

Photomicrograph of cross section of compact bone (not decalcified).

There are three types of lamellae in bone, named according to their location.

1. Circumferential lamellae (external and internal). The external circumferential lamellae consist of a few layers which extend around the outer margin of the bone; the internal circumferential lamellae are around the inner margin, bordering the marrow cavity.

2. Concentric or Haversian lamellae that are arranged in concentric layers around individual Haversian canals.

3. Interstitial lamellae that fill in the spaces between the numerous Haversian systems.

The *Haversian system* is the unit of structure of compact bone (Fig. 18). It consists of (1) a *central Haversian canal,* (2) three to five or more *concentric lamellae* of bone around the canal, (3) *lacunae,* between lamellae, containing *bone cells* or *osteocytes,* and (4) *canaliculae.*

(Note: Sharpey's fibers do not penetrate Haversian systems.)

OSSIFICATION OF BONE. The chemical incorporation of mineral matter with preosseous material (ostein, osteoid) during bone formation is known as *ossification* and occurs first in small, specific areas called *ossification centers.* From these first centers, the formation and ossification of bone gradually spreads toward the periphery until the bone is completely formed and growth has terminated. Ossification of bone begins before birth in all bones except the carpal bones of the wrist, some of the tarsal bones of the ankle, and the coccyx or "tail bone."

GROWTH OF BONES. Before considering how specific bones grow, it will be profitable to review a few facts concerning formation and growth of osseous tissue. Bone is formed either directly from a membranous precursor or by endochondral bone forming where a cartilaginous model intervenes and is replaced by bone. Once bone starts to form by either of the two types of bone formation mentioned above, it "grows" or increases in amount only by new bone being deposited on the surface of bone already formed. This type of growth is called *appositional* growth. The student must realize that bone formation and bone growth can be occurring simultaneously in a single bone.

Growth of membrane bones (*intramembranous bone formation* or *subperiosteal bone formation,* as it is referred to in certain areas) is a relatively simple process. These bones increase in size by new bone being deposited on one or more surfaces of bone already formed.

Growth of bone replacing a cartilaginous precursor is often confusing for a beginning student since it involves several different processes affecting both cartilage and bone occurring more or less simultaneously within a single bone. A general statement of the growth of endochondral bone will be given, and then a description of the growth of a specific long bone will be added in an attempt to clarify the subject.

In the developing embryo, at the sites where the bones forming the skeleton will finally be found, the embryonic connective tissue, called *mesenchyme,* becomes condensed and gives rise to cartilage. This cartilage then grows in two ways.

1. Primarily by means of *interstitial growth,* in which the increment takes place within the semisolid matrix of the developing cartilage so that it "expands" in one or more directions.

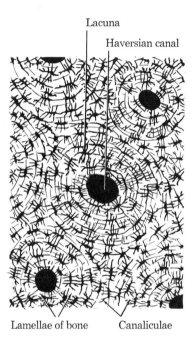

Fig. 18. A Haversian system.

2. To a much lesser degree by means of *appositional growth,* in which new cartilage is added to the surface of cartilage already formed.

With the growth of the cartilage, a miniature cartilaginous skeletal model is formed. A separate cartilaginous model for each adult bone is represented and can be identified by its shape. Modification of the connective tissue covering the cartilaginous model results in the multipotential cells of its deepest layer being converted to bone-forming cells (osteoblasts). These osteoblasts accompanied by small blood vessels form the *periosteal bud* which begins to penetrate into the center of the cartilaginous model where the cartilage has started to degenerate and calcify. On reaching the area of calcified cartilage, the osteoblasts begin to produce bone along the edges of the spicules of calcified cartilage and the replacement of cartilage by bone has started. The area where bone replacement first occurs is called a *primary center of ossification.* Primary centers of ossification appear usually between the fifth and twelfth week of embryonic life. The replacement of cartilage by bone and the addition of new bone by means of the appositional growth mechanism continues and spreads from the center towards the periphery until all of the cartilage has been replaced (except a thin layer over articular surfaces) and the growth of the bone stopped.

During the time that the osteoblasts are producing bone, a second process, involving the destruction and remodelling of the newly formed bone, begins and tends to more or less parallel the formation of bone. In this way the marrow cavities are formed and the proportion and shape of the growing bone maintained. The final bone becomes a strong but lightweight organ, well adapted to carry out the functions required.

GROWTH OF A LONG BONE. In the long bones, at the time of birth, bone replacement of the cartilaginous model has spread from the primary centers of ossification in the shaft (diaphysis) throughout most of the length of the bone, leaving only the ends of the shaft and the extremities (epiphyses) cartilaginous (Fig. 19). Shortly after birth the epiphyses (*secondary centers of ossification*) appear and the replacement by bone from these secondary centers spreads peripherally. During growth in length of a long bone, the areas of bone formation for the epiphyses are separated from the areas of advancing bone formation of the diaphysis by an area of growing cartilage called the *epiphyseal plate.* Relatively little growth in length occurs on the epiphyseal side of the plate. The growth in length of any long bone is due primarily to interstitial growth of cartilage on the shaft side (diaphyseal side) of the epiphyseal plate. This area is called the *metaphysis* and can be identified even grossly since it occupies the area where the shaft "flares" to meet the epiphysis. It should be impressed on the student that a metaphysis is present only in a growing bone and is not found in the mature bone of the adult. The growth and elongation of long bones continues for a long time after birth, until the replacement by bone finally overtakes the growing cartilage, and the bone of the diaphysis fuses with the bone of the epiphyses. Growth then stops.

Growth in width of the long bone is due primarily to intramembranous or subperiosteal bone formation. The cells of the osteogenic layer of the periosteum deposit bone on the surface of the bone of the diaphysis and at the same time the bone is resorbed from the inner surface of the bone bordering the marrow cavity. This delicately co-

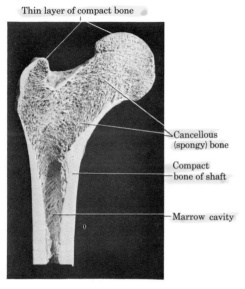

Thin layer of compact bone

Cancellous (spongy) bone

Compact bone of shaft

Marrow cavity

Photograph of the upper portion of a right femur cut longitudinally.

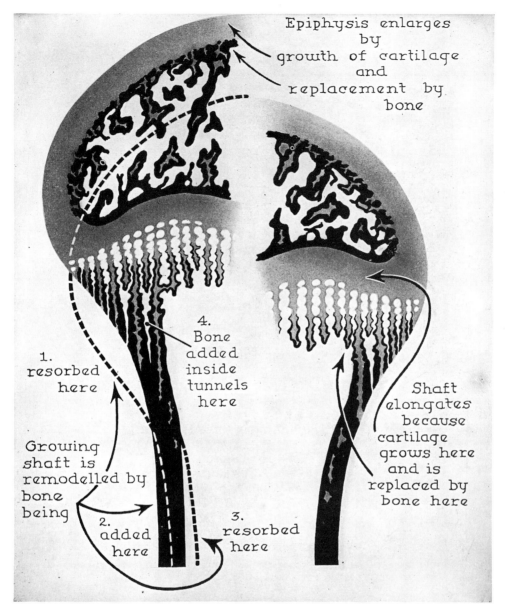

Epiphysis enlarges
by
growth of cartilage
and
replacement by
bone

4.
Bone
added
inside
tunnels
here

1.
resorbed
here

Growing
shaft is
remodelled by
bone
being

2.
added
here

3.
resorbed
here

Shaft
elongates
because
cartilage
grows here
and is
replaced by
bone here

Fig. 19.   Diagram showing surfaces on which bone is deposited and resorbed to account for the remodeling that takes place at the ends of growing long bones that have flared extremities. (From Ham. *J. Bone & Joint Surg.,* 34A:701, 1952.)

ordinated formation and resorption of bone maintains the proper thickness of the diaphysis as the bone grows.

In each long bone there are at first a minimum of three *centers of ossification*. The center for the shaft, called the *diaphysis,* appears first and for this reason is also referred to as the *primary center* of ossification. Then at least one center of ossification appears for each extremity. These centers are known as *secondary centers* of ossification, or *epiphyses* (singular, epiphysis). Some bones will develop more than one center of ossification for an extremity. When this occurs, the centers will unite with each other to form the epiphysis, which will finally unite with the diaphysis or shaft of the bone. The cartilaginous junction between the epiphysis and the diaphysis in long bones is known as the *epiphyseal plate* and remains cartilaginous until growth in length of the bone is completed.

BONY MARKINGS.   The surfaces of bones are not smooth and regular, but present many roughened areas, depressions, and prominences known as *bony markings*. Function plays an important part in the formation of these surface markings. Because of weight bearing, the ends of long bones enlarge and their surfaces are very smooth and hard, covered by a thin layer of hyaline cartilage. The areas of tendinous attachment of muscles produce a variety of prominences of different shapes and sizes, and the course of blood vessels—particularly along the inner surface of the flat bones of the skull—leave depressions that mark their course.

Before starting a more detailed study of the skeletal and muscular systems of the body, the student should learn the terms applied to specific bony markings and be able to define each term.

Classification of Bony Markings

A. Nonarticular surfaces
  1. Process—any decided, roughened bony prominence. These are classified according to size as follows:
     a. Trochanter—found only on the femur. A relatively large, blunt type of process.
     b. Tuberosity—a large, blunt or rounded prominence.
     c. Tubercle—a small, blunt or rounded prominence.
  2. Spine—a pointed projection of bone. A spine may be long and sharply pointed or short and blunted.
  3. Crest—a prominent, roughened border, which may be relatively broad.
  4. Foramen—a hole through a bone. Sizes of foramina are extremely variable.
  5. Fossa—a saucer-like depression.
B. Articular surfaces
  1. Head—a rounded articular surface joined to the shaft of the bone by a constricted portion called the neck.
  2. Condyle—a relatively large articular surface (either concave or convex) joined directly to the shaft of the long bone.

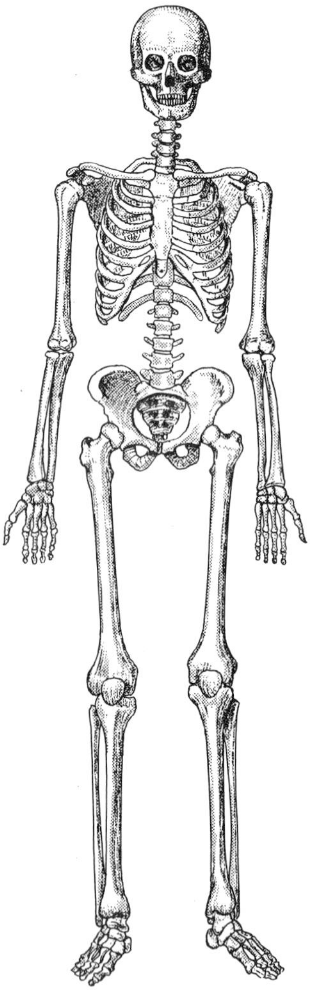

Fig. 20.   The skeleton.

BONES AS PART OF THE SKELETAL SYSTEM

THE SKELETON

DEFINITION.   The skeleton consists of a series of bones, supplemented in a few areas by cartilage, which are joined together to form the supportive framework of the body (Fig. 20).

NUMBER OF BONES.   In the adult there are usually 206 separate bones. This number may vary slightly due to the appearance of certain anomalies such as extra ribs, where the number may be increased to 208, or when there is a failure of certain bones to ossify and the number would be less than 206.

DIVISION OF THE ADULT SKELETON.

Axial skeleton
  Skull   22 bones
    cranium   8 bones
    face   14 bones
  Vertebral column   26 bones
    cervical vertebrae   7 bones
    thoracic vertebrae 12 bones
    lumbar vertebrae   5 bones
    sacrum   1 bone (5 fused bones)
    coccyx   1 bone (3 to 5 fused bones)
  Sternum   1 bone
  Ribs   24 bones
  Hyoid   1 bone
  Ossicles (ear bones)   6 bones
    malleus   2 bones
    incus   2 bones
    stapes   2 bones
Appendicular skeleton
  Shoulder girdle   4 bones
    clavicle   2 bones
    scapula   2 bones
  Upper extremity   60 bones
    humerus   2 bones
    ulna   2 bones
    radius   2 bones
    carpals   16 bones
    metacarpals   10 bones
    phalanges   28 bones
  Os coxae   2 bones
  Lower extremity   60 bones
    femur   2 bones
    fibula   2 bones
    tibia   2 bones
    patella   2 bones
    tarsals   14 bones
    metatarsals   10 bones
    phalanges   28 bones

                                TOTAL   206 bones

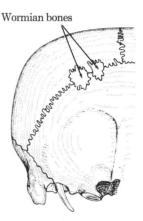

Wormian bones

Fig. 21.   Wormian bones.

In addition to the bones listed, there are a variable number of small bones called *sesamoid bones*. They are found near the attachments (insertions) of certain tendons, and function to change the direction of pull of the tendon to give a greater mechanical leverage. With the exception of the patella, a sesamoid bone included in the list of bones of the lower extremity, the sesamoid bones are unnamed, variable in number, and are usually found in association with tendons of the hands and feet.

The *sutural (Wormian) bones* are small additional bones that form in the line of the sutures of the cranium (Fig. 21).

CLASSIFICATION OF BONES. The bones of the skeleton are classified as follows: long bones, short bones, flat bones, and irregular bones. A description of the bones in each of these groups is given on pages 16 and 17.

FUNCTIONS OF THE SKELETON.

1. Gives shape to the body.
2. Affords attachment for muscles. The bones of the skeleton serve as levers making movement of the body possible.
3. The bones of the axial skeleton form more or less solid-walled compartments which serve to protect vital organs such as the brain, heart, lungs, and some of the reproductive organs.
4. Serves as a storehouse for calcium.
5. The bone marrow of the skeleton is the site for the formation of certain blood cells of the body.

AGE DIFFERENCES. No attempt will be made to discuss all of the minute differences in the skeleton of the newborn, the adult, and the aged. However, attention will be called to the obvious differences.

The skull of the newborn (Fig. 22) is disproportionately large. The cranial portion, which accounts for seven eighths of the bulk of the skull, is due to the relatively large size of the contained brain which has attained three fourths of its adult size at birth. The small size of the facial portion, one eighth of the skull mass, is due primarily to the absence of teeth and their associated alveolar processes, along with the rudimentary state of development of the maxillary air sinuses and nasal cavity. At birth, the transverse and anteroposterior measurements of the maxilla are greater than the vertical measurement of the bone. In the adult, the vertical measurements become greater than the other two. In old age, with the loss of teeth and the resorption of the alveolar processes, the shift is again toward the infantile proportions (Fig. 23). The absence of teeth in the mandible accounts for the rudimentary development of that bone and the very obtuse angle (175°) between the ramus and the body of the mandible in the newborn. With the eruption of the teeth and the growth of the alveolar processes there is a gradual decrease of the obtuseness of the mandibular angle until it reaches about 100° to 120° in the adult. In old age, with loss of the teeth and resorption of the alveolar processes, the appearance of the mandible is again quite like that of the newborn except that the mandibular angle is not quite so obtuse (140°).

SEX DIFFERENCES. For the person trained and skilled in the field of Osteology, sexing of skeletal material is a relatively easy task. In general, we can state that the bones of the female skeleton are smaller, lighter, and the bony markings less pronounced than those of the male of the same "racial" group. The female skeleton differs from the male in the following ways.

The female skull is generally smaller with an average cranial capacity about 10 per cent less than that of the male.

The glabella, supraorbital ridges, and mastoid processes are not as well developed.

The air sinuses and facial bones containing them are smaller.

The upper margin of the orbit is quite sharp.

The forehead is more vertical and somewhat rounded due to the retention of the frontal eminences, an infantile characteristic.

The maxilla, the mandible, and the teeth are smaller.

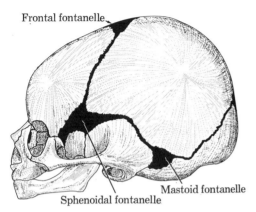

Frontal fontanelle

Mastoid fontanelle

Sphenoidal fontanelle

Fig. 22.   Skull of a newborn. Lateral aspect.

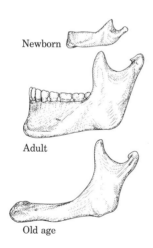

Newborn

Adult

Old age

Fig. 23.   Age changes in the mandible.

Bones as Part of the Skeletal System

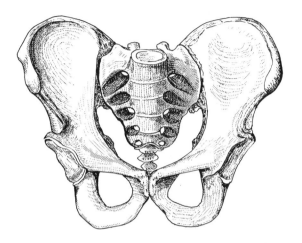

Fig. 24A.   Male pelvis.

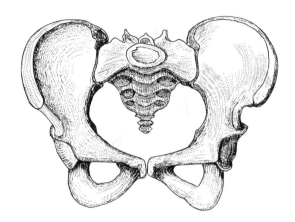

Fig. 24B.   Female pelvis.

The pelvic bones offer the most reliable criteria for sexing skeletal material (Fig. 24A and B). This is not surprising since in the female they serve as the bony portion of the birth canal through which the fetus must pass. The depth of the female pelvis is less than that of the male, the ilia are less sloped, and the anterior iliac spines are farther apart.

The superior opening of the lesser pelvis is larger and more rounded.

The pelvic cavity is shallower and wider.

The sacrum is wider, shorter, and is less curved in its upper part.

The obturator foramen is smaller and more triangular in shape.

The inferior pelvic outlet is larger, and the coccyx (tailbone) is more movable.

The sciatic notches are shallow and wide, and the ischial spines are directed more outwardly.

The acetabula are smaller and are directed more anteriorly.

Both the ischial spines and the acetabula are more widely separated.

The pubic symphysis is shallower and there is a more rounded pubic arch in the female, which in the male is narrower and forms an angular junction.

These sex differences are present and obvious in the fetus as early as the fourth month.

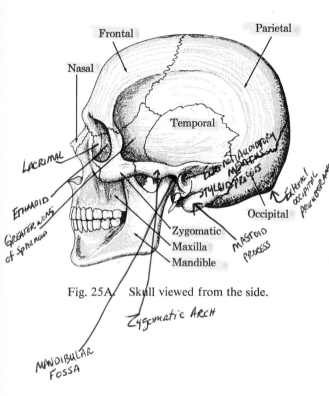

Fig. 25A. Skull viewed from the side.

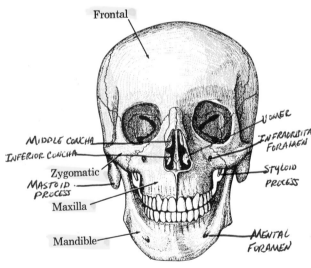

Fig. 25B. Skull viewed from the front.

BONES OF THE AXIAL SKELETON

THE SKULL (FIGS. 25A AND B AND 26)

LOCATION. The skull is balanced on the upper end of the vertebral column. It articulates with the 1st cervical vertebra.

COMPONENTS. The skull is made up of 22 flattened, curved, and/or irregularly shaped bones.

ARTICULATIONS. In the adult, except for the mandible (jaw bone), the bones of the skull are joined together by immovable joints called *sutures* (Fig. 27). Some of the bones have very irregular edges which interlock. Between some, the edges are smooth and beveled (slanted) and overlap one another. In this latter type, fibrous tissue is interposed between the articular surface of the bones and helps bind them together more firmly. However, they are always immovable.

DIVISIONS. The skull consists of a *cranial portion* and a *facial portion* (Figs. 28 and 29).

NUMBER OF BONES. The number of bones is 22, eight forming the cranium and 14 forming the face.

SKULL OF THE NEWBORN. At birth the cranial part of the skull is relatively large. In comparison, the face is small and undeveloped. At this time the bones of the skull are not completely ossified, the spaces between the bony portions being membranous tissue. These membranous areas are known as *fontanelles* and there are usually six of them in the newborn (Fig. 30A and B). They are described in relation to their location.

Frontal or anterior fontanelle is the largest of the six and is diamond-shaped. It is located in the front part of the cranium, between the two parietal bones and the two segments of the frontal bone. Normally, this fontanelle is closed, i.e., the membrane replaced by bone, by the middle of the second year.

Occipital or posterior fontanelle is small and triangular in shape. It is located at the junction of the occipital and parietal bones. It closes within a few months after birth.

Lateral fontanelles are four small, irregularly-shaped spaces. Two are called the sphenoidal fontanelles and are located one on either side of the skull at the junction of the frontal, parietal, temporal, and sphenoid bones. The remaining two, one on either side of the skull, are at the junction of the occipital, parietal, and temporal bones, and are called the mastoid fontanelles. These four fontanelles are closed within a month or two after birth.

The floor of the cranial cavity forms three saucer-shaped depressions or fossae, arranged in descending levels from front to back. These fossae are the anterior, middle, and posterior cranial fossae.

In the floor of the cranial cavity there are a number of openings or foramina for the transmission of the cranial nerves and blood vessels. Starting anteriorly, the major openings or foramina to be observed and identified are:

1. Foramen cecum—between the frontal bone and the crista galli of the ethmoid bone. It transmits a small vein.

2. Optic foramen of the sphenoid bone. It transmits the optic nerve and the ophthalmic artery.

3. Superior orbital fissure of the sphenoid bone. It transmits the oculomotor, trochlear, ophthalmic division of the trigeminal, and the

abducent nerves, a branch of the middle meningeal artery, and the ophthalmic veins.

4. Foramen rotundum of the sphenoid bone. It transmits the maxillary branch of the trigeminal nerve.

5. Foramen ovale of the sphenoid bone. It transmits the mandibular branch of the trigeminal nerve and a small vessel. Occasionally the lesser superficial petrosal nerve passes through this foramen.

6. Foramen spinosum of the sphenoid bone. It transmits the middle meningeal vessels and a branch of the mandibular nerve.

7. Foramen lacerum. It transmits the internal carotid artery with its sympathetic plexus of nerves.

8. Jugular foramen. It transmits the inferior petrosal sinus, transverse sinus, arterial branches, and the glossopharyngeal, vagus, and accessory nerves.

9. Foramen magnum of the occipital bone. This large foramen transmits the spinal cord.

10. Hypoglossal canal of the occipital bone. It transmits the hypoglossal nerve and a small artery.

The Cranium

The cranium is made up of eight bones which form a strong, dome-shaped case that extends above and behind the face and encloses the brain. It consists of the following bones: the *frontal* (single), the *parietals* (paired), the *occipital* (single), the *temporals* (paired), the *sphenoid* (single), and the *ethmoid* (single).

Frontal Bone (Figs. 25A and B and 28)

LOCATION. This bone forms the front and upper part of the cranium (forehead).

SHAPE. It resembles a cockle shell.

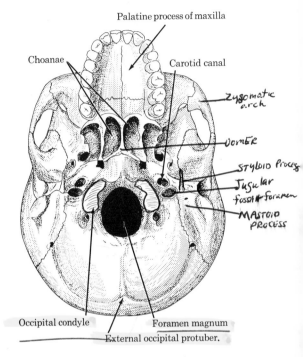

Fig. 26. Base of the skull.

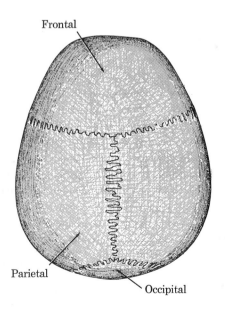

Fig. 27. Sutures of the cranium.

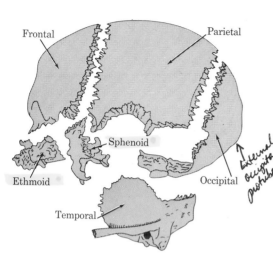

Fig. 28.   Bones of the cranium.

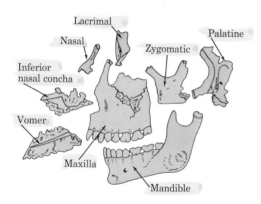

Fig. 29.   Bones of the face.

DESCRIPTION.   The bone consists of two portions—the *squama,* which corresponds to the forehead, and the *horizontal portion* which helps form the upper parts of the orbits or eye sockets. At birth the frontal bone consists of two halves joined by a suture. The suture usually disappears by the sixth year; however, the suture may persist throughout life, and when it does, it is called the *metopic suture.* This bone contains several air spaces which vary markedly in size and extent, called the *frontal sinuses.*

ARTICULATIONS.   The frontal bone articulates with 12 bones: two parietals, the sphenoid, the ethmoid, two nasals, two maxillae, two lacrimals, and two zygomatics.

Parietal Bones, Right and Left (Figs. 25A and 28)

LOCATION.   The two parietal bones form the top and upper sides of the cranium.

SHAPE.   Each parietal bone is shaped rather like a square saucer.

DESCRIPTION.   The outer surface of each bone is convex and almost smooth. The inner concave surface is marked by shallow grooves which radiate upwards from the inferior border of the bone. These grooves mark the course of blood vessels (middle meningeal vessels) going to the brain.

ARTICULATIONS.   Each parietal bone articulates with five bones —the opposite parietal, the frontal, the occipital, the sphenoid, and the temporal.

Occipital Bone (Figs. 26 and 28)

LOCATION.   The occipital bone forms the back and part of the floor of the cranium.

SHAPE.   This bone is trapezoid in outline.

DESCRIPTION.   The occipital bone consists of two portions, the *squama* and a *basilar portion,* which are separated by a large opening, the *foramen magnum,* which transmits the spinal cord. The squama is the portion of the bone which extends behind the foramen magnum and then bends upward to form the back of the cranium. The external surface of the squama is convex and near its middle has a prominence called the *occipital protuberance.* The rough areas and lines are for muscle attachments. The inner concave surface has several broad grooves which indicate the course of venous sinuses of the brain. The basilar portion of the occipital bone extends forward and upward. On either side of the foramen are two portions of bone which join the squama and basilar portions. These portions of bone support two smooth oval prominences, the *occipital condyles,* which articulate with the condylar surfaces on the 1st cervical vertebra.

ARTICULATIONS.   The occipital bone articulates with six bones —two parietals, two temporals, the sphenoid, and the first cervical vertebra.

Temporal Bones, Right and Left (Figs. 25A and 28)

LOCATION.   These bones form the sides and part of the floor of the cranium.

SHAPE.   The temporal bones are irregularly shaped.

DESCRIPTION.   The temporal bone consists of four portions— the *squama,* the *tympanic, mastoid,* and *petrous* portions.

The squama forms the upper and front part of the bone. It is thin and scale-like. Extending forward and slightly outward from the lower third of the squama is a ridge of bone which ends in a thin, arched bony process, called the *zygomatic process.* Below the beginning of this ridge of bone is an opening, the *external auditory meatus,* which leads into the bony ear. In front of and slightly above the external auditory meatus is a concave articular fossa for the articular process of the mandible.

The mastoid portion projects behind and below the external auditory meatus and forms a cone-shaped prominence called the *mastoid process.* The bone of this process is filled with many small spaces known as *mastoid air cells.* These air cells communicate with the middle ear and form a possible route for the spread of infections involving the middle ear.

The petrous portion is wedge-shaped and helps form the floor of the skull. This portion of the bone contains the essential part of the organ of hearing. On the lower surface of the petrous portion is a rather long, slender spine, the *styloid process.* On the internal posterior surface is an opening, the *internal auditory meatus,* which transmits the auditory and facial nerves.

The tympanic portion of the bone lies below the squama and in front of the mastoid process. It forms the greater part of the external auditory meatus.

ARTICULATIONS. Each temporal bone articulates with five bones —the mandible, zygomatic, sphenoid, parietal, and occipital.

Sphenoid Bone (Fig. 28)

LOCATION. The sphenoid forms the anterior part of the floor of the cranium.

SHAPE. This is a rather large, irregularly-shaped bone that is usually described as resembling a bat with its wings spread.

DESCRIPTION. The sphenoid consists of a *body* and two *pterygoid processes.* The body of the bone is a rather elongated, box-shaped portion which lies in the midline of the floor of the cranium between the occipital bone behind and the ethmoid bone in front. This part of the bone is hollow and forms two or more cavities, the *sphenoid air sinuses,* which communicate with the nasal cavity. On the back part of this portion of the bone is a marked depression called the *sella turcica,* which holds the pituitary gland.

The greater wings of the sphenoid are rather large, bony processes which extend laterally from the body. They curve upward and backward to form part of the lateral wall of the orbit and a portion of the greater wing fits between the frontal and temporal bones and forms the lateral wall of the cranium. The lesser wings are thin, triangular processes of bone which project from the upper and front parts of the body. They form the back part of the roof of the orbit and part of the floor of the cranium.

Between the greater and lesser wings is an obliquely directed space, the *superior orbital foramen,* which transmits several blood vessels.

The pterygoid processes extend vertically downward from the body of the sphenoid. Each process consists of two plates of bone, the *medial* and *lateral pterygoid plates.* They enclose a shallow fossa

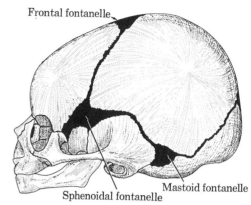

A. Skull viewed from the side.

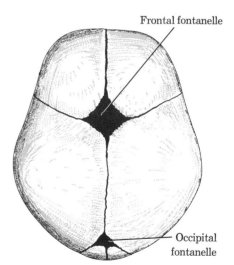

B. Skull viewed from above.

Fig. 30. Fontanelles of a newborn.

called the *pterygoid fossa.* The medial plate helps form the posterior part of the lateral wall of the nasal cavity.

ARTICULATIONS.   The sphenoid articulates with 12 bones—the vomer, ethmoid, frontal, two temporals, two parietals, occipital, two zygomatics, and two palatines.

Ethmoid Bone *(Figs. 28 and 31)*

LOCATION.   It is located in the front part of the floor of the cranial cavity, lying between the orbits, and forms the roof of the nasal cavity.

SHAPE.   This bone is somewhat cup-shaped.

DESCRIPTION.   For descriptive purposes, it is considered in four parts—the *cribriform plate, perpendicular plate,* and the *two labyrinths.*

The cribriform plate is the horizontal portion, the lower surface of which forms the roof of the nasal cavity. The upper surface of the cribriform plate contributes to the floor of the cranial cavity. This plate of bone is perforated by a number of small openings for the passage of the olfactory nerves (nerves of smell).

The perpendicular plate is a thin, rectangular piece of bone which projects downward into the nasal cavity and forms the upper part of the nasal septum.

The two labyrinths or lateral masses consist of a number of thin-walled spaces known as the *ethmoid air cells* or *sinuses.* Extending below these are two, curved, scroll-like pieces of bones known as *conchae.* The upper is called the superior and the one below it is called the middle concha. They contribute to the lateral wall of the nasal cavity.

ARTICULATIONS.   The ethmoid bone articulates with 15 bones of which four are cranial bones and 11 are bones of the face. The cranial bones are the sphenoid, the sphenoidal conchae (two), and the frontal. The facial bones with which the ethmoid articulates include two nasals, two maxillae, two lacrimals, two palatines, two inferior nasal conchae, and the vomer.

The Face

The skeleton of the face is made up of irregularly-shaped bones. It is attached to the cranial portion of the skull and lies below and in front of most of the cranium. The bones of the face include the *nasals* (paired), *maxillae* (paired), *lacrimals* (paired), *zygomatics* or *malars* (paired), *palatines* (paired), *inferior nasal conchae* (paired), *vomer* (single), and *mandible* (single).

Nasal Bones *(Figs. 25B and 29)*

LOCATION.   They lie side by side in the midline of the upper part of the face and form the root and part of the bridge of the nose.

SHAPE.   These are small, narrow, oblong bones.

DESCRIPTION.   Each bone has two surfaces—outer and inner—and four borders—superior, inferior, medial, and lateral.

The outer (facial) surface from above downward is at first concave, then convex. It is slightly convex from side to side. The inner (nasal) surface parallels the contour of the outer surface.

The superior border is narrow but thick, and its many serrations fit comparable serrations on the frontal bone. The inferior border is

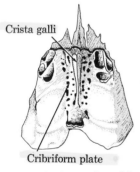

Crista galli

Cribriform plate

Fig. 31.   Ethmoid bone viewed from above.

thin. The cartilaginous framework of the lower half of the nose and nostrils attaches to the inferior border. The medial border is thick above and tapers to a thin border below; it articulates with the nasal bone of the opposite side. The lateral border is slightly serrated and articulates with the maxilla.

ARTICULATIONS. The nasal bone articulates with four bones— the frontal bone above, the other nasal bone medially, the frontal process of the maxilla laterally, the frontal and ethmoid bones posteriorly, and the nasal cartilage inferiorly.

Maxillae (Upper Jaw Bones) (Fig. right and Fig. 29)

These are among the largest bones of the face.

LOCATION. They form the major part of the skeleton of the upper and midportion of the face (the upper jaw).

SHAPE. Irregular.

DESCRIPTION. Each maxilla contributes to the formation of three cavities—the orbit, the nasal cavity, and the roof of the mouth. For descriptive purposes each maxilla consists of a *body,* and *four processes*—frontal, zygomatic, alveolar, and palatine.

The body is a pyramidal-shaped structure. It contains a large cavity or air space called the maxillary sinus that fills most of the body. It has four surfaces—anterior (facial), posterior (infratemporal), superior (orbital), and medial (nasal).

The anterior (facial) surface is directed anteriorly and laterally. On this surface can be seen two fossae, the incisive and canine; a series of eminences along its inferior margin; a foramen (the infraorbital foramen); a notch (the nasal notch); and a spine (the anterior nasal spine). The *incisive fossa* is a depression just below the horizontal margin of the nasal opening above the incisor teeth. The *canine fossa* is a depression lateral to the incisive fossa and below the infraorbital foramen. The eminences are a series of tapered prominences along its inferior margin that correspond to the roots of the teeth which project into the bone. The *infraorbital foramen* is a hole just below the orbit that transmits the infraorbital vessels and nerve. The *nasal notch* is an opening or concavity that marks the entrance into the nasal cavity. The *nasal spine* is a pointed process that, together with its counterpart from the opposite side, forms a sharp anteriorly directed *spinous process.*

The posterior surface (infratemporal) is directed laterally and posteriorly. The zygomatic process merges into a marked ridge at the inferior margin, and separates the posterior and anterior surfaces. The *alveolar canals* open near the center of this surface. They transmit the posterior superior alveolar vessels and nerves.

The superior (orbital) surface lies horizontally, for the most part, and forms the floor of the orbit. It is smooth and triangular in shape.

The medial (nasal) surface is irregular in its upper posterior portion. Below is a smooth concave area that forms part of the inferior meatus of the nasal cavity.

The *maxillary sinus* is a large, thin-walled cavity within the body of the maxilla. The maxillary sinuses vary in size, even on the two sides of the same individual.

The *frontal process* is a plate of bone that projects upward between the nasal bones and the orbit. It helps form part of the lateral

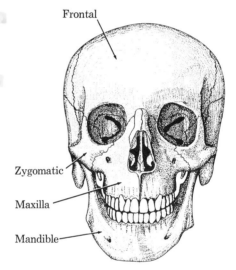

Frontal

Zygomatic

Maxilla

Mandible

Skull viewed from the front.

wall of the nasal cavity. Its posterior border is grooved and it articulates with a matched groove on the lacrimal bone, to form the *lacrimal fossa* which holds the lacrimal sac (part of the lacrimal or tear apparatus of the eye).

The *zygomatic process* is the lateral projection of the maxilla, which articulates with the zygomatic bone and forms the anterior end of the zygomatic arch.

The *alveolar process* on the inferior portion of the body of the maxilla contains eight cavities for the roots of half of the upper teeth. The two maxillae, articulated, present a horseshoe-shaped arch (the *alveolar arch*), containing 16 cavities for the roots of the upper teeth. The midpoint of this arch is the *alveolar point*.

The *palatine process* is horizontally positioned and, with its fellow of the opposite side, forms the hard palate of the roof of the mouth. Anteriorly, near the midline junction between the two palatine processes, are several openings or foramina for the transmission of small blood vessels.

AGE DIFFERENCES. The most marked changes in the maxilla due to age are associated with the development and eruption of the teeth (see page 24).

ARTICULATIONS. The maxilla articulates with two cranial and seven facial bones, nine bones in all. The cranial bones are the frontal and ethmoid. The facial bones with which the maxilla articulates are the nasal, zygomatic, lacrimal, palatine, vomer, inferior nasal concha, and the opposite maxilla.

Lacrimal Bone (Fig. left)

LOCATION. This bone is found in the medial wall of the orbit.

SHAPE. Rectangular.

DESCRIPTION. It is the smallest bone of the face. It presents two surfaces—a lateral (orbital) and a medial (nasal), and four borders—anterior, posterior, superior, and inferior.

The lateral surface is divided into two areas by a vertical ridge, the *posterior lacrimal crest.* The area in front of the crest is grooved, and articulates with a corresponding groove on the frontal process of the maxilla, forming the *lacrimal sulcus,* which houses the lacrimal sac and the beginning of the nasolacrimal duct. The larger area behind the crest is smooth and contributes to the formation of the medial wall of the orbit. The lower anterior portion of the lacrimal bone forms a small hook-like process, the *lacrimal hamulus.* This process articulates with the maxilla, and completes the groove for the nasolacrimal duct.

The medial surface is divided into two areas by a vertical groove, comparable to the crest on the lateral surface. The portion of the bone in front of the groove forms part of the nasal cavity (*middle meatus*). The area behind the groove is rough and articulates with the ethmoid bone.

The borders are all slightly serrated for articulation with adjacent bones.

ARTICULATIONS. The lacrimal bone articulates with two cranial and two facial bones, four bones in all. The cranial bones are the frontal and ethmoid. The facial bones with which the lacrimal bone articulates are the maxilla and inferior nasal concha.

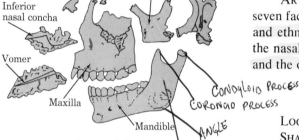

Bones of the face.

Zygomatic (Malar) Bone (Figs. 25B and 29)

LOCATION.   Located in the upper lateral part of the face, this bone forms the prominence of the cheek.

SHAPE.   Roughly diamond-shaped.

DESCRIPTION.   This bone contributes to the formation of the lateral wall of the orbit and a small bit of the floor, and to the temporal and infratemporal fossae. It presents two surfaces, *malar* and *temporal;* four processes, *maxillary, temporal, orbital,* and *frontosphenoidal;* and four borders, *maxillary, orbital, temporal,* and *zygomatic.*

The malar surface is slightly convex. Near its center is a small foramen (*zygomaticofacial*) for the transmission of the zygomatico-facial vessels and nerve.

The temporal surface is concave. It is directed backward and medially. It has a roughened articular area along its medial extent for articulation with the adjacent maxilla. The remainder of its surface is concave and smooth. In the middle of this area is the *zygomatico-temporal foramen* for transmission of the vessels and nerve of the same name.

The maxillary process articulates with the maxilla.

The temporal process projects posterolaterally and is serrated for articulation with the zygomatic process of the temporal bone.

The orbital process contributes to the formation of the orbit. It projects backward and medially from the infralateral rim of the orbit.

The frontosphenoidal process is directed upward, is quite thick and serrated for articulation with the frontal bone.

The maxillary border of the zygomatic bone is directed antero-inferiorly. It is a roughened, beveled border, articulating with the maxilla.

The orbital border forms roughly one third of the orbital rim.

The temporal border is convex above and concave below. Above it is continuous with the temporal line; below it is continuous with the upper margin of the zygomatic arch.

The zygomatic border is smooth and wavy.

ARTICULATIONS.   The zygomatic (malar) bone articulates with four bones—maxilla, temporal, frontal, and sphenoid.

Palatine Bone (Figs. 29 and 32)

LOCATION.   It lies behind the maxilla where it contributes to the formation of the back part of the nasal cavity, the back part of the hard palate of the mouth, and the floor of the orbit.

SHAPE.   It is an irregularly-shaped bone.

DESCRIPTION.   This bone has two parts, a *vertical* and a *horizontal portion,* and three processes—the *pyramidal, sphenoidal,* and *orbital.*

The horizontal part is roughly quadrilateral in shape and forms the back part of the hard palate, separating the nasal cavity and the mouth. Its anterior margin is serrated and articulates with the palatine process of the maxilla. Its posterior margin is smooth and concave and affords attachment for the structures of the soft palate.

The vertical part is roughly oblong in shape and forms part of the lateral wall of the nasal cavity.

The pyramidal process extends laterally and posteriorly from the angle of junction between the vertical and horizontal portion.

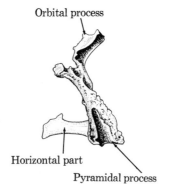

Orbital process

Horizontal part

Pyramidal process

Fig. 32.   Right palatine bone. Posterior aspect.

The sphenoidal process is a thin, narrow plate of bone that extends upward and medially from the upper posterior margin of the vertical portion.

The orbital process is above and in front of the sphenoidal process. It is directed upward and laterally. The orbital surface of this process contributes to the formation of the floor of the orbit.

ARTICULATIONS.   The palatine bone articulates with six bones—maxilla, sphenoid, ethmoid, inferior nasal concha, vomer, and the other palatine.

Inferior Nasal Concha (Figs. 29 and 33)

LOCATION.   It is positioned horizontally and forms part of the lateral wall of the nasal cavity.

SHAPE.   It is an irregular, thin, scroll-like piece of bone.

DESCRIPTION.   This bone has two surfaces, medial and lateral; two extremities, anterior and posterior; and two borders, superior and inferior.

The medial surface is convex. Several grooves for vessels run longitudinally.

The lateral surface is concave. It forms a part of the inferior meatus.

The anterior extremity is bluntly pointed.

The posterior extremity is more elongated and pointed.

The superior border is thin and presents two thin projections—the *lacrimal process* is anterior and articulates with the lacrimal bone, and the *ethmoid process* is posterior, broad, and joins the uncinate process of the ethmoid bone.

The inferior border is unarticulated; the margin is rounded and fairly thick.

ARTICULATIONS.   The inferior nasal concha articulates with four bones—maxilla, ethmoid, lacrimal, and palatine.

Vomer (Fig. 29)

LOCATION.   It is located in the median plane, where it forms the lower and back portion of the nasal septum.

SHAPE.   It is a thin bone, roughly quadrilateral in shape.

DESCRIPTION.   This bone has two lateral surfaces and four borders—superior, inferior, anterior, and posterior.

Each lateral surface of the vomer presents a well-defined groove, the *nasopalatine groove,* which runs obliquely downward and forward. The nasopalatine vessels and nerve lie in this groove.

The superior border is flared and wide and has a deep medial furrow for articulation with the sharp projection from the sphenoid.

The inferior border is irregular and fits into a groove between the left and right maxillary and palatine bones.

The anterior border of the vomer is long and is directed obliquely downward and forward. Its upper half is joined to the perpendicular plate of the ethmoid bone; its lower half is grooved to receive the cartilage of the nasal septum.

The posterior border is free, smooth, and concave.

ARTICULATIONS.   The vomer articulates with six bones—two cranial, four facial—and the septal cartilage. The cranial bones are the sphenoid and ethmoid. The facial bones with which the vomer articulates are two maxillae and two palatine bones.

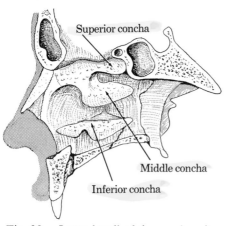

Fig. 33.   Lateral wall of the nasal cavity.

Mandible (Figs. 29 and 34)

LOCATION.   It forms the lower part of the face, the lower jaw.

SHAPE.   Irregular.

DESCRIPTION.   The mandible has two parts—a horizontal portion, called the *body,* and two vertically positioned *rami.*

The body is a thick, horseshoe-shaped bone with two surfaces—external and internal, and two borders—superior (alveolar) and inferior.

In the midline of the external surface is a faint ridge, the *symphysis.* This ridge spreads apart below to enclose a triangular-shaped prominence, the *mental protuberance.* The inferior margin or base of this protuberance is indented in the midline, but elevated slightly on either side to form the *mental tubercles.* Just below the incisor teeth is a slight depression called the *incisive fossa.* On either side, below the second premolar tooth, is a hole, the *mental foramen* which transmits the mental vessels and nerve. The *oblique line* is a faint ridge that extends from the mental tubercle, obliquely upwards and backwards to the anterior border of the ramus, with which it is continuous.

The internal surface forms the concave surface of the horseshoe. In back of the symphysis are two small projections, the *mental spines.* On the internal surface, extending from the lower portion of the symphysis upward and backward to the ramus, is a ridge of bone, the *mylohyoid line.*

The superior (alveolar) border contains 16 cavities or sockets for the roots of the teeth of the lower jaw.

The inferior border is rounded and thicker in front than behind.

The ramus is positioned nearly vertically and is quadrilateral in shape. It presents two surfaces—medial and lateral; four borders—upper, lower, anterior, and posterior; and two processes—the coronoid and the condyloid processes.

The lateral surface is flat and relatively smooth.

The medial surface presents a hole near its center, the *mandibular foramen,* where the inferior alveolar vessels and nerve emerge. On the front margin of the foramen and bounding it medially is a flap of bone, the *lingula mandibulae.*

The upper border is thin, concave, and presents two processes—an anterior process called the *coronoid* and a posterior process, the *condyloid.* The concavity between the two processes is termed the *mandibular notch.*

The lower (inferior) border is round and thick. Its anterior portion is continuous with the lower border of the body.

The anterior border is thin above and thicker below where it is continuous with the oblique line and body of the mandible.

The posterior border is rounded and thick, and where it joins the inferior border it forms the *angle of the mandible.*

The coronoid process (the more anterior process) of the ramus is a flat, somewhat triangular-shaped prominence that varies in size and shape.

The condyloid process is thicker than the coronoid process. It consists of an articular condyle, below which is a constricted neck that is continuous with the upper posterior part of the ramus.

AGE DIFFERENCES.   The most marked differences in the mandible due to age changes are associated with the development and eruption of the teeth. (See page 24).

ARTICULATIONS.   The mandible articulates with the two temporal bones.

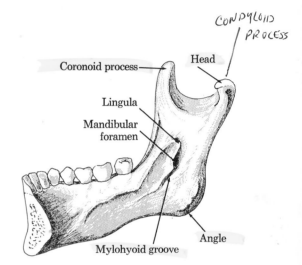

CONDYLOID PROCESS

Coronoid process

Head

Lingula

Mandibular foramen

Mylohyoid groove

Angle

Fig. 34.   Mandible. Medial surface.

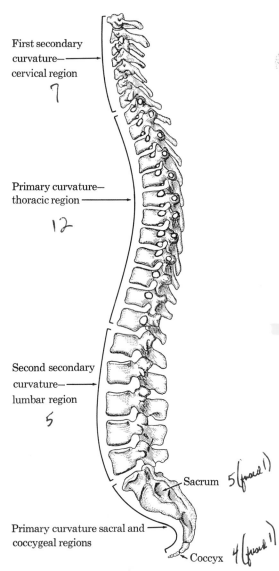

First secondary curvature—cervical region

7

Primary curvature—thoracic region

12

Second secondary curvature—lumbar region

5

Sacrum 5 (fused)

Primary curvature sacral and coccygeal regions

Coccyx 4 (fused)

Fig. 36.   Vertebral column.

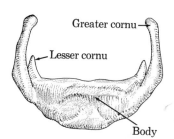

Greater cornu
Lesser cornu
Body

Fig. 35.   Hyoid bone.

THE HYOID BONE (FIG. 35)

LOCATION.   A small isolated bone located in the upper anterior part of the neck.

SHAPE.   It is a U-shaped bone.

DESCRIPTION.   It consists of a *central body* which is directed anteriorly, and two pairs of processes, the greater and lesser cornua. The *greater cornua,* a pair of relatively large processes, extend horizontally backward from the lateral borders of the body of the hyoid. The greater cornua decrease slightly in thickness as they progress posteriorly, and each ends in a rounded, enlarged tubercle. Two smaller cone-like processes, the *lesser cornua,* extend obliquely upward and laterally from the upper lateral margin of the body, at the junction of the greater cornua and the body of the hyoid bone. From the tip of each lesser cornu, a ligament (the stylohyoid ligament) extends to the styloid process of the temporal bone and helps to suspend the bone in its proper position in the body.

THE VERTEBRAL COLUMN (FIG. 36)

COMPOSITION.   This is a flexible column, formed by 24 separate vertebrae, the sacrum, and the coccyx.

NUMBER OF BONES.   There are 26 separate bones in the vertebral column.

LOCATION.   It is located along the posterior wall of the trunk, in the midline. Above, the vertebral column articulates with the skull; below, with the two os coxae (pelvic bones).

LENGTH OF COLUMN.   About 27 inches.

APPEARANCE.   Viewed from the side, the vertebral column in the adult presents four curves. The curves in the thoracic and the sacrococcygeal regions are concave anteriorly. They are known as primary curves since they are present in the fetus. The curves in the cervical and lumbar regions are convex anteriorly and are known as the secondary curves. They appear when the child learns to hold up its head (cervical curve) and to sit upright (lumbar curve).

The Vertebrae

CLASSIFICATION.   These bones are named according to the regions they occupy, and their numbers vary in the different regions.

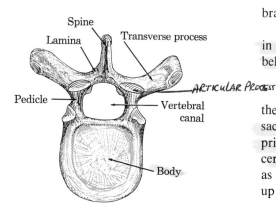

Spine
Lamina
Transverse process
Pedicle
ARTICULAR PROCESS
Vertebral canal
Body

Fig. 37.   A typical thoracic vertebra seen from above.

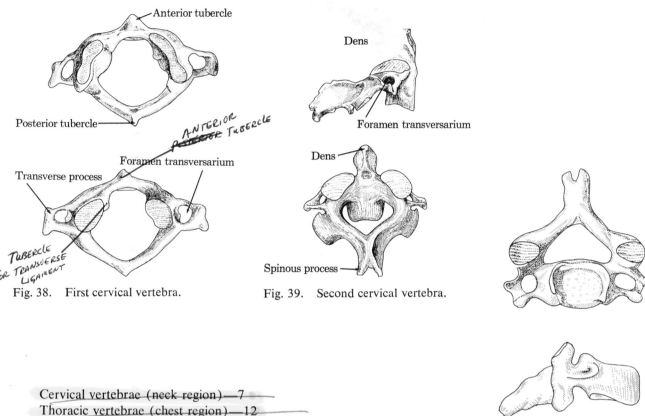

Fig. 38.   First cervical vertebra.

Fig. 39.   Second cervical vertebra.

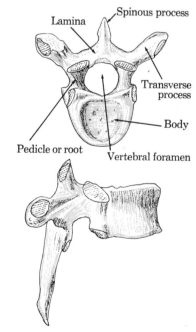

Fig. 40.   A cervical vertebra. Superior and lateral view.

Fig. 41.   A thoracic vertebra. Superior and lateral view.

Cervical vertebrae (neck region)—7
Thoracic vertebrae (chest region)—12
Lumbar vertebrae (lower back)—5
Sacral vertebrae (pelvis)—5, fused into 1 bone known as the sacrum

Coccygeal vertebrae (tail)—4, fused into 1 bone called the coccyx

APPEARANCE.   Except for the 1st and 2nd cervical vertebrae and the sacrum and coccyx, the vertebrae have certain characteristics in common. (Fig. 37.) Anteriorly each vertebra has a *body,* and directed posteriorly is the *vertebral arch.* Together these two segments form the *vertebral foramen,* which encloses the spinal cord. The vertebral arch is made up of two *pedicles,* two *laminae,* and has four *articular processes,* two *transverse processes, and* one *spinous process.*

VARIATIONS IN THE BASIC APPEARANCE.   Cervical vertebrae (Figs. 38, 39, and 40). They are the smallest of the single vertebrae. A foramen is present in each transverse process. The spinous processes are usually bifid. The 1st cervical vertebra, also called the *atlas,* has no body and no spinous process. It appears as a "ring" of bone. The 2nd cervical vertebra, or *axis,* has a well developed process (the *dens* or *odontoid process*) which projects upward from the body and forms a pivot around which the atlas revolves.

Thoracic vertebrae (Fig. 41). These vertebrae are larger than the cervical and smaller than the lumbar vertebrae and increase in size from above downward. Except for the 11th and 12th vertebrae, they have articular facets on the sides of the bodies and on the transverse processes, which articulate with the heads and tubercles of the ribs. The spinous processes are long and are directed obliquely downward.

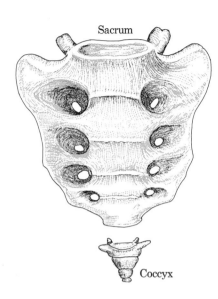

Fig. 43.   Sacrum and coccyx. Anterior aspect.

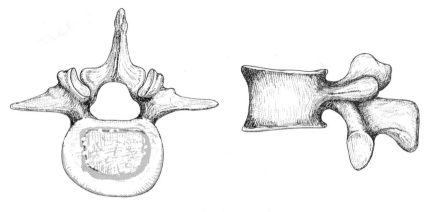

Fig. 42.   A lumbar vertebra.

A.   Superior view.   B.   Lateral view.

Lumbar vertebrae (Fig. 42). These are the largest of the single, or unfused, vertebrae. There are neither foramina in the transverse processes nor facets on the sides of the bodies of these vertebrae. The spinous process is quadrilateral in shape and thick and broad, and projects nearly straight posteriorly.

Sacral Vertebrae (Figs 43 and 44). The five sacral vertebrae are fused to form a single, large, triangular-shaped bone, the sacrum. It is curved so that it presents a concave surface anteriorly and a convex surface posteriorly. The sacrum articulates above with the last lumbar vertebra, laterally with the pelvic bones and below with the coccyx.

Coccygeal Vertebrae (Figs. 43 and 44). Normally the last four vertebrae are fused to form the coccyx; it may be formed by fusion of three to five vertebrae. These vertebrae are rudimentary and consist of only the body and poorly developed transverse processes.

BONES OF THE THORAX

The thoracic skeleton is a cagelike structure that encloses and protects two vital organs, the heart and the lungs (Fig. 45).

COMPONENTS. It is formed by the *bodies of the thoracic vertebrae,* 12 pairs of *ribs* and *associated costal cartilages,* and the *sternum* or breast bone.

SHAPE. It resembles a flattened cone in shape, being broad below and narrow above. It is flattened anteroposteriorly and is longer behind than in front.

SEX DIFFERENCES. The thoracic cavity in the male has a greater capacity than in the female. In the male, the sternum is positioned one vertebra higher than in the female, and the upper ribs are not quite so movable in the male.

The Ribs (Figs. 46 and 47)

The ribs are arched strips of bone that form the greater part of the bony thorax. The length of the ribs increases from the 1st to the 7th, then decreases again to the 12th.

NUMBER. Usually there are 12 pairs of ribs. This number may vary so that there may be 11 or 13 pairs.

ARTICULATIONS. The ribs articulate with the vertebrae behind and attach by segments of cartilage with the sternum in front.

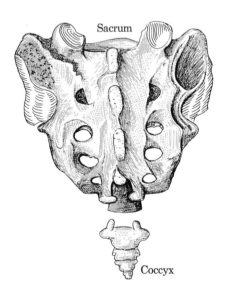

Fig. 44.   Sacrum and coccyx. Posterior aspect.

Carpal Bones (Figs. 57 and 58)

The eight bones of the wrist are arranged in two transverse rows. In the proximal row from the lateral to the medial side they are *scaphoid* (navicular), *lunate, triquetrum* (triangular), *and pisiform;* in the distal row, lateral to medial, they are *trapezium* (greater multangular), *trapezoid* (lesser multangular), *capitate,* and *hamate.*

ARTICULATIONS. The scaphoid articulates with five bones—proximally with the radius, distally with the trapezium and trapezoid, and medially with the capitate and lunate.

The lunate articulates with five bones—proximally with the radius, distally with the capitate and hamate, laterally with the scaphoid, and medially with the triquetrum.

The triquetrum articulates with three bones—distally with the hamate, laterally with the lunate, anteriorly with the pisiform, and proximally with a cartilaginous articular disc which extends between it and the distal extremity of the ulna.

The pisiform articulates with only one bone—the triquetrum.

The trapezium articulates with four bones—proximally with the scaphoid, distally with the first metacarpal, medially with the trapezoid and second metacarpal.

The trapezoid articulates with four bones—proximally with the scaphoid, distally with the second metacarpal, laterally with the trapezium, and medially with the capitate.

The capitate articulates with seven bones—proximally with the scaphoid and lunate; distally with the second, third, and fourth metacarpals; laterally with the trapezoid; and medially with the hamate.

The hamate has a hook-like process of bone called the hamulus, that projects anteriorly from the distal portion of its anterior surface. The hamate articulates with five bones—proximally with the lunate, distally with the fourth and fifth metacarpals, medially with the triquetrum, and laterally with the capitate.

The closely fitting articular surfaces of the carpal bones, and the numerous ligaments that bind them together, greatly restrict the movements in the wrist as to both the extent and kind of movement (gliding primarily).

Metacarpal Bones (Fig. 57 and Fig. 58)

These are the bones of the palm of the hand. They are identified by numbers from one to five, beginning on the lateral side with the metacarpal of the thumb. Each bone has a shaft and two extremities: *base* (carpal) and *head* (digital). The base of each bone is nearly cuboidal in shape, but slightly wider behind than in front. At its base, each metacarpal articulates with the distal row of carpal bones and at the sides with the adjacent metacarpal bone or bones.

The shaft of the metacarpals is slightly curved, presenting a concave curve anteriorly and a convexity posteriorly. The digital extremity has an anteroposteriorly convex articular surface called a *head,* which articulates with the proximal end of the proximal phalanx. The heads of the metacarpals form the knuckles on the back of the hand.

ARTICULATIONS. The metacarpal bones articulate proximally as follows:

The first metacarpal articulates with the trapezium.

The second metacarpal articulates with the trapezium, trapezoid, capitate, and third metacarpal.

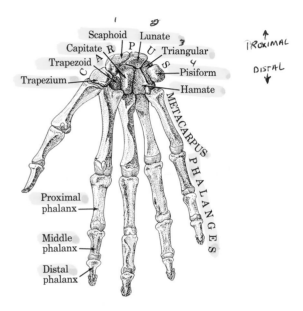

Fig. 57. Bones of the hand. Palmar aspect.

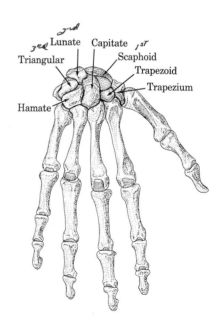

Fig. 58. Bones of the hand. Dorsal aspect.

The third metacarpal articulates with the capitate, second metacarpal, and fourth metacarpal.

The fourth metacarpal articulates with the capitate, hamate, third metacarpal, and fifth metacarpal.

The fifth metacarpal articulates with the hamate and fourth metacarpal.

Distally they articulate with the bases of the proximal phalanges.

Phalanges (Fig. 57 and Fig. 58, p. 45)

There are 14 phalanges: two for the thumb and three for each of the remaining four fingers. They are identified as proximal, middle, and distal phalanges, or as the first, second, and third phalanges, starting proximally. In shape they are not unlike the metacarpals, except for the distal or third phalanx. This bone is short and its distal portion is flattened anteroposteriorly; its distal margin is horseshoe-shaped.

ARTICULATIONS.   The proximal phalanges articulate proximally with the metacarpals and distally with the middle phalanges. The middle phalanges articulate with adjacent phalanges at both ends. The terminal phalanges articulate proximally with the distal extremity of the middle phalanges.

PELVIC GIRDLE AND LOWER EXTREMITY

The bones of the lower extremities are attached to the axial skeleton by means of the os coxae. These bones, with the sacrum, form a solid, firm, bony pelvis (the pelvic girdle).

Bones of the Pelvic Girdle

Os Coxae

The hip bone is large and irregularly shaped (Figs. 59 and 60). The adult bone is formed by the fusion of three distinct and separate bony segments demonstrable in the newborn: the *ilium, ischium,* and the *pubis.* These three bony segments are united in a bowl-shaped articular cavity, the *acetabulum,* on the lateral surface of the bone in its narrowest part.

LOCATION.   The right and left hip bones, together with the sacrum form the bony framework of the lower part of the body cavity.

SHAPE.   Each hip bone is irregular.

DESCRIPTION.   Because of the complexity of each bone, no attempt will be made to describe it in detail. Certain characteristic features will be listed and described and the illustrations should be referred to for orientation.

THE ILIUM.   This segment forms the greater part of the hip bone. It consists of a *body,* which makes up roughly two fifths of the acetabulum, and the *ala,* the large, thin, fan-shaped blade above. Its upper free margin (the *crest*) is convex, thickened, and rough. The crest ends anteriorly in a blunted process which is the *anterior superior iliac spine.* Roughly two inches below is a second less prominent process, the *anterior inferior iliac spine.* Posteriorly the crest ends in smaller but comparable processes called the *posterior superior iliac spine,* below which is a second process, the *posterior inferior iliac*

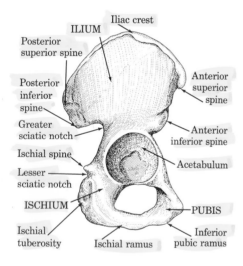

Fig. 59.   Os coxae. Lateral aspect.

spine. The inner surface of the ala is concave, its outer surface is convex. Both surfaces afford attachments for muscles of the pelvis and buttocks. The two bones are so positioned that the anterior superior spines are widely separated, while the posterior superior spines are only about four inches apart. The posterior inner surface of each ala is very rough from the level of the posterior inferior spine, forward and upward. This is the articular surface that fits a comparable surface on the sacrum to form the nearly immovable sacroiliac joint. Immediately below the articular surface of the ilium is a large concavity, the *greater sciatic notch,* which terminates below in a prominent pointed spinous process, the *spine of the ischium.* The junction between the ilium and the ischium lies just below the angle of the sciatic notch.

THE ISCHIUM. This segment forms the lower and posterior part of the hip bone. It consists of a *body* which contributes to the lower and posterior two fifths of the acetabulum, and an *inferior ramus.* Just below its junction with the ilium the sharp pointed spine of the ischium projects backwards from its posterior border. Below the spine is a small concavity that marks the *lesser sciatic notch.* Below the level of the spine is a thick, short segment of the ischium, formerly called the superior ramus, which projects almost vertically downward and very slightly backward, and ends in a large, rough enlargement of the ramus called the *ischial tuberosity.* This tuberosity bears the weight of the body when an individual is sitting erect. From the anterior margin of the ischial tuberosity a flattened, relatively narrow bar of bone, the *inferior ramus,* extends obliquely forward, upward, and medially to merge with a comparable bar of bone (the inferior ramus of the pubis) that descends from the body of the pubic bone or pubis.

THE PUBIS. This segment contributes to the formation of the anteromedial one fifth of the acetabulum. From this acetabular portion of the bone, a flattened bar of bone, the *superior ramus of the pubis,* extends medially for about an inch before it expands to form the *body* of the pubic bone. The body of the pubis is roughly rectangular in shape. Medially it presents an oval, roughened articular surface which forms a slightly movable joint with the body of the pubis of the opposite side. This junction is called the *pubic symphysis.* The *obturator foramen* is a large, triangular-shaped "hole" in the lower half of the hip bone. It is enclosed by the rami of the pubis and the ischium, and the constricted portion of the bone containing the acetabulum. In the intact body this space is closed almost completely by a thin layer of fibrous tissue.

The Bony Pelvis

This is formed by the two hip bones in front and laterally, and the sacrum and coccyx posteriorly. It forms a bony girdle, open above and below, that serves to protect and contain some of the abdominal organs. It is divided into two parts: the *false pelvis,* which is the area located between the iliac ala (blades), and the *true pelvis,* the smaller area bounded by the lower half of the pelvic bones (including the area of the acetabulum, the ischium, and the pubic bones), the sacrum, and the coccyx. The true pelvis is important in the female since it represents the bony limiting boundaries of the birth canal. The female pelvis shows certain definite sex differences from the true pelvis in the

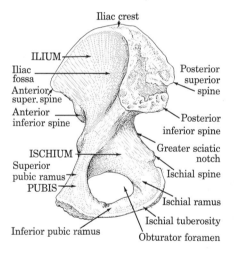

Fig. 60.   Os coxae. Medial aspect.

male (Fig. 24, p. 25). These sex differences consist of the following modifications in the female:

1. The bones are less rugged.
2. The pelvis has less depth.
3. The ilia are less vertical in position.
4. The anterior superior spines are farther apart.
5. The superior opening into the true pelvis is larger and more rounded.
6. The sacrum is wider, shorter, and less sharply curved.
7. The ischiopubic rami diverge more so as to form a wide, more rounded arch. In the male, these rami form a rather acute angle. (See Fig. 24, p. 25.)
8. The ischial tuberosities turn outward and are more everted.
9. The inferior opening of the true pelvis is larger.

ARTICULATIONS. The hip bone articulates with three bones—the sacrum, the femur, and the pelvic bone of the opposite side.

Bones of the Lower Extermity

These include *bones of the thigh and leg,* which are the femur, the patella or knee cap, the tibia, and the fibula, and *bones of the foot,* which include the tarsal (ankle) bones, the metatarsal bones, and the phalanges (toes).

The Femur (Figs. 61 and 62)

The femur is the largest, longest, and strongest bone of the skeleton. In the standing position, the femur is not positioned vertically, rather it is directed obliquely downward and medially so as to approach the femur of the opposite side in its lower part. This convergence of the two bones brings the knee joints nearer the line of gravity for the body. Since the female pelvis is broader than that of the male, the degree of convergence is greater in women and accounts for the fact that most women are "knock-kneed."

LOCATION. It is the bone of the thigh located between the hip and the knee.

SHAPE. It is a typical long bone.

DESCRIPTION. The femur has a shaft (body) and two extremities—upper and lower.

The upper extremity consists of a *head, neck,* and the *greater* and *lesser trochanters* (Figs. 61 and 62). The head is a nearly spherical articular prominence that is directed upward, medially, and very slightly anteriorly. The surface of the head is smooth except for an oval area near the center of the head called the *fovea capitis femoris.* It affords attachment for the ligamentum teres which fastens the head of the femur in the acetabulum of the hip bone.

The neck is a relatively thick segment of bone extending between the head and the shaft of the femur. It is inclined upward, medially, and slightly forward forming, in the adult male, a less acute angle than in the adult female, due to the width of the female pelvis.

The trochanters are two bony prominences that project from the upper end of the femur at the junction of the neck and shaft of the bone. The greater trochanter is the larger of the two. It projects upward and slightly posterolaterally from the upper and outer line of

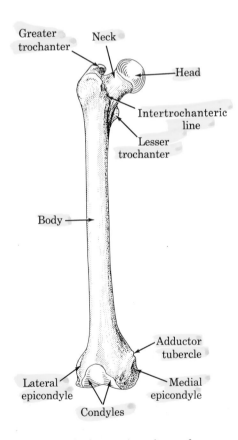

Fig. 61. Right femur. Anterior surface.

junction between neck and shaft. The lesser trochanter is a smaller, conical elevation directed posteromedially. It lies at a lower level, in line with the lower and inner point of junction between the neck and the shaft. The *intertrochanteric line* is a narrow, roughened strip extending from the greater trochanter obliquely downward and medially (on the front of the bone) to the lesser trochanter. The *intertrochanteric crest* is a raised, rounded crest of bone on the posterior aspect of the femur that extends from the greater trochanter obliquely downward and medially to the lesser trochanter.

The shaft is cylindrical in shape and smooth except for a vertical, roughened ridge down the posterior surface of the bone, the *linea aspera,* which gives attachment for most of the thigh muscles. The linea aspera, both above and below, divides into two roughened, diverging lines. Above, one line is directed toward the lesser trochanter and the other toward the greater trochanter; below, the lines diverge and merge with the *supracondylar ridges,* one with the lateral and one with the medial ridge. The *gluteal tuberosity* is the roughened upward extension of the linea aspera that goes to the base of the greater trochanter. The *pectineal line* extends from the linea aspera to the base of the lesser trochanter. Below, where the lines of the linea aspera diverge, they enclose a triangular space, the popliteal surface of the femur.

The lower extremity is the large, distal, expanded portion of the femur. It includes the two articular eminences, the *medial* and *lateral condyles;* the *intercondyloid fossa;* the *intercondyloid line;* and the *medial* and *lateral epicondyles.*

The condyles are two smooth, anteroposteriorly convex, articular surfaces. The lateral condyle is the wider and the more prominent of the two. The medial condyle is longer. This increased length allows for proper articulation with the tibia. Viewed from below, the articular surfaces are roughly U-shaped, with the open part of the U directed posteriorly. The space between the two condyles posteriorly is the intercondyloid fossa and is limited above by a ridge, the intercondyloid line. Where the two condyles merge below and in front, a deep groove forms a trochlear-like patellar surface over which the patella glides. The epicondyles are raised eminences of bone, one associated with each condyle. The medial epicondyle is a large, convexly-rounded process above and medial to the medial condyle. Where the medial supracondylar ridge joins the epicondyle is a small tubercle, the *adductor tubercle.* The lateral epicondyle is smaller and less prominent than its medial counterpart.

ARTICULATIONS. The femur articulates with three bones—proximally with the hip bone, distally with the tibia, below and anteriorly with the patella.

The Patella or Knee Cap (Fig. 63)

LOCATION. The patella lies in front of the knee joint in the tendon of the quadriceps femoris muscle.

SHAPE. Roughly triangular.

DESCRIPTION. This is a small, rather flat bone. It is positioned so that its apex is down. The upper three fourths of its posterior surface is a smooth articular surface with a vertical ridge which matches and fits into the groove on the trochlear patellar surface of the femur.

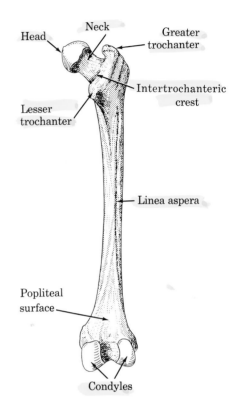

Fig. 62. Right femur. Posterior surface.

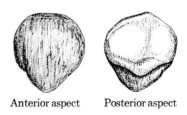

Anterior aspect   Posterior aspect

Fig. 63. Patella. Anterior and posterior surfaces.

ARTICULATIONS. The patella articulates with only one bone—the femur.

Two bones form the supportive framework of the leg, the large, medially positioned *tibia* and the long, slender, laterally positioned *fibula.*

The Tibia (Figs. 64 and 65)

The tibia is the second longest bone of the skeleton, exceeded only by the femur.

LOCATION. It is the more medial of the two bones of the leg, and extends between the knee and the ankle.

SHAPE. It is one of the long bones.

DESCRIPTION. Like all long bones it has a shaft (body) and two extremities—upper and lower.

The upper extremity is large and expanded to form two condyles that articulate with and bear the weight transmitted by the femur. On the upper surface of the condyles are two concave articular surfaces, separated by an irregular, non-articular, rough strip from which projects the *intercondylar eminence.* On the front of the tibia, about an inch below the level of the articular surfaces, is an oval-shaped eminence, the *tibial tuberosity.* Immediately below the margin of the lateral condyle on the posterolateral side of the bone is a small articular facet for the head of the fibula.

The shaft of the tibia presents three surfaces: medial, lateral, and posterior; and three margins: medial, anterior, and interosseous. Three structures of the shaft warrant special mention.

1. The *soleal line* (*popliteal line*) on the posterior surface, that extends obliquely downward and medially from the fibular articular facet to the medial margin.

2. The anterior margin, that extends from the tibial tuberosity above to the anterior margin of the medial malleolus below. This border is sharp and prominent above, rounded, and not so prominent below. It is subcutaneous and easily palpated through its entire extent. The medial surface, except where it affords attachment for the tendons of the sartorius, gracilis, and the semitendinous, is also subcutaneous and is therefore subject to injury.

3. The interosseous margin is directed laterally and affords attachment for the thin fibrous interosseous membrane which fills the gap between the tibia and fibula.

The lower extremity is smaller and less expanded than the upper extremity. It consists of a medial, downward, bony projection called the *medial malleolus,* and articular surfaces. The inferior articular surface, which is continuous medially with the articular surfaces on the lateral side of the malleolus, is smooth, slightly concave from front to back, and is for articulation with the talus, one of the bones of the ankle. The lower portion of the lateral surface presents a smooth, depressed articular area for articulation with the fibula.

ARTICULATIONS. The tibia articulates with three bones—proximally with the femur, laterally (at both extremities) with the fibula, and distally with the talus.

The Fibula (Figs. 64 and 65)

LOCATION. It is the more lateral of the two bones of the leg, located between the knee and the ankle.

SHAPE. A long, slender bone with a slightly twisted shaft.

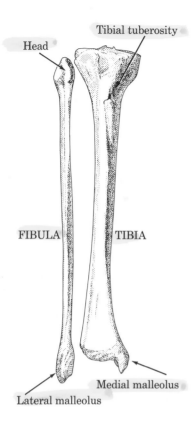

Fig. 64. Right tibia and fibula. Anterior aspect.

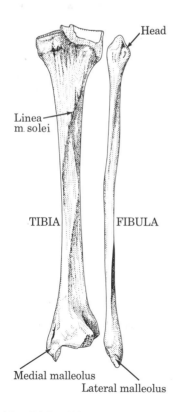

Fig. 65. Right tibia and fibula. Posterior aspect.

DESCRIPTION.   The bone has a shaft (body) and two extremities —upper and lower.

The upper extremity presents a small, knob-like enlargement, the *head,* on which is a small, smooth articular surface for articulation with the lateral condyle of the tibia. This bone does not enter into the formation of the knee joint.

The shaft of the bone is extremely slender in relation to the length of the fibula. It is slightly twisted on its long axis. The bony markings are limited to margins and areas of surface roughness for attachments of muscles. One margin, the *interosseous,* is directed medially and affords attachment for the interosseous membrane that extends between the fibula and the tibia.

The lower extremity is pyramidal in shape and about the size of a thumb. It is flatter and more pointed than the upper extremity. It extends beyond the lower, lateral margin of the tibia to form the *lateral malleolus.* The lower extremity of the fibula articulates with a concave depression on the lateral side of the lower extremity of the tibia to which it is firmly bound by the interosseous membrane and ligaments. The medial free surface extending below the tibia has a smooth surface for articulation with the talus. On the posterior margin of the malleolus is a groove, the *malleolar sulcus,* for the tendons of the two peronei (plural of peroneous) muscles. The fibula is essential in the formation of the ankle joint.

ARTICULATIONS.   The fibula articulates with two bones—the tibia and the talus.

The foot is modified to serve as a weight bearing structure and for locomotion. The bones entering into the formation of the foot and their arrangement are designed to form a stable structure, somewhat limited in range of movement.

Tarsal Bones (Ankle Bones) (Figs. 66 and 67)

The seven tarsal bones are the talus, calcaneus, navicular, medial, intermediate and lateral cuneiforms, and the cuboid. The talus and calcaneus are the largest of these seven bones and are so aligned as to receive the entire weight of the body.

The Talus

The talus is the second largest tarsal bone (the largest is the calcaneus). It consists of a *body,* a constricted *neck* portion, and a *head.* The upper face of the body is a smooth, trochlear-shaped articular surface, convex from front to back, that articulates with the tibia. This articular surface continues onto the sides of the body, where it is concave, to articulate medially with the medial malleolus of the tibia, and laterally with the lateral malleolus of the fibula. The inverted U-shaped space, into which the articular portion of the body fits, restricts the movement at this joint to flexion and extension. Below, the talus rests on and articulates with the calcaneus. Anteriorly, the talus articulates with the navicular bone.

ARTICULATIONS.   The talus articulates with four bones—the tibia, fibula, calcaneus, and navicular.

The Calcaneus

This is the largest bone of the ankle. Through the talus above it, the calcaneus receives the entire weight of the body and in turn it

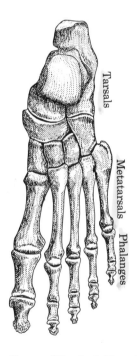

Fig. 66.   Bones of the foot. Dorsal aspect.

transmits this weight to the ground. It is roughly rectangular in shape with its long axis directed forward, upward, and very slightly laterally. It extends inferiorly and posteriorly beyond the talus to form the heel. Its posterior portion is convexly curved, somewhat expanded, and affords attachments for the tendons of the powerful extensor muscles of the foot. From the front part of its medial surface a stout process of bone, the *sustentaculum tali,* projects medially. Viewed from above, three smooth articular surfaces can be seen, two on the body of the bone and one on the sustentaculum tali, for articulation with the talus. The anterior surface of the bone also presents a smooth surface for articulation with the cuboid bone.

ARTICULATIONS. The calcaneus articulates with two bones—the talus and the cuboid.

The Navicular Bone.

This is a "boat-shaped" bone located on the medial side of the foot, between the talus behind and the cuneiforms in front. Its posterior surface is smooth and concave for articulation with the talus. Its anterior surface, generally convex from side to side, presents three distinct facets for articulation with the three cuneiform bones.

ARTICULATIONS. The navicular articulates with four bones—the talus, and the medial, intermediate, and lateral cuneiforms.

The Cuboid

As the name implies, this bone is roughly cuboidal in shape. It is located on the lateral side of the foot, lateral to the navicular and the lateral cuneiform, in front of the calcaneus, and behind the fourth and fifth metatarsals. On its posterior, medial, and anterior surfaces are smooth articular surfaces for articulation with each of the above mentioned bones.

ARTICULATIONS. The cuboid articulates with five bones—the calcaneus, navicular, lateral cuneiform, fourth and fifth metatarsals.

The Cuneiforms

These bones are identified by their position—medial, intermediate, and lateral, and are all more or less wedge-shaped. The medial is the largest and the intermediate the smallest of the three. They lie in a row immediately behind the first three metatarsals and a portion of the fourth, and articulate anteriorly with these bones.

ARTICULATIONS. The medial cuneiform articulates with four bones—navicular, intermediate cuneiform, and first and second metatarsals. The intermediate cuneiform articulates with four bones—navicular, medial and lateral cuneiforms, and the second metatarsal. The lateral cuneiform articulates with six bones—navicular, cuboid, intermediate cuneiform, and second, third and fourth metatarsals.

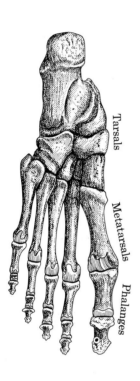

Fig. 67.   Bones of the foot. Plantar aspect.

The Metatarsals (Figs. 66 and 67)

There are five metatarsal bones, numbered from one to five, starting on the medial side of the foot. In general, these bones are similar in form to the metacarpal bones of the hand, but differ in the following characteristics.

The metatarsal bones are longer and more slender.

Their anterior ends (heads) show little expansion, but the articular surface extends farther onto the dorsal surface of the shaft than in the metacarpals.

All of the metatarsals lie parallel to one another. This limits the movement of the great toe when compared to the freedom of movement possible in the thumb.

The first metatarsal is a short, thick, strong bone designed to support and transmit the weight of the body to the ground.

ARTICULATIONS. The head of each metatarsal bone articulates with the proximal phalanx of the corresponding digit in front. At their bases the metatarsals articulate with one or more tarsal bones (see above).

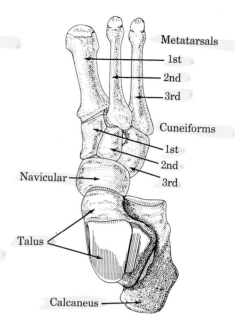

Fig. 68. Bones forming the medial longitudinal arch of the right foot.

Phalanges of the Foot (Figs. 66, p. 51 and 67, p. 52)

There are 14 phalanges in the foot and their arrangement is similar to the phalanges of the hand. In the foot, however, the phalanges are short, and even vestigial in the fifth digit.

Arches of the Foot

Normally, the bones of the foot are not placed flatly on the ground, rather, they are arranged in the form of two longitudinal arches—medial and lateral—and one transverse arch. The shapes of the bones of the ankle and the metatarsals are important factors in the formation of the arches, but their maintenance is dependent on the ligaments that bind the bones together and the tendons of muscles that help to support them.

The *medial longitudinal arch* is formed by nine bones: the calcaneus, the talus, the navicular, the three cuneiforms and the first three metatarsals. (Fig. 68.)

The *lateral longitudinal arch* is formed by four bones: the calcaneus, the cuboid, and the fourth and fifth metatarsals. (Fig. 69.)

The *transverse arches* of the foot, for the most part, consist of a series of incomplete arches (half-domes) that are difficult to define sharply, particularly in the mid-tarsal area. There are complete arches in the area of the metatarsal-tarsal junctions. These arches are reinforced by the short intertarsal ligaments, the intrinsic muscles of the first and fifth toes and by the tendon of the peroneus longus muscle.

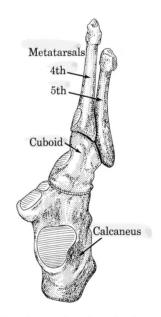

Fig. 69. Bones forming the lateral longitudinal arch of the right foot.

4

THE ARTICULAR SYSTEM

To form a functional skeletal system the separate bones of the body must be securely joined together. Their junctures are called joints or articulations. In some joints the opposing surfaces of the bones are so close together and securely fastened that little or no movement can take place. Most of the joints of the body, however, allow variable amounts of movement between adjacent bones.

CLASSIFICATION

On the basis of the amount of movement that can take place, joints are classified as *immovable* and *movable*. The latter are subdivided into slightly and freely movable joints.

Immovable Joints (Junctura fibrosa or Synarthroses)

The immovable joints of the body are restricted in number and distribution in the adult body. They occur between bones formed directly from membrane such as the bones of the skull (except for the mandible). Among this type of articulation are the joints called *sutures,* which unite the bones of the cranium. A variation of the immovable form of joint occurs in the immature long bones of the skeleton at the epiphyseal plate. Here the epiphysis of the bone is joined to the diaphysis by a narrow, intervening plate of hyaline cartilage. This is a temporary joint, found only in growing bones; by adulthood the epiphyseal cartilage is replaced by bone, i.e., the epiphyses are closed.

CHARACTERISTICS OF SUTURAL JOINTS. The articular surfaces of adjacent bones are either beveled and overlap each other (squamous suture) or they are serrated and interlock (serrate suture) (Fig. 70). In either case the articulating surfaces fit snugly together and are securely joined by a thin layer of dense fibrous connective tissue, the *sutural ligament.*

FUNCTION. Immovable joints afford maximum stability, and in the cranium form a rigid, nearly solid-walled, cranial cavity that contains and affords protection for the soft, delicate tissue of the brain.

Slightly Movable Joints (Junctura cartilaginea or Amphiarthroses)

These joints are found where stability and strength are more important than movement. (Fig. 71.)

CHARACTERISTICS OF SLIGHTLY MOVABLE JOINTS. The adjacent bony articular surfaces are separated slightly and are held in close

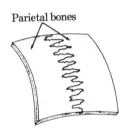
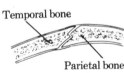

Parietal bones

Temporal bone

Parietal bone

Fig. 70.   Sutures. A type of immovable joint.

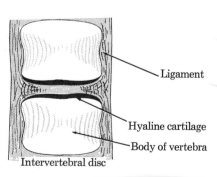

Ligament

Hyaline cartilage

Body of vertebra

Intervertebral disc

Fig. 71.   Slightly movable joint.

approximation to each other by a tough fibrocartilaginous disc, i.e., between the bodies of the vertebrae, or by interosseous fibers that form a ligament connecting the adjacent bones, i.e., the inferior tibio-fibular joint.

FUNCTION.   Slightly movable joints afford strong, stable junctions in which the range of movement is restricted.

Freely Movable Joints (Junctura synovialis or Diarthroses)

Most of the joints of the body belong in this group. (Fig. 72.)

CHARACTERISTICS OF FREELY MOVABLE JOINTS.   The articular surfaces of the adjacent bones are hard, smooth, and free of periosteum. These surfaces are covered with a thin layer of hyaline cartilage. There are ligaments that hold the bones in approximation to each other and enclose the articular ends of the bones in an articular capsule that is lined by a synovial membrane. The synovial membrane secretes a fluid called synovia, which serves to lubricate the joint and prevent friction between the two articular bony surfaces. A freely movable joint may have a fibrocartilaginous articular disc or meniscus that divides the joint cavity completely or incompletely. When present, such a divider is attached at its outer edges to the fibrous capsule. Its free surfaces are covered by synovial membrane.

VARIETIES OF FREELY MOVABLE JOINTS.   These joints can be subdivided either on the basis of the shape of the surfaces of the adjacent articulating bones or by the kind of movement each joint is capable of performing. Using the first criterion, we can subdivide the synovial joints as follows:

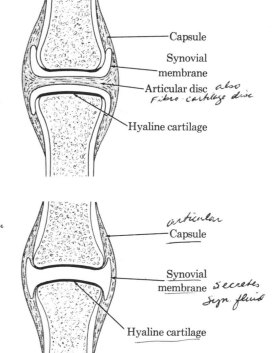

Fig. 72.   Freely movable joints, (above) with and (below) without an intervening articular disc.

Ginglymus (hinge joint) *elbow*	Cotyloid or Enarthrosis *hip + shoulder*
Trochoid (pivot joint) *wrist or head*	(ball-and-socket joint)
Condyloid *fingers*	Plane or Arthrodia
Sellaris (saddle joint) *thumb*	(gliding joint) *carpals*
Spheroid (convex head in	
concave fossa)	

If we subdivide on the basis of the movement permitted at a joint, we find that some joints will allow movement in only one plane and around a single axis. These are the uniaxial joints. Other joints permit movement in two planes, around two axes that are at right angles to each other. These are called biaxial joints, and the movements allowed are flexion and extension around one axis and abduction and adduction around a second axis. A third group includes multiaxial articulations. This variety is best illustrated by a long bone (humerus) that has a single axis center at its proximal end, which allows the distal end of the extremity to execute a wide, sweeping, circular movement (circumduction), involving numerous axes. Freely movable joints classified according to this method include:

Uniaxial Joints	Hinge joints (ginglymus) *elbow joint*
	Pivot joints (trochoid) *wrist + head*
Biaxial Joints	Saddle joints (sellaris) *thumb*
	Condyloid joints *fingers*
Multiaxial Joints	Ball-and-socket joints *hip + shoulder*
	(cotyloid or enarthrosis)
	Gliding joints *carpals*
	(plane or arthrodia)

KINDS OF MOVEMENT IN JOINTS

Gliding

This is the simplest type of movement occurring in movable joints and occurs in some degree in all of them. In a few joints, it is the only type of motion that can take place.

Angular

This kind of movement increases or decreases the angle between two articulated bones and is of four types: *flexion,* which decreases the angle between two articulated bones; *extension,* which increases the angle between two articulated bones; *abduction,* in which an extremity moves laterally, away from the median plane of the body—in abduction of the digits of the hand or foot, the fingers or toes are spread apart, away from the median longitudinal axis which bisects the middle finger or toe; and *adduction,* in which an extremity moves medially, toward the median plane of the body—in adduction of the digits of the hand or foot, the fingers or toes are brought together, toward the median longitudinal axis which bisects the middle finger or toe.

Circumduction

This movement occurs only at the shoulder or hip joint. During circumduction the distal end of the extremity swings freely, ascribing a circle, while the proximal end is attached at a single central point.

Rotation

During rotation a bone moves around a longitudinal axis. This longitudinal axis may be in one bone and a second bone may "rotate" around it, or the bone may rotate around its own axis.

In this book only four joints will be discussed in any detail—the shoulder and elbow joints, the hip, and the knee. All joints will be listed, indicating classification and range of movement of each joint.

ARTICULATIONS OF THE SHOULDER, ELBOW, HIP, AND KNEE

The Shoulder Joint (Fig. 73)

BONES.   The articulation at the shoulder involves the rounded, smooth head of the humerus and the shallow, glenoid fossa of the scapula.

CLASSIFICATION.   This is a ball-and-socket joint of the synovial (diarthrodial) or freely movable class of joints.

STRUCTURES FORMING THE JOINT.   The components of this joint include the adjacent articular surfaces of the humerus and scapula, the glenoid labrum, the articular capsule lined by the synovial membrane, and three ligaments—coracohumeral, glenohumeral, and transverse humeral.

The *glenoid labrum* is a triangular-shaped fibrocartilaginous rim of tissue, connected by its broad base to the bony margin of the glenoid fossa. Its apex is free and sharp. It deepens the fossa and protects its bony margin.

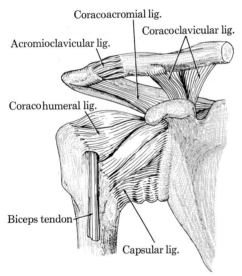

Coracoacromial lig.

Acromioclavicular lig.

Coracoclavicular lig.

Coracohumeral lig.

Biceps tendon

Capsular lig.

Fig. 73.   Shoulder joint viewed from the front.

MOVEMENTS. In a sense, the elbow is a "three joints in one capsule" arrangement, one joint occurring between the humerus and the ulna; one between the humerus and the radius; and the third between the proximal ends of the radius and the ulna. Ordinarily in considering the movements that occurs at the elbow, we describe it as a simple hinge joint capable of flexion and extension only. However, movement also occurs between the radius and the ulna (involving the capitulum of the humerus and the fovea of the radius), resulting in supination and pronation of the hand. In spite of the fact that the proximal radioulnar joint is included within the joint capsule of the elbow, it is treated as a separate entity (the radioulnar joint) and includes both the proximal and distal areas of bony articulation between these two bones.

BLOOD SUPPLY. The blood supply to the elbow joint is derived from branches given off the network of anastomosing vessels arising from the brachial, radial, and ulnar arteries.

NERVE SUPPLY. The joint is supplied by one branch from the ulnar nerve, one from the musculocutaenous, and two from the median nerve.

The Hip Joint

BONES. The articulation of the hip joint involves the acetabulum of the pelvic bone, and the smooth, rounded head of the proximal end of the femur.

CLASSIFICATION. It is a ball-and-socket joint of the freely movable or synovial (diarthrodial) class of articulations.

STRUCTURES. The components of this joint include the head of the femur, the acetabulum of the pelvic bone, the glenoid labrum, the articular capsule lined by the synovial membrane, and five ligaments—ligamentum capitis femoris (ligamentum teres femoris), transverse acetabular, iliofemoral, ischiofemoral (ischiocapsular), and pubofemoral (pubocapsular) (Figs. 77 and 78).

The *glenoid labrum* is a triangular-shaped strip of fibrocartilage that forms an incomplete ring around the margin of the acetabulum. The apex of the triangle is sharp and free. The labrum serves to deepen the cup-like acetabulum that receives the head of the femur.

The *articular capsule* is a relatively thick, dense, very strong, fibrous structure that encloses the joint. It is attached above to the margin of the acetabulum (behind) and the labrum (in front). Where the labrum is deficient, it is attached to the transverse acetabular ligament that spans the space where the labrum is missing.

The *ligamentum capitis femoris* (ligamentum teres femoris) is a short, strong, oval ligament extending between the acetabular depression and the head of the femur. Its apex is attached to the head of the femur at the roughened fovea capitis femoris. Its base is attached to the wall of the acetabulum by two thickened bands that straddle the acetabular notch.

The *transverse acetabular ligament* is a dense, flattened, fibrous ligament that bridges the acetabular notch where the labrum is deficient, thus completing the circular cartilaginous ring formed by the labrum, and creating a foramen through which nutrient vessels enter the joint.

The *iliofemoral ligament* is an inverted Y-shaped ligament at the front of the joint, where it merges with and strengthens the capsule

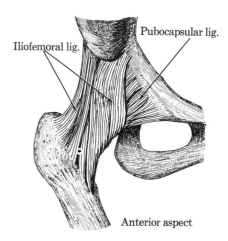

Fig. 77.   Hip joint. Anterior aspect.

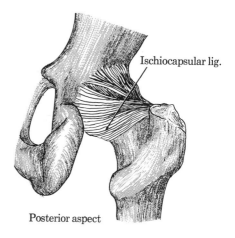

Fig. 78.   Hip joint. Posterior aspect.

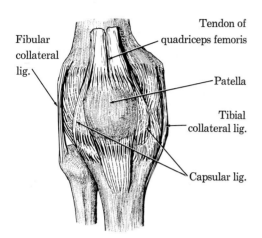

Fig. 79.   Knee joint. Anterior aspect.

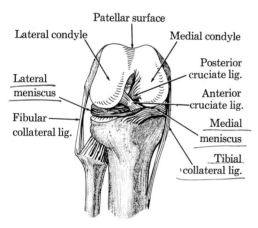

Fig. 80.   Knee joint dissected. Anterior aspect.

at this point. Above, it is attached to the anterior inferior spine of the ilium. Below, it fans out and forms two stout bands, one of which attaches to the upper part of the intertrochanteric line, and the other to the lower part of the intertrochanteric line of the femur.

The *ischiofemoral* ligament (ischiocapsular ligament) is a dense, strong, triangular-shaped ligament that extends from the ischium below and behind the joint capsule to the inner margin of the trochanteric fossa of the femur. Its deep fibers merge with and form part of the capsule.

The *pubofemoral ligament* (pubocapsular ligament) is a narrow band of fibers that extends from its attachment along the obturator crest and the superior pubic ramus above, to the neck of the femur where it merges with the fibrous capsule.

MUSCLES.   The muscles associated with the hip joint are above, the gluteus minima and the rectus femoris; in front, the iliopsoas; medially, the obturator externus and the pectineus; and behind, the piriformis, the superior and inferior gemelli (singular, gemellus), the obturator internus and externus, and the quadratus femoris.

MOVEMENTS.   The hip joint is capable of flexion, extension, abduction, adduction, rotation, and circumduction.

BLOOD SUPPLY.   The hip joint is supplied by the articular branches of the obturator, superior and inferior gluteals, and the medial femoral circumflex arteries.

NERVE SUPPLY.   Branches from the femoral, sciatic, obturator, and accessory obturator nerves and fibers from the sacral plexus supply the hip joint.

The Knee Joint

The knee joint is the largest, weakest, and most superficial joint in the body.

BONES.   The bones forming the knee joint are the distal end of the femur and the proximal end of the tibia. The articulation between the distal end of the femur and the patella is also involved.

CLASSIFICATION.   The knee joint is usually described as a hinge joint between the distal end of the femur and the proximal end of the tibia. Actually it is three joints in one: two arthrodial (gliding) joints, one between each of the two condyles of the femur and the corresponding condyles of the tibia, and a third atypical arthrodial joint between the femur and the patella. All belong to the synovial (diarthrodial) or freely movable class of articulation.

STRUCTURES.   The components of the knee joint include the articular surfaces of the femur, tibia, and patella; the medial and lateral menisci (singular, meniscus); the articular capsule lined by the synovial membrane; nine ligaments—anterior cruciate, posterior cruciate, transverse, coronary, oblique popliteal, arcuate popliteal, tibial collateral, fibular collateral, ligamentum patellae; and medial and lateral patellae retinacula (Figs. 79, 80, 81, and 82).

The *menisci* (Fig. 83) are two crescent-shaped strips of fibrous cartilage that cover roughly the peripheral two thirds of the articular surface of each tibial condyle. They are attached along their thickened, convex, outer margins to the outer edge of the tibial condyle and to the inside of the adjacent part of the capsule. Their centrally directed margins are thin and free. Their under surfaces that are in contact with the tibia are flat; the upper surfaces are concave and serve to deepen the condylar surfaces of the tibia for the reception of the condyles of the femur. The medial meniscus is the larger of the two and roughly oval in shape. Anteriorly, it narrows down to attach to the anterior intercondylar fossa of the tibia in front of the anterior cruciate ligament. Behind, it is broader, and it attaches to the posterior intercondylar fossa in front of the posterior cruciate ligament. The lateral meniscus, nearly circular in shape, covers most of the articular surface of the lateral condyle. Its anterior end is attached to the tibia between the anterior cruciate ligament, which lies in front and somewhat medial to it, and the intercondylar eminence of the tibia which projects behind it. Its posterior end attaches to the tibia in front of the posterior end of the medial meniscus.

The *articular capsule* is a thin, strong structure, reinforced by the fibrous bands of the fascia lata and the tendons of the thigh muscles. Behind, the capsule attaches so as to exclude the cruciate ligaments from the joint cavity proper. In front, the capsule is reinforced by the quadriceps muscles and their tendons and by the fascia lata and extensions from its thickened iliotibial band. Laterally, the iliotibial band reinforces the capsule along with the oblique popliteal and fibular collateral ligaments. Behind are the cruciate and the oblique popliteal ligaments along with the tendon of the semimembranous muscle. On the medial side of the capsule, the tibial collateral ligament along with the tendons of the semimembranosus and sartorius muscles reinforce the capsule.

The *cruciate ligaments* are two relatively short but strong fibrous structures located between the two articular surfaces of the condyles of the tibia, nearer the posterior than the anterior margins of the joint. The synovial membrane lining the capsule is reflected around the cruciate ligaments so that, although the ligaments are within the capsule, they are outside of the joint cavity proper. These ligaments are so named because as they extend from their attachments they cross each other forming a letter "X." The *anterior* cruciate ligament is attached to the tibia at a slight depression in front of the intercondylar eminence. It extends obliquely upward, backward, and laterally to attach to the posteromedial part of the lateral condyle of the femur. The *posterior* cruciate ligament is shorter and stronger than the anterior. It is attached to the posterior intercondylar fossa of the tibia, and extends upward, forward, and medially to attach to the anterolateral part of the medial epicondyle of the femur.

The *transverse ligament* extends horizontally between the narrowed anterior end of the medial meniscus and the anterior convex margin of the lateral meniscus. (Fig. 83.)

The *coronary ligaments* are actually part of the capsule itself, where it extends between and connects the menisci to the bony margin of the tibia.

The *oblique popliteal ligament* is broad and flat, and extends from the upper limit of the intercondylar fossa and posterior surface of the femur above, obliquely downward and medially, to attach along the posterior uppermost margin of the tibia.

The *arcuate popliteal ligament* attaches above to the lateral condyle of the femur and sweeps downward merging with the posterior surface of the capsular ligament. The fibers along this attachment converge and attach by two slips to the head of the fibula.

The *tibial collateral ligament* is a broad, vertically positioned, flat, fibrous band along the medial side of the knee joint, nearer its

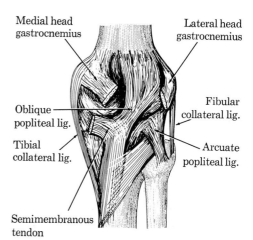

Fig. 81.   Knee joint. Posterior aspect.

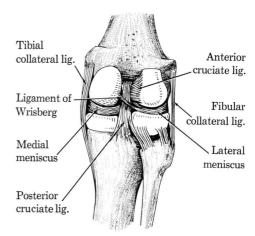

Fig. 82.   Knee joint dissected. Posterior aspect.

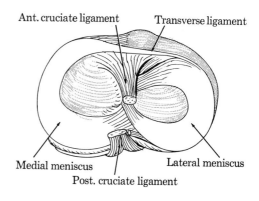

Fig. 83.   Knee joint. Menisci.

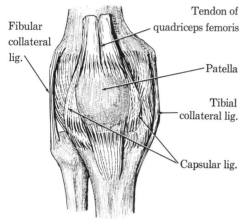

Fibular collateral lig.

Tendon of quadriceps femoris

Patella

Tibial collateral lig.

Capsular lig.

Knee joint dissected.

posterior than its anterior limit. It is attached to the medial condyle of the femur above and to the medial condyle and the medial surface of the tibia about an inch below the condyle.

The *fibular collateral ligament* is a strong, cord-like structure that extends between the lateral condyle of the femur and the head of the fibula. It is not attached to the lateral meniscus.

The *ligamentum patellae* is the name of that portion of the quadriceps tendon extending from the apex of the patella to the tuberosity of the tibia. (Fig. 79.)

MUSCLES. The muscles associated with the knee joint are in front and at the sides, the quadriceps femoris; medially, the sartorius, gracilis, semimembranosus, and semitendinosus; behind, the popliteus, plantaris, and the two heads of the gastrocnemius; and laterally, tendons of the biceps femoris and popliteus.

MOVEMENTS. The knee joint allows movements of flexion and extension, and some rotation in the flexed position.

BLOOD SUPPLY. The joint is supplied by branches of the femoral, popliteal, anterior tibial, and the lateral femoral circumflex arteries.

NERVE SUPPLY. The knee joint receives branches from the obturator, femoral, tibial, and common peroneal nerves.

LIST OF ARTICULATIONS

ARTICULATIONS OF THE SKULL

Mandibular articulation—between the mandible and temporal bone of the skull.
　Class of joint—synovial (diarthrosis)
　　Variety—ginglymus (hinge)—arthrodial
　Movements—mixed gliding and rolling; rotation

Atlanto-occipital articulation—between the atlas (first cervical vertebra) and the occipital bone of the skull.
　Class of joint—synovial (diarthrosis)
　　Variety—condyloid
　Movements—mixed gliding and rolling

Atlanto-axialis articulation
Medial—between the odontoid process (dens) of the axis and the anterior arch of the atlas and its transverse ligament.
　Class of joint—synovial (diarthrosis)
　　Variety—pivot
　Movement—rotation
Lateral—between the articular processes of the atlas and the axis.
　Class of joint—synovial (diarthrosis)
　　Variety—gliding
　Movement—gliding

ARTICULATIONS OF THE TRUNK

Intervertebral articulations
Between the bodies of the vertebrae.
　Class of joints—cartilaginous
　　Variety—symphysis (synarthrosis)

　　Movements—flexion; extension and lateral flexion; rotation
Between the vertebral arches.
　Class of joints—synovial (diarthrosis)
　　Variety—gliding
　Movement—gliding

Costovertebral articulations—between ribs and vertebrae.
　Class of joints—synovial (diarthrosis)
　　Variety—gliding
　Movements—gliding; rotation

Sternocostal articulations—between the sternum and the cartilages of the true ribs (except 1st rib).
　Class of joints—synovial (diarthrosis)
　　Variety—gliding
　Movements—gliding; rotation

ARTICULATIONS OF THE SHOULDER GIRDLE

Sternoclavicular articulation—between the medial end of the clavicle and the manubrium of the sternum.
　Class of joint—synovial (diarthrosis)
　　Variety—gliding
　Movements—gliding; rotation

Acromioclavicular articulation—between the acromial process of the scapula and the lateral end of the clavicle.
　Class of joint—synovial (diarthrosis)
　　Variety—gliding
　Movements—gliding; rotation

ARTICULATIONS OF THE UPPER EXTREMITY

Humeroscapular (shoulder) articulation—between the head of the humerus and the glenoid fossa of the scapula.
    Class of joint—synovial (diarthrosis)
        Variety—ball-and-socket
    Movements—flexion; extension; abduction; adduction; rotation; circumduction

Elbow articulation—between the humerus and the ulna, humerus and radius.
    Class of joint—synovial (diarthrosis)
        Variety—hinge
    Movements—flexion; extension

Radioulnar articulation
Proximal—between the head of the radius and the radial notch of the ulna.
    Class of joint—synovial (diarthrosis)
        Variety—pivot
    Movements—gliding; rotation
Distal—between the head of the ulna and the ulnar notch of the radius.
    Class of joint—synovial (diarthrosis)
        Variety—pivot
    Movements—gliding; rotation

Radiocarpal (wrist) articulation—directly, between the distal end of the radius and carpal bones: scaphoid (navicular), lunate, and triquetrum.
    Class of joint—synovial (diarthrosis)
        Variety—condyloid
    Movements—flexion; extension; abduction; adduction; circumduction

Intercarpal articulations—between the carpal bones of the proximal row; between the carpal bones of the distal row; and between the proximal and distal rows.
    Class of joints—synovial (diarthrosis)
        Variety—gliding
    Movement—gliding

Carpometacarpal articulations
Of the thumb: Between the trapezium (greater multangular) and proximal end of the 1st metacarpal.
    Class of joint—synovial (diarthrosis)
        Variety—saddle joint
    Movements—gliding; rotation
Of the four medial digits: Between the distal surfaces of the trapezium (greater multangular), trapezoid (lesser multangular), capitate, and hamate, and the proximal ends of the 2nd, 3rd, 4th, and 5th metacarpals.
    Class of joint—synovial (diarthrosis)
        Variety—gliding
    Movement—gliding

Intermetacarpal articulations—between the medial and lateral aspects of the proximal ends of the 2nd, 3rd, 4th, and 5th metacarpals.
    Class of joints—synovial (diarthrosis)
        Variety—gliding
    Movement—gliding

Metacarpophalangeal articulations
Of the four medial digits: Between the distal surfaces of the proximal end of the 1st phalanx.
    Class of joint—synovial (diarthrosis)
        Variety—hinge joint
    Movements—flexion; extension
Of the four medial digits: Between the distal ends of the 2nd, 3rd, 4th, and 5th metacarpals and the proximal ends of the 1st phalanges of the 2nd, 3rd, 4th, and 5th fingers.
    Class of joints—synovial (diarthrosis)
        Variety—condyloid
    Movements—flexion; extension; abduction; adduction; circumduction

Interphalangeal articulations—between the adjacent phalanges of each finger.
    Class of joints—synovial (diarthrosis)
        Variety—hinge joint
    Movements—flexion; extension

ARTICULATIONS OF THE PELVIS

Sacroiliac articulation—between the sacrum and the ilium.
    Class of joint—cartilaginous
        Variety—symphysis
    Movement—practically none, except due to compression of the cartilage

Pubic symphysis—between the two pubic bones.
    Class of joint—cartilaginous
        Variety—symphysis
    Movement—practically none, except due to compression of the cartilage

ARTICULATIONS OF THE LOWER EXTREMITY

Coxal (hip joint) articulation—between the head of the femur and the acetabulum of the pelvic bone.
    Class of joint—synovial (diarthrosis)
        Variety—ball-and-socket
    Movements—flexion; extension; abduction; adduction; rotation; circumduction

Tibio-femoral articulation (knee joint)—between the distal end of the femur and the proximal end of the tibia.
    Class of joint—synovial (diarthrosis)

Variety—hinge joint
Movements—flexion; extension

Tibio-fibular articulations

Proximal joint—between the lateral condyle of the tibia and the head of the fibula.

Class of joint—synovial (diarthrosis)
Variety—gliding
Movement—gliding

Distal joint—between the lateral side (fibular notch) of the tibia and the medial side of the lower extremity of the fibula.

Class of joint—cartilaginous
Variety—syndesmosis
Movement—slight yielding of the articular ligament

Talo-crural articulation (ankle joint)—between the distal end of the tibia (and its medial malleolus) and the talus; and between the lateral malleolus of the fibula and the talus.

Class of joint—synovial (diarthrosis)
Variety—hinge joint
Movements—flexion; extension

Intertarsal articulations—between the tarsals (bones of the ankle)

Class of joints—synovial (diarthrosis)
Varieties—gliding: posterior talocalcaneal joint
gliding: talocalcaneonavicular joint
saddle joint, gliding: calcaneocuboid joint
gliding: cuneonavicular joint
gliding: cuboideonavicular joint
gliding: intercuneiform joints
gliding: cuneocuboid joint
Movements—restricted gliding movements

Tarsometatarsal articulations—medial tarsometatarsal joint: between the medial cuneiform and the base of the 1st metatarsal; intermediate tarsometatarsal joint: between the intermediate cuneiform and the base of the 2nd metatarsal, and between the lateral cuneiform and the base of the 3rd metatarsal; lateral tarsometatarsal joint: between the lateral cuneiform and cuboid, and the base of the 4th metatarsal; and the cuboid and the 5th metatarsal.

Class of joints—synovial (diarthrosis)
Variety—arthrodial joints, gliding
Movement—slight gliding

Intermetatarsal articulations—between the medial and lateral aspects of the bases of adjacent metatarsal bones.

Class of joints—synovial (diarthrosis)
Variety—gliding
Movement—slight gliding

Metatarsophalangeal articulations—between the distal ends of the metatarsal bones and the bases of the proximal row of phalanges.

Class of joints—synovial (diarthrosis)
Variety—condyloid joints
Movements—flexion; extension; abduction; adduction

Interphalangeal articulations—between adjacent phalanges of each toe.

Class of joints—synovial (diarthrosis)
Variety—hinge joints
Movements—flexion; extension

5

THE MUSCULAR SYSTEM

MUSCLE TISSUE

While contractility is a property of the protoplasm of all living cells, it is only in muscle cells that this property reaches its maximum degree of differentiation and full utilization.

DEFINITION. Muscle is one of the four fundamental tissues of the body.

DERIVATION. It is derived from mesoderm.

COMPONENTS. Muscle tissue consists of *muscle cells* and the *associated fibrous connective tissues* which invest and serve to "harness" these cells so that their function (contraction) can be effectively utilized.

MUSCLE CELLS. *General Characteristics.* The structural unit of muscle is the muscle cell (fiber). All muscle cells are so modified (elongated) by their functional requirements that they look more like fibers than cells. In fact muscle cells are usually called muscle "fibers." Each muscle cell appears as an elongated fiber enclosed in a distinct cell membrane and containing one oval nucleus, (smooth muscle cells) or more than one (striated or cardiac muscle cells). The cytoplasm of the cell is known specifically as *sarcoplasm.* In the sarcoplasm, numerous fine fibrils called *myofibrils* are arranged parallel to the long axis of the muscle fiber. These myofibrils are thought to be the structures responsible for contraction of the muscle cell.

Function. The primary function of a muscle cell is *contraction.*

Classification. Based on morphologic and physiologic criteria, there are three kinds of muscle cells.

Smooth Muscle (non-striated; involuntary)
Cardiac Muscle (striated; involuntary)
Skeletal Muscle (striated; voluntary)

Smooth muscle is the simplest of the three kinds of muscle. Each muscle cell (fiber) is an elongated, spindle-shaped cell that has an elongated oval nucleus in the center of the cell   (see Fig. right). There are no cross striations or banding of the fiber and there is no sarcolemma enclosing the fiber. Smooth muscle is an involuntary muscle that cannot be "willed" to contract. It forms the muscular walls of internal organs and tubular structures (i.e., the stomach, intestines, uterus, urinary bladder, bile ducts, and blood vessels) and the arrectores pilorum muscles of the hair follicles in the skin. Smooth muscle usually contracts slowly and rhythmically.

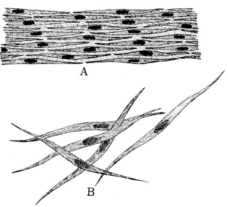

Smooth muscle and teased smooth muscle fibers.

65

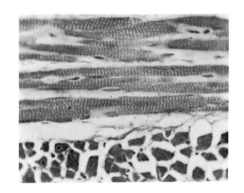

Fig. 84. Striated muscle, longitudinal and cross section.

Cardiac muscle or heart muscle is found only in the walls of the heart. This muscle shares some characteristics with smooth muscle, some with striated muscle, and it has several specific characteristics of its own. Cardiac muscle cells (fibers) are elongated, cylindrical cells that show faint cross striations (these characteristics are shared with striated muscle). The oval nuclei are centrally located and the muscle's action is involuntary (these characteristics are shared with smooth muscle). Characteristics peculiar to cardiac muscle are branching of the muscle fibers, and intercalated discs. The latter are markings that extend either straight or stepwise across the fiber at varying intervals and are interpreted as being the double layer of sarcolemma (a thin structureless membrane enclosing the fiber) of two adjacent cells. (See Fig. 11, p. 9.)

Skeletal (striated) *muscle* makes up the voluntary musculature of the body and is under the "willed" control of the individual. This kind of muscle makes up the "meat" of the body. Skeletal muscle cells (fibers) are elongated, cylindrical, multinucleated cells with peripherally located oval nuclei. The fibers show distinct cross-striations, and each fiber is enclosed within a membrane called the sarcolemma (Fig. 84). Unlike smooth muscle, skeletal muscle does not contract rhythmically. Its contractions are rapid, powerful, and intermittent.

ASSOCIATED FIBROUS CONNECTIVE TISSUE. The contraction (shortening) of an elongated muscle cell (fiber) would never produce movement by itself, unless the ends of the cell were in some way attached to the structure to be moved. These cells, therefore, must be "harnessed" to a structure that effects movement, if the shortening (contraction) of the muscle fiber is to produce a "pull" on the structure. Fibrous connective tissue closely associated with the muscle cells (fibers) harnesses the muscle cells (Figs. 85 and 86). A fine mesh-

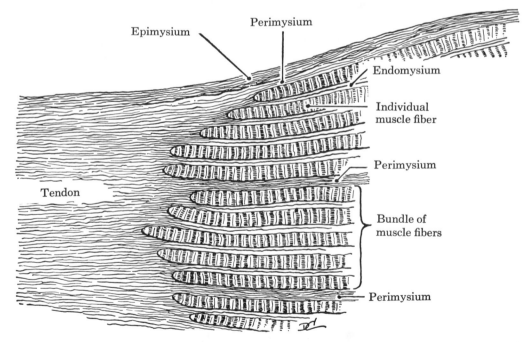

Fig. 85. Diagram of a longitudinal section of a muscle, showing how muscles terminate in tendons. The connective tissue of the epimysium, the perimysium, and the endomysium is continuous with the connective tissue of the tendon. The sarcolemma covering each muscle fiber also is adherent to the connective tissue of the tendon. (From Ham and Leeson. *Histology,* 4th ed. J. B. Lippincott Co.)

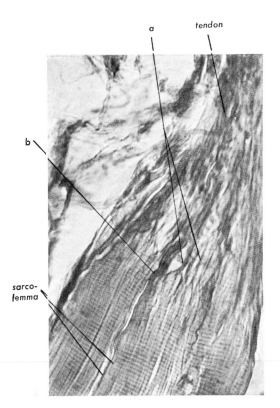

a   tendon

b

sarco-
lemma

Fig. 86. Section from human tongue, showing connection of striated muscle and its tendon. The fibrils of the tendon apparently are connected with myofibrils at (a) and with sarcolemma at (b). Photomicrograph. Mallory-azan stain. X500. (After von Herrath and Abramow. From Bloom and Fawcett. *A Textbook of Histology*. 8th ed. W. B. Saunders Company.)

work of reticular connective tissue fibers, the *endomysium,* surrounds each muscle cell. Groups of muscle cells (fibers), arranged in parallel, are bound together in bundles, called fasciculi, by a coarser fibrous connective tissue called the *perimysium*. This extends throughout each muscle, merging with adjacent endomysium surrounding individual muscle cells (fibers), and extending to the surface of the muscle to merge with a dense, fibrous connective tissue sheath, the *epimysium,* which forms a sheath that encloses the entire skeletal muscle. These connective tissues are continuous with the dense, white fibrous tissue (tendon) that attaches the muscle to some structure to be moved, usually a bone.

SKELETAL MUSCLES

DEFINITION. Each voluntary or skeletal muscle of the body is an organ of the muscular system.

LOCATION. Skeletal muscles are found throughout the entire body where, for the most part, they occupy the area between the skin and the bones of the skeletal system (Fig. 87).

FUNCTION. Skeletal muscles effect movement of various parts of the body. This is accomplished by contraction of the striated muscle cells (fibers) that form the skeletal muscles, and by the fact that the extremities of each muscle are firmly attached to structures (usually bones) that can be brought closer together or "moved."

BLOOD SUPPLY. Skeletal muscles are very vascular organs. The blood vessels supplying a muscle are usually "muscular" branches of

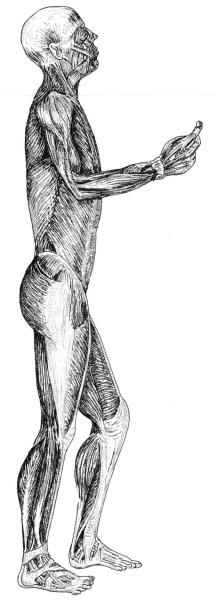

Fig. 87. Muscles of the body.

the larger, named vessels of the area. The muscular branches of the vessels, accompanied by the nerve supplying the muscle, penetrate the epimysium enclosing the muscle and are distributed throughout the entire organ by way of the connective tissue that forms the supporting framework (the perimysium and the endomysium). Within the muscle, the blood vessels branch repeatedly and finally form an anastomosing vascular network of capillaries, supplying the individual muscle cells. Generally the capillaries are arranged parallel to the muscle fibers with short, transverse, communicating branches given off throughout the length of the fiber (Fig. 88).

LYMPHATICS. The lymphatic vessels of skeletal muscle are found in the connective tissue forming the perimysium and the epimysium.

NERVE SUPPLY. Skeletal muscles are supplied by peripheral nerves containing both efferent (motor) and afferent or sensory (pain and proprioceptive) fibers. Each muscle receives at least one or, if the muscle is large, two or more nerves which enter the epimysium, together with the muscular artery, to be distributed to the muscle fibers. After the nerve has penetrated the epimysium, it begins to separate into individual fibers, and throughout its course nerve fibers "peel off" from the main nerve, until finally all of the fibers are separated. In this way the individual nerve fibers are widely distributed throughout the body of the muscle to supply muscle fibers.

The efferent or motor fibers terminate on a muscle fiber at a neuromuscular *motor end plate* where the nerve fiber contacts but does not penetrate the sarcolemma of the muscle fiber. The afferent or sensory fibers contact the muscle fibers either by way of specialized endings called *neuromuscular spindles* or by way of simple, naked branches of the axis cylinder of the nerve.

At this point it should be emphasized that a skeletal muscle fiber will not contract unless an impulse is transmitted to it by a nerve, and when a muscle fiber is thus stimulated, it responds with a maximum contraction. This is the "all or none" law of muscle contraction. If it is true that muscle fibers respond either maximally or not at all, how is it possible to have degrees of strength of contraction of a muscle so essential in delicate, precisely controlled movements which occur in the body? These movements, for the most part, are produced by relatively small muscles in which each muscle fiber is supplied by a single nerve fiber. In such a muscle, if the nerve is stimulated so strongly that all of the nerve fibers are activated, all of the muscle fibers supplied by the nerve contract. However, if the strength of the stimulus is such that only a few of the nerve fibers are activated, a corresponding number of muscle fibers contract and the force of the movement produced is decreased. In other words, the number of nerve fibers stimulated determines the number of muscle fibers contracting, and the nature of the movement produced.

In the large muscles of the body that produce the more generalized movements, each muscle fiber is not supplied by a single nerve fiber. A single nerve fiber (axon) will divide into a number of terminal branches, each of which will supply a muscle fiber. Thus a single nerve fiber (axon) may supply as many as 100 separate muscle fibers. However, these muscle fibers will not be in a restricted, closely bunched group within the muscle, but will be widely and uniformly scattered throughout the entire muscle. The relationship of nerve fiber to the number of muscle fibers it activates to contract is important from the functional aspect of muscle.

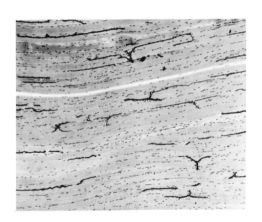

Fig. 88. Photomicrograph of a longitudinal section of striated muscle. The blood vessels were injected to show the relation of the capillaries to the muscle fibers.

FORM. Thin and quadrilateral in shape.

ORIGIN. Superior nuchal line and from the mastoid process of the temporal bone.

INSERTION. Galea aponeurotica.

ACTION OF THE EPICRANIUS. The frontalis portion elevates the eyebrows and draws the scalp forward, at the same time producing transverse wrinkles on the forhead. The occipitalis draws the scalp backward.

NERVE SUPPLY OF THE EPICRANIUS. Facial nerve.

Muscles of the Face (Fig. 90)

Superficial Muscles of the Face (The Mimetic Muscles). The muscles of this group are referred to as the "mimetic" muscles or the muscles of facial expression. They differ from most of the muscles in that they are not enclosed in a muscle fascia, and at least one of their attachments is in the deep layer of the skin thus making it possible to produce a wide range of facial expressions. The following muscles are included in this group.

Orbicularis oculi	Mentalis
Procerus	Depressor labii inferioris
Nasalis	Triangularis
Levator labii superioris	Risorius
Zygomaticus	Orbicularis oris

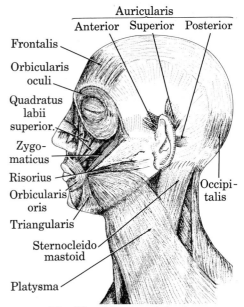

Fig. 90. Muscles of the face.

Orbicularis oculi

The sphincter muscle of the eye.

LOCATION. Encircles the eye (Fig. 90).

FORM. Flat, sphincter muscle.

ORIGIN. Nasal part of the frontal bone, adjacent portion of the frontal process of the maxilla, and the medial palpebral ligament.

INSERTION. Fibers form a complete elliptical circle and insert where they arise.

ACTION. Closes the eyelids, pulls the skin of the forehead, temple, and cheek toward the medial side of the orbit.

NERVE SUPPLY. Facial nerve.

Procerus

LOCATION. Over the root of the nose.

FORM. Small, triangular muscle.

ORIGIN. Fascia covering the junction of the nasal bone and nasal cartilage.

INSERTION. Skin between and above the eyebrow.

ACTION. Draws medial angle of the eyebrow downward, and causes transverse wrinkle at the root of the nose.

NERVE SUPPLY. Facial nerve.

Nasalis

Has two parts—transverse and alar.

LOCATION. Along side of and over the bridge of the nose.

FORM. Small, triangular muscle.

Transverse Part

ORIGIN. From maxilla, just lateral to the incisive fossa.

INSERTION.   With fibers of the opposite muscle, over the bridge of the nose, and with the aponeurosis of the procerus muscle.

ACTION.   Compresses the ala.

NERVE SUPPLY.   Facial nerve.

Alar Part

ORIGIN.   Greater alar cartilage.

INSERTION.   Skin at the tip of the nose.

ACTION.   Depresses the tip of the nose and draws the ala toward the septum.

NERVE SUPPLY.   Facial nerve.

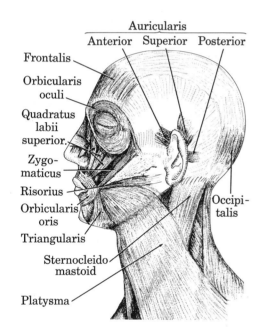

Levator labii superioris (Quadratus labii superioris)

LOCATION.   Front part of the face at the side of the nose (Fig. 90).

FORM.   A three-headed muscle.

Angular Head

ORIGIN.   Frontal process of the maxilla.

INSERTION.   By two slips—one inserts on the greater alar cartilage and skin of the nose, the other into the corner of the upper lip.

Infraorbital Head

ORIGIN.   Maxilla, above infraorbital foramen.

INSERTION.   Upper lip.

Zygomatic Head

ORIGIN.   Malar surface of the zygomatic bone.

INSERTION.   Upper lip.

ACTION.   Elevates the upper lip. The angular head dilates the nostrils and the whole muscle in action produces an expression of contempt and disdain.

NERVE SUPPLY.   Facial nerve.

Zygomaticus

LOCATION.   Lies obliquely at the side of the cheek, extending from the corner of the mouth upward and laterally (Fig. 90).

FORM.   Flattened cylindrical shape.

ORIGIN.   Zygomatic bone.

INSERTION.   Corner of the mouth.

ACTION.   Draws the corner of the mouth laterally and upward as in laughing.

NERVE SUPPLY.   Facial nerve.

Mentalis

LOCATION.   On the chin.

FORM.   Short, thick, tapered muscle.

ORIGIN.   Incisive fossa of the mandible.

INSERTION.   Skin over the chin.

ACTION.   Wrinkles the skin over the chin, raises and protrudes the lower lip, and expresses doubt and disdain.

NERVE SUPPLY.   Facial nerve.

Depressor labii inferioris (Quadratus labii inferioris)

LOCATION.   Below the mouth.
FORM.   Quadrangular.
ORIGIN.   Oblique line of the mandible.
INSERTION.   Skin of the lower lip.
ACTION.   Draws the lower lip downward and slightly laterally, and produces an expression of irony.
NERVE SUPPLY.   Facial nerve.

Triangularis

LOCATION.   Below the corner of the mouth (Fig. 90).
FORM.   A flat, triangular muscle.
ORIGIN.   Oblique line of the mandible.
INSERTION.   Corner of the mouth.
ACTION.   Depresses the corner of the mouth.
NERVE SUPPLY.   Facial nerve.

Risorius

LOCATION.   Extends laterally from the corner of the mouth (Fig. 90).
FORM.   Flat, ribbon-like muscle.
ORIGIN.   Fascia over the masseter muscle.
INSERTION.   Skin at the corner of the mouth.
ACTION.   Retracts the corner of the mouth and produces an unpleasant, grinning expression.
NERVE SUPPLY.   Facial nerve.

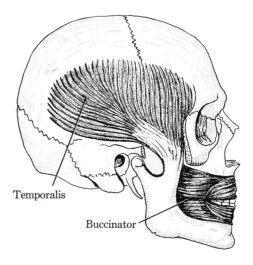

Fig. 91. Buccinator and temporalis muscles.

Orbicularis Oris

LOCATION.   Encircles the mouth (Fig. 90).
FORM.   A sphincter muscle.
ORIGIN.   From various muscles that insert into the lips and from some muscles that form the lips.
INSERTION.   Skin of the lips.
ACTION.   Closes the lips and the superficial part of the muscle brings the lips together and protrudes them forward.
NERVE SUPPLY.   Facial nerve.

Deep Muscles of the Face. Under this grouping will be discussed the buccinator muscle and the muscles of mastication—temporalis, masseter, medial pterygoid, and lateral pterygoid.

Buccinator

LOCATION.   Muscle of the cheek (Fig. 91).
FORM.   Flat, quadrangular muscle.
ORIGIN.   Pterygomandibular raphe (a tendinous strip between the buccinator and the superior pharyngeal constrictor muscles), and the outer surfaces of the alveolar processes of the maxilla and mandible adjacent to the molar teeth.
INSERTION.   Deepest layer of the orbicularis oris muscle.
ACTION.   Presses lips and cheeks against the teeth.
NERVE SUPPLY.   Facial nerve.

Temporalis

LOCATION.   At the side of the head, above the ear (Figs. 91 and 92).

FORM.   Large, fan-shaped muscle.

ORIGIN.   From the temporal fossa the fibers converge and pass downward behind the zygomatic arch.

INSERTION.   On the coronoid process of the mandible.

ACTION.   Closes the jaws and retracts the mandible.

NERVE SUPPLY.   Branch of the mandibular division of the trigeminal nerve.

Masseter

LOCATION.   In the cheek (Fig. 92).

FORM.   Thick, quadrilateral muscle.

ORIGIN.   From the zygomatic arch.

INSERTION.   Into the lateral surface of the ramus and the angle of the mandible.

ACTION.   Closes the jaws.

NERVE SUPPLY.   Branch of the mandibular division of the trigeminal nerve.

Medial (Internal) pterygoid

LOCATION.   On the medial surface of the ramus of the mandible.

FORM.   Thick, quadrilateral muscle.

ORIGIN.   The lateral pterygoid plate of the sphenoid and the palatine bone.

INSERTION.   The medial surface of the ramus of the mandible near the mandibular angle.

ACTION.   Closes the jaws.

NERVE SUPPLY.   Branch of the mandibular division of the trigeminal nerve.

Lateral (External) pterygoid

LOCATION.   On the medial side of the upper part of the mandible, lateral to the upper half of the internal pterygoid.

FORM.   Short, rather thick, pyramidal muscle that arises by two heads.

ORIGIN.   The upper head from the great wing of the sphenoid, the lower head from the lateral pterygoid plate of the sphenoid.

INSERTION.   On the neck of the mandible.

ACTION.   Opens the mouth, moves the mandible sideways and protrudes it.

NERVE SUPPLY.   Branch of the mandibular division of the trigeminal nerve.

Extrinsic Muscles of the Ear (Fig. 90)

These small muscles are of relatively little importance in Man. When Man learned to stand upright and could turn his head to catch the sound of approaching danger, there was no longer the need to turn the ears for this purpose. Without purpose of function these muscles decreased in size, and gradually the voluntary control of them has diminished. There are relatively few individuals who can voluntarily control the movements of their ears.

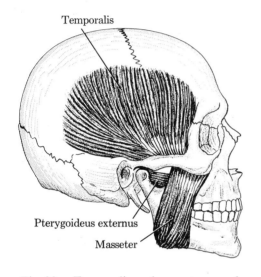

Temporalis

Pterygoideus externus

Masseter

Fig. 92.   Temporalis and masseter muscles.

These muscles include three small, triangular-shaped muscles—the *auricular anterior, auricular superior,* and *auricular posterior.* They are designed and positioned to draw the ear forward, upward, or backward, and are innervated by branches of the facial nerve.

MUSCLES OF THE NECK

Superficial Neck Muscle

Platysma

LOCATION.   A broad sheet of superficial muscle in the neck that extends from the lower jaw to the region of the clavicle (Fig. 90).

FORM.   Thin, quadrilateral muscle.

ORIGIN.   Fascia over the anterior thorax and shoulder.

INSERTION.   Fibers extend upward and medially. The anterior fibers from the two sides interlace below the chin and some merge with the fibers of muscles about the mouth and insert into the skin and subcutaneous tissue of the lower part of the face. Deeper fibers insert into the mandible below the oblique line of the mandible.

ACTION.   Produces obliquely directed wrinkles in the skin of the neck, and depresses the lower jaw and the corner of the mouth. Produces an expression of melancholy.

NERVE SUPPLY.   Branch of the facial nerve.

Lateral Neck Muscles

The lateral neck muscles include the sternocleidomastoid and the trapezius.

Sternocleidomastoid

LOCATION.   Lateral and anterior part of neck (Figs. 90 and 93).

FORM.   Flattened cylindrical muscle.

ORIGIN.   Anterior surface of the manubrium of the sternum, and upper margin of the medial end of the clavicle.

INSERTION.   Mastoid process of the temporal bone, and lateral half of the superior nuchal line of the occipital bone.

ACTION.   The muscle contracting on one side turns the head to the opposite side and turns the face upward. Both muscles contracting at the same time pull the head forward and downward.

NERVE SUPPLY.   Accessory nerve (11th cranial).

Trapezius

While this muscle extends into the area of the neck and is the muscle primarily responsible for producing the surface contour of the lateral side of the neck and the slope of the upper part of the shoulder above the clavicle and spine of the scapula, it is actually a superficial muscle of the back and will be described on page 79 with these muscles.

Suprahyoid Muscles

This group of muscles includes the mylohyoideus, geniohyoideus, digastricus, and stylohyoideus.

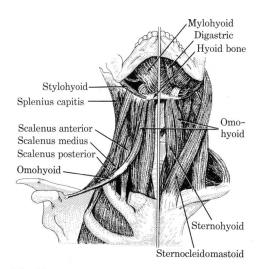

Fig. 93.
Muscles of the neck and floor of the mouth.

Mylohyoideus

Forms the floor of the mouth (Fig. 93).

ORIGIN.   Mylohyoid line of the mandible (from the symphysis to the third molar tooth).

INSERTION.   Median raphe (dense fibrous connective tissue that extends between the chin and the hyoid bone).

ACTION.   Raises the hyoid bone (and the tongue).

NERVE SUPPLY.   Branch from the mandibular division of the trigeminal nerve.

Geniohyoideus

A narrow, strap-like muscle that lies above the mylohyoideus inside the mouth.

ORIGIN.   Inferior mental spine of the mandible.

INSERTION.   Hyoid bone.

ACTION.   Pulls hyoid bone and tongue forward.

NERVE SUPPLY.   Branch of the hypoglossal nerve.

Digastricus

A two-bellied muscle joined by an intermediate, short, round tendon. It lies below the mandible.

ORIGIN.   Anterior belly—inner surface of the mandible near the midline. Posterior belly—mastoid notch of the temporal bone.

INSERTION.   Into an intermediate tendon between the two muscle bellies which is in turn bound by a loop of fibrous connective tissue to the hyoid bone.

ACTION.   Raises the hyoid bone; helps to open the jaws when the hyoid bone is fixed.

NERVE SUPPLY.   Anterior belly by branch of the mandibular division of the trigeminal nerve. Posterior belly by a branch of the facial nerve.

Stylohyoideus

A slender muscle that crosses in front of the posterior belly of the digastricus (Fig. 93).

ORIGIN.   Styloid process of the temporal bone.

INSERTION.   Body of the hyoid bone.

ACTION.   Draws the hyoid bone upward and backward.

NERVE SUPPLY.   Branch of the facial nerve.

Infrahyoid Muscles

This group of muscles includes the sternohyoideus, sternothyroideus, thyrohyoideus, and omohyoideus. For the most part these muscles are narrow, ribbon-like muscles that (except for the sternothyroideus) have one attachment on the hyoid bone and are the antagonists of the suprahyoid group of muscles.

Sternohyoideus

ORIGIN.   The manubrium of the sternum, the medial end of the clavicle, and the costoclavicular ligament (Fig. 93).

INSERTION.   The hyoid bone.

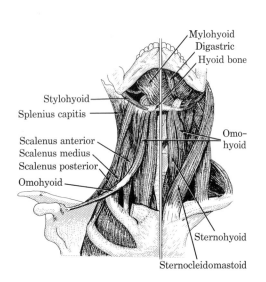

Mylohyoid
Digastric
Hyoid bone
Stylohyoid
Splenius capitis
Scalenus anterior
Scalenus medius
Scalenus posterior
Omohyoid
Omo-hyoid
Sternohyoid
Sternocleidomastoid

ACTION.   Pulls the hyoid bone downward.

NERVE SUPPLY.   Branch of the ansa hypoglossi ($C_1C_2C_3$).

Sternothyroideus

ORIGIN.   The manubrium of the sternum and the first costal cartilage.

INSERTION.   Thyroid cartilage of the larynx.

ACTION.   Pulls the thyroid cartilages downward.

NERVE SUPPLY.   Branch of the ansa hypoglossi ($C_1C_2C_3$).

Thyrohyoideus

ORIGIN.   Thyroid cartilage.

INSERTION.   Hyoid bone.

ACTION.   Pulls the hyoid bone downward, or if the hyoid is "fixed," elevates the thyroid cartilage.

NERVE SUPPLY.   Branch of the hypoglossal nerve (C_1C_2).

Omohyoideus

Has two narrow bellies joined by a central tendon (Fig. 93).

ORIGIN.   Inferior belly—from the superior border of the scapula. Superior belly—from the central tendon which is anchored to the clavicle by a fold of deep cervical fascia.

INSERTION.   Hyoid bone.

ACTION.   Pulls the hyoid bone downward.

NERVE SUPPLY.   Branch of the ansa hypoglossi ($C_1C_2C_3$).

Anterior Vertebral Muscles

This group of muscles include the longus colli, longus capitis, rectus capitis anterior, and rectus capitis lateralis. These muscles lie deep, in front of the vertebral column. As a group they flex and rotate the head. The rectus capitis, contracting on one side, bends the head laterally.

Lateral Vertebral Muscles

These muscles include the scalenus anterior, scalenus medius, and scalenus posterior (Fig. 93).

These muscles extend from the vertebrae to the first and second ribs. Together they raise the first and second ribs (assist in inspiration). If the ribs are fixed, they flex the neck and bend the head forward. Acting on one side, they bend the neck to one side.

MUSCLES OF THE UPPER EXTREMITY

MUSCLES FROM THE AXIAL SKELETON TO THE SHOULDER GIRDLE

Trapezius	Serratus Anterior
Levator Scapulae	Subclavius
Rhomboids: Major and Minor	Pectoralis Minor

Trapezius

LOCATION.   A superficial muscle of the back of the neck and the upper part of the back (Fig. 94).

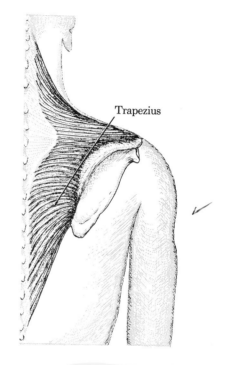

Fig. 94.   Trapezius muscle.

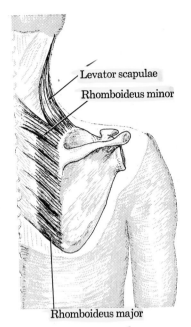

Fig. 95.   Levator scapulae and rhomboids, major and minor, muscles.

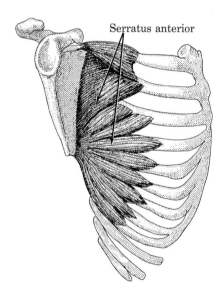

Fig. 96.   Serratus anterior muscle.

FORM.   Flat, broad, and triangular.

ORIGIN.   Occipital bone, nuchal ligament along spines of cervical vertebrae to spine of the 7th cervical vertebra, and spines of all 12 thoracic vertebrae.

INSERTION.   The lateral one third of the clavicle and the medial margin of the acromion and the upper lip of the spine of the scapula.

ACTION.   Rotates the inferior angle of the scapula laterally and forward, elevates and approximates the scapulae, extends the head.

NERVE SUPPLY.   Accessory nerve (11th cranial).

(Elevate Scapula) *Levator scapulae*

LOCATION.   On back and side of neck, between the upper cervical vertebrae and the scapula (Fig. 95).

FORM.   Long, thick, strap-like muscle.

ORIGIN.   By tendinous slips from the transverse processes of the first four cervical vertebrae.

INSERTION.   Upper medial (vertebral) border of the scapula from the medial angle to the root of the spine.

ACTION.   Rotates the lateral angle (glenoid fossa) downward. If the scapula is fixed, extends the neck and rotates it to the same side.

NERVE SUPPLY.   Anterior rami of the third and fourth cervical nerves, and the dorsal scapular nerve ($C_3C_4C_5$).

Rhomboids (major and minor)

Since these muscles are more or less continuous, they will be treated as one muscle. The minor is a narrow band of fibers above the major. (Fig. 95.)

LOCATION.   Upper medial part of the back between the vertebrae and the scapula.

FORM.   Flat, quadrangular muscle.

ORIGIN.   From the lower part of the nuchal ligament and the spinous processes of the 7th cervical vertebra and the first five thoracic vertebrae. Fibers of the muscle are directed obliquely downward and laterally.

INSERTION.   Medial (vertebral) border of the scapula from the root of the spine to the inferior angle.

ACTION.   Elevates and approximates the scapulae.

NERVE SUPPLY.   Dorsal scapular nerve (C_5).

Action   Adduction & downward rotation

Serratus anterior

LOCATION.   Wraps around the posterior and lateral wall of the thorax (Fig. 96).

FORM.   Flat, quadrangular muscle.

ORIGIN.   By finger-like digitations from the lateral faces of the first eight ribs.   *serrated*

INSERTION.   Along the anterior surface of the medial (vertebral) border of the scapula.

ACTION. Holds the scapula against the thoracic wall, draws the scapula forward and laterally, and rotates the lateral angle (glenoid fossa) upward.

NERVE SUPPLY. Long thoracic nerve ($C_5C_6C_7$).

Subclavius *Skip*

LOCATION. A small muscle located between the clavicle and the 1st rib.

FORM. A small, short, triangular muscle.

ORIGIN. Anterior surface of the 1st rib and its cartilage.

INSERTION. Inferior face of the clavicle.

ACTION. Works over one joint—the sternoclavicular. Draws the clavicle (and attached scapula) downward and slightly forward.

NERVE SUPPLY. Subclavius nerve (C_5C_6).

Pectoralis minor *Deep*

LOCATION. Anterior thoracic wall, deep to the pectoralis major (Fig. 97).

FORM. Flat, triangular muscle.

ORIGIN. Anterior surfaces of 3rd, 4th, and 5th ribs.

INSERTION. Medial border of the coracoid process of the scapula.

ACTION. Depresses shoulder and draws the scapula down and medially toward the thorax.

NERVE SUPPLY. Medial pectoral (anterior) thoracic nerve (C_7C_8). *Action — abduction + downward rotation*

MUSCLES FROM THE AXIAL SKELETON TO THE HUMERUS

These muscles include the pectoralis major (an anterior muscle) and the latissimus dorsi (a posterior muscle).

Pectoralis major

LOCATION. The superficial muscle of the anterior thoracic wall (Figs. 98 and 99).

FORM. Large, flat, triangular muscle.

ORIGIN. Anterior face of the sternal half of the clavicle, lateral anterior surface of the sternum as low as the 6th or 7th rib, and cartilages of the first six or seven ribs.

INSERTION. Crest of the greater tubercle of the humerus.

ACTION. Works over one joint—the shoulder joint. Adducts and draws the arm forward across the chest, at the same time rotating it medially. *Action — Flexion Some Medial Rotation*

NERVE SUPPLY. Lateral pectoral nerve ($C_5C_6C_7$) and part of the medial pectoral nerve (C_8T_1). *Horizontal Flexion*

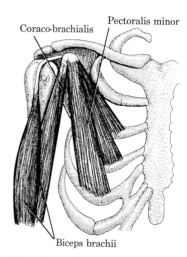

Fig. 97. Pectoralis minor, coracobrachialis, and biceps brachii muscles.

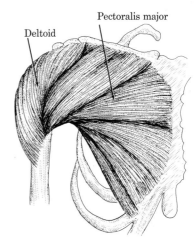

Fig. 98. Pectoralis major and deltoid muscles.

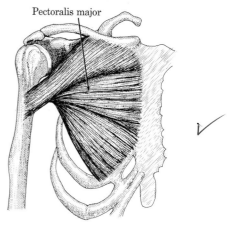

Fig. 99. Pectoralis major muscle.

Latissimus dorsi

LOCATION.   It is located in the lower part of the back and along the lateral wall of the thorax (Fig. 100). It is superficial except where it is covered by the trapezius muscle.

FORM.   Large, thin, flat, triangular muscle.

ORIGIN.   Is tendinous from the lumbodorsal fascia. Arises from the spinous processes of the lower six thoracic, all of the lumbar and upper sacral vertebrae, and the posterior half of the iliac crest. By small, fleshy digitations from the lower three or four ribs and the inferior angle of the scapula.

INSERTION.   Tendon extends behind the humerus and inserts into the floor of the intertubercular groove of the humerus.

ACTION.   Works over one joint—the shoulder. Pulls the arm backward and medially; rotates it medially. This muscle is used in swimming with the crawl stroke.   *Adduction*

NERVE SUPPLY.   Thoracodorsal nerve ($C_6C_7C_8$).

MUSCLES FROM THE SHOULDER GIRDLE TO THE HUMERUS

These include the subscapularis, infraspinatus, supraspinatus, and teres minor, which reinforce the shoulder joint and are attached to the capsule itself, and the teres major, deltoid, and coracobrachialis.

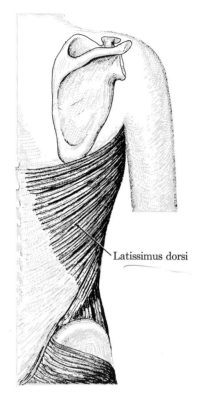

Fig. 100.   Latissimus dorsi muscle.

Subscapularis

LOCATION.   Deep muscle of the shoulder. It lies between the serratus anterior and the anterior surface of the scapula (Fig. 101).

FORM.   Flat, triangular muscle.

ORIGIN.   Subscapular fossa of the scapula.

INSERTION.   Lesser tubercle of the humerus.

ACTION.   Helps stabilize the shoulder joint. It works over one joint—the shoulder—and is a powerful medial rotator of the arm. Depending on the position of the arm, this muscle can flex or extend, abduct or adduct.

NERVE SUPPLY.   Subscapular nerve (C_5C_6).

Action - Big Inward rotator

Supraspinatus

LOCATION.   On the posterior surface of the scapula, above the spine (Fig. 102).

FORM.   Thick, triangular-shaped muscle.

ORIGIN.   Supraspinous fossa of the scapula.

INSERTION.   Highest impression on the greater tubercle of the humerus.

ACTION.   Works over one joint—the shoulder. Reinforces shoulder joint. Abducts arm. Weak lateral rotator.

NERVE SUPPLY.   Suprascapular nerve (C_5C_6).

Action - Abduction

Infraspinatus

LOCATION.   On posterior surface of the scapula below the spine (Fig. 102).

FORM.   Thick, triangular muscle.

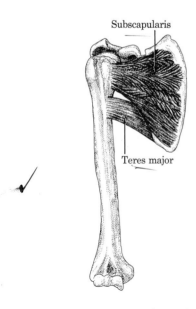

Fig. 101.   Subscapularis and teres major muscles.

ORIGIN.   Infraspinous fossa of scapula.

INSERTION.   Middle impression on the greater tubercle of the humerus.

ACTION.   Works over one joint—the shoulder. Reinforces the shoulder joint. Lateral rotator. Upper part abducts; lower part adducts.

NERVE SUPPLY.   Axillary nerve (C_5C_6).

Action   outward rotater

Teres minor

LOCATION.   Just below and fused with the infraspinatus (Fig. 102).

FORM.   Narrow, elongated muscle.

ORIGIN.   Dorsal surface of lateral (axillary) margin of the scapula.

INSERTION.   Lowest impression on the greater tubercle of the humerus.

ACTION.   Works over one joint—the shoulder. Reinforces the shoulder joint. Lateral rotator and weak adductor of the arm.

NERVE SUPPLY.   Axillary nerve (C_5C_6).

Action - Outward Rotator

Teres major

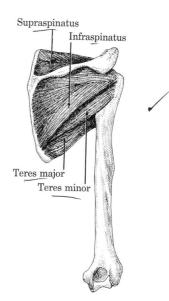

Fig. 102.   Supraspinatus, infraspinatus, teres major and teres minor muscles.

LOCATION.   Along lateral (axillary) margin of the scapula (Figs. 101, 102, and 103).

FORM.   Thick, slightly flattened, cylindrical muscle.

ORIGIN.   Dorsal face of the inferior angle of the scapula.

INSERTION.   Crest of the lesser tubercle of the humerus.

ACTION.   Works over one joint—the shoulder. Adducts, extends, and medially rotates the arm.

NERVE SUPPLY.   Subscapular nerve (C_5C_6).

Action   Latismus helper

Deltoid

LOCATION.   A large superficial muscle that covers the shoulder joint (front, side, and back) (Figs. 98 and 103).

FORM.   Large, triangular muscle.

ORIGIN.   Anterior margin and upper face of the lateral third of the clavicle, lateral margin and upper face of the acromion, and the lower lip of the spine of the scapula.

INSERTION.   Deltoid tubercle on the lateral side of the humerus.

ACTION.   Works over one joint—the shoulder. Abducts the arm. Anterior fibers flex; posterior fibers extend the arm.   *abduction*

NERVE SUPPLY.   Axillary nerve (C_5C_6).   *Big*

Coracobrachialis   *help stabilize Shoulder*

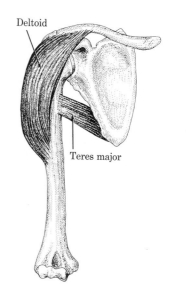

Fig. 103.   Teres major and deltoid muscles.

LOCATION.   Upper medial side of the arm (Fig. 97, p. 81).

FORM.   Roughly quadrangular in shape.

ORIGIN.   From the apex of the coracoid process of the scapula (by common tendon of origin with the short head of the biceps brachii).

INSERTION.   Impression on the middle third of the medial face of the shaft of the humerus.

ACTION.   Works over one joint—the shoulder. Draws the humerus forward and medially.

NERVE SUPPLY.   Musculocutaneous nerve (C_6C_7).

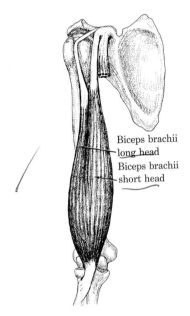

Fig. 104.   Biceps brachii muscle.

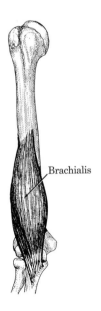

Fig. 105.   Brachialis muscle.

MUSCLES OF THE ARM

These muscles include the biceps brachii, brachialis, and triceps brachii. The coracobrachialis is also considered a muscle of the arm group.

Biceps brachii

LOCATION.   The superficial muscle of the anterior aspect of the arm (Figs. 97 and 104).

FORM.   Two-headed muscle, fusiform in shape.

ORIGIN.   The long head arises from the supraglenoid tubercle of the scapula. The short head arises with the coracobrachialis from the apex of the coracoid process of the scapula by common tendon.

INSERTION.   Into the tuberosity of the radius. *radial tuberosity*

ACTION.   Works over three joints—the shoulder, elbow, and the radioulnar joint. Flexes the arm and forearm; supinates the forearm and hand.

NERVE SUPPLY.   Musculocutaneous nerve (C_5C_6).

Brachialis

LOCATION.   The deep muscle of the lower half of the arm (Fig. 105).

FORM.   Flat, fusiform muscle.

ORIGIN.   Arises from the lower half of the anterior surface of the humerus.

INSERTION.   Into the ulnar tuberosity and anterior surface of the coronoid process.

ACTION.   Works over one joint—the elbow. Flexes the forearm.

NERVE SUPPLY.   Radial nerve (C_5C_6). *True flexor of the elbow*

Triceps brachii

LOCATION.   On the posterior aspect of the arm (Figs. 106 and 107).

FORM.   Large, three-headed muscle.

ORIGIN.   The long head arises from the infraglenoid tubercle of the scapula; the lateral head arises from the posterior face of the shaft of the humerus above the radial groove; and the medial head arises from the posterior face of the shaft of the humerus below the radial groove.

INSERTION.   Into the olecranon process of the ulna.

ACTION.   Works over two joints—the shoulder and elbow. The long head extends and adducts the arm; the whole muscle extends the forearm.

NERVE SUPPLY.   Radial nerve ($C_6C_7C_8$).

MUSCLES OF THE FOREARM (ANTERIOR ASPECT)

These muscles consist of a superficial and a deep group.

Superficial Anterior Muscles of the Forearm

These muscles include the pronator teres, flexor carpi radialis, palmaris longus, flexor carpi ulnaris, and flexor digitorum sublimis.

Fig. 106. Triceps brachii muscle, long head and lateral head.

Fig. 107. Triceps brachii muscle. A portion of the lateral head has been cut away in order to expose a portion of the medial head and the radial nerve.

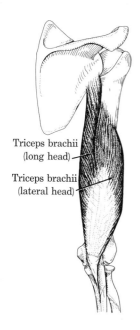

Triceps brachii (long head)

Triceps brachii (lateral head)

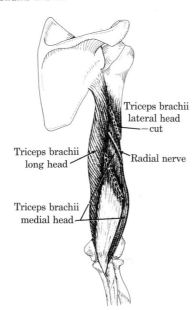

Triceps brachii lateral head —cut

Triceps brachii long head

Radial nerve

Triceps brachii medial head

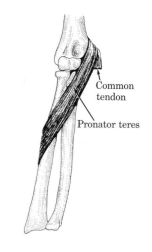

Common tendon

Pronator teres

Fig. 108.   Pronator teres muscle.

Pronator teres

LOCATION.   On the upper medial side of the forearm (Fig. 108).

FORM.   Two-headed, quadrangular muscle.

ORIGIN.   The humeral head arises by common tendon from the medial epicondyle of the humerus; the ulnar head arises from the medial side of the coronoid process of the ulna.

INSERTION.   Into the middle third of the lateral face of the shaft of the radius.

ACTION.   Works over two joints—the elbow and the radioulnar joint. Pronates the forearm and hand; assists in flexing the forearm.

NERVE SUPPLY.   Median nerve (C_6C_7).

Flexor carpi radialis

LOCATION.   On the upper medial part of the forearm (Fig. 109).

FORM.   Flat, fusiform muscle.

ORIGIN.   Arises by common tendon from the medial epicondyle of the humerus.

INSERTION.   Into the base of the second metacarpal bone.

ACTION.   Works over three joints—elbow, wrist, and the radioulnar joint. Flexes the forearm; flexes and abducts the wrist; pronates the forearm and hand.

NERVE SUPPLY.   Median nerve (C_6C_7).

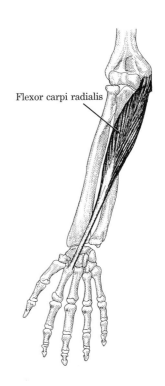

Flexor carpi radialis

Fig. 109.   Flexor carpi radialis muscle.

Palmaris longus

LOCATION.   On the upper medial part of the forearm (Fig. 110).

FORM.   Short, narrow, fusiform muscle.

ORIGIN.   Arises by common tendon from the medial epicondyle of the humerus.

INSERTION.   By long slender tendon into the central part of the transverse carpal ligament and palmar aponeurosis.

ACTION.   Works over two joints—elbow and wrist. Assists in flexing the forearm; flexes the wrist joint; tenses the palmar aponeurosis.

NERVE SUPPLY.   Median nerve ($C_7C_8T_1$).

Flexor carpi ulnaris

LOCATION.   Along the ulnar side of the forearm (Fig. 111).

FORM.   Flat, somewhat triangular, two-headed muscle.

ORIGIN.   The humeral head arises by common tendon from the medial epicondyle of the humerus; the ulnar head arises from the medial margin of the olecranon and upper two thirds of the dorsal margin of the ulna.

INSERTION.   Into the pisiform bone.

ACTION.   Works over two joints—elbow and wrist. Assists in flexing the forearm; flexes and adducts the wrist.

NERVE SUPPLY.   Ulnar nerve (C_8T_1).

Flexor digitorum sublimis

LOCATION.   The deepest of the superficial muscles—below the flexor carpi ulnaris and above the flexor digitorum profundus (Fig. 112).

FORM.   Flat, fusiform muscle with three separate heads of origin.

ORIGIN.   The humeral head arises by common tendon from the medial epicondyle of the humerus and the ulnar collateral ligament; the ulnar head arises from the medial side of the coronoid process above the origin of the pronator teres; the radial head arises from the oblique line of the radius.

INSERTION.   By four tendons that extend under the transverse carpal ligament and go to the four medial digits; each tendon splits to insert into the sides of the second phalanx (Fig. 115).

ACTION.   Works over several joints—elbow, wrist, carpometacarpal, metacarpophalangeal, and first interphalangeal joints. Assists in flexing elbow and wrist; flexes first the middle, then the proximal phalanges.

NERVE SUPPLY.   Median nerve ($C_7C_8T_1$).

Deep Anterior Muscles of the Forearm

These include the flexor digitorum profundis, flexor pollicis longus, and pronator quadratus.

Flexor digitorum profundus

LOCATION.   The ulnar side of the forearm (Fig. 113).

FORM.   Flat, fusiform muscle.

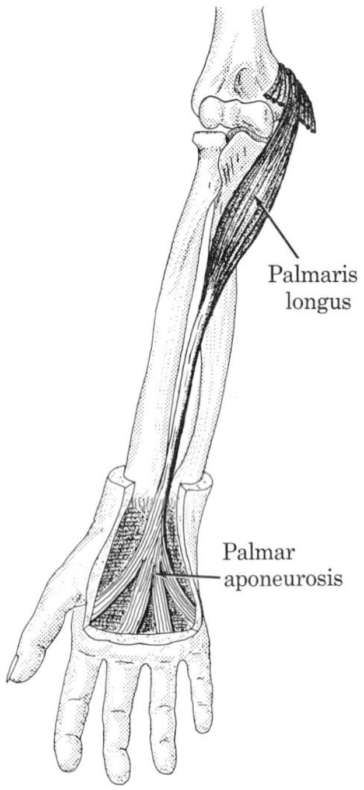

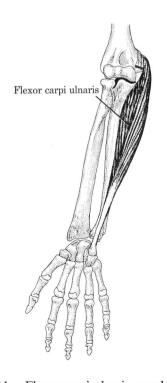

Fig. 110.   Palmaris longus muscle and the palmar aponeurosis.

Fig. 111.   Flexor carpi ulnaris muscle.

ORIGIN. Arises by common tendon from the lateral epicondyle of the humerus.

INSERTION. By a long, thin tendon which extends under the tensor retinaculum and then fuses with the tendon of the communis going to the little finger.

ACTION. Works over two joints—elbow and wrist. Assists in extending forearm; extends wrist and little finger.

NERVE SUPPLY. Branch of the radial nerve (C_7C_8).

Extensor carpi ulnaris

LOCATION. Medial to the extensor digiti quinti proprius (Figs. 118 and 119).

FORM. Fusiform muscle.

ORIGIN. By common tendon from the lateral epicondyle of the humerus, and by the aponeurosis from the dorsal margin of the ulna.

INSERTION. Into the tubercle of the ulnar side of the base of the fifth metacarpal bone.

ACTION. Works over two joints—elbow and wrist. Extends forearm; extends and adducts hand.

NERVE SUPPLY. Branch of the radial nerve ($C_6C_7C_8$).

Deep Posterior Muscles of the Forearm

These muscles include the supinator, abductor pollicis longus, extensor pollicis brevis, extensor pollicis longus, and extensor indicis proprius.

Supinator

LOCATION. Winds around the upper part of the radius (Fig. 119).

FORM. Broad, flat, triangular muscle.

ORIGIN. By common tendon from the lateral epicondyle of the humerus, and from the radial collateral ligament of the elbow joint.

INSERTION. Into the lateral edge of the radial tuberosity and the oblique line of the radius, and into the anterior, lateral, and posterior face of the upper part of the radius.

ACTION. Works over two joints—elbow and radioulnar joint. Flexes the forearm; supinates the forearm and hand.

NERVE SUPPLY. Branch of the radial nerve ($C_5C_6C_7$).

Abductor pollicis longus

LOCATION. Radial side of the forearm (Fig. 119).

FORM. Fusiform muscle.

ORIGIN. From the dorsal surface of the interosseous membrane and adjacent portions of the radius and ulna.

INSERTION. Into the base of the first metacarpal bone.

ACTION. Works over two joints—wrist and first carpometacarpal joint. Flexes and abducts hand; abducts thumb.

NERVE SUPPLY. Branch of the radial nerve ($C_6C_7C_8$).

Extensor pollicis brevis

LOCATION. On radial side of the forearm just distal to the abductor pollicis longus (Fig. 119).

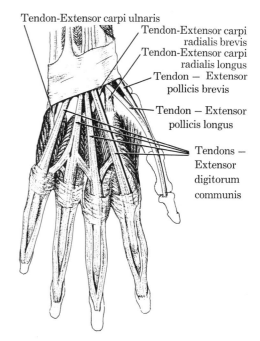

Tendon-Extensor carpi ulnaris

Tendon-Extensor carpi radialis brevis
Tendon-Extensor carpi radialis longus
Tendon — Extensor pollicis brevis
Tendon — Extensor pollicis longus
Tendons — Extensor digitorum communis

Fig. 120. Method of insertion of the extensor digitorium communis muscles.

FORM.   Fusiform muscle.

ORIGIN.   From the dorsal face of the shaft of the radius below the adbuctor pollicis longus.

INSERTION.   Into the base of the proximal phalanx of the thumb.

ACTION.   Works over several joints—wrist, carpometacarpal, and metacarpophalangeal joints. Abducts the hand; extends and abducts the proximal phalanx of the thumb.

NERVE SUPPLY.   Branch of the radial nerve ($C_6C_7C_8$).

Extensor pollicis longus

LOCATION. Lower two thirds of the dorsal surface of the forearm (Fig. left).

FORM.   Long, tapered muscle.

ORIGIN.   From the middle third of the dorsal face of the shaft of the ulna and from the adjacent interosseous membrane.

INSERTION.   Into the base of the terminal phalanx of the thumb.

ACTION.   Works over several joints—wrist, carpometacarpal, metacarpophalangeal, and interphalangeal joints. Extends and abducts the hand and thumb.

NERVE SUPPLY.   Branch of the radial nerve ($C_6C_7C_8$).

Extensor indicis proprius

LOCATION. Toward the medial side of the forearm (Fig. left).

FORM. Tapered muscle.

ORIGIN.   From the dorsal face of the shaft of the ulna and adjacent interosseous membrane.

INSERTION.   Joins the tendon of the extensor digitorum communis to the index finger.

ACTION.   Works over several joints—wrist, carpometacarpal, metacarpophalangeal, and interphalangeal joints. Extends hand and index finger.

NERVE SUPPLY.   Branch of the radial nerve ($C_6C_7C_8$).

MUSCLES OF THE TRUNK

The muscles of the trunk will be grouped and described according to the area in which they are functionally active, as follows: deep muscles of the neck (suboccipital) and the back, muscles of the thorax, muscles of the abdomen, muscles of the pelvic floor, and muscles of the gluteal region and hip.

The deep muscles of the neck and back are of greater concern to the professional anatomist and to the physician, particularly the orthopedist, than they are to the average beginning student in anatomy. These muscles are numerous, and their attachments are difficult to visualize and remember if not worked with constantly. For that reason, except for the *erecta spinae* (sacrospinalis) they will be treated in this text in a very general manner. Details can be obtained from any medical textbook of Anatomy if the student is interested.

DEEP MUSCLES OF THE NECK (SUBOCCIPITAL)

These muscles extend from the 1st and/or 2nd vertebrae to the skull (occipital bone). As a group they extend the head and rotate it. The last muscle listed for the group, the obliquus capitis superior, also bends the head laterally.

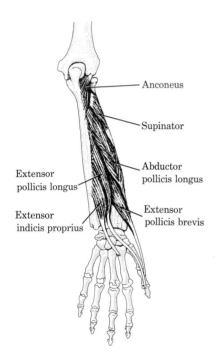

Anconeus

Supinator

Abductor pollicis longus

Extensor pollicis longus

Extensor indicis proprius

Extensor pollicis brevis

Rectus Capitis Posterior Major   *Obliquus Capitis Superior*
Rectus Capitis Posterior Minor   **Obliquus Capitis Inferior**

DEEP MUSCLES OF THE BACK

This is a complex posterior group of muscles which extends from the skull to the pelvis. Functionally they act as a single muscle to extend the entire vertebral column. If the muscles on one side contract, the vertebral column is rotated and bent in that direction. This groups includes the following muscles. *[handwritten: Keep spine erect   Extion & lateral Flexion]*

Erector spinae (Sacrospinalis)	*Multifidus*
Splenius Capitis	*Rotatores*
Splenius Cervicis	*Intertransversii*
Semispinalis	*Interspinalis*

Erector spinae (Sacrospinalis). In the bony groove between the spines of the vertebrae and the ribs posteriorly, lies a large muscle mass, the erector spinae. In its lower extent (in the sacral and lumbar area) it is a solid and thick mass. As it extends superiorly it divides into three muscular columns which gradually decrease in size as they ascend and reach their insertions into the vertebrae of the thoracic and cervical regions, the ribs, and the cranium.

ORIGIN.   Dorsal surface of the sacrum, spines of all lumbar and last thoracic vertebrae, and posterior part of the crest of the ilium.

As the muscle mass splits, it forms three muscle columns (Fig. 121), which in turn are subdivided as follows.

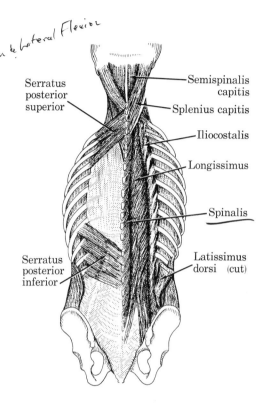

Serratus posterior superior		Semispinalis capitis
		Splenius capitis
		Iliocostalis
		Longissimus
		Spinalis
Serratus posterior inferior		Latissimus dorsi (cut)

Fig. 121.   Muscles of the back.

Lateral Column	Intermediate Column	Medial Column
Iliocostalis	Longissimus	Spinalis
I. lumborum	L. thoracis (dorsi)	S. thoracis (dorsi)
I. thoracis (dorsi)	L. cervicis	S. cervicis
I. cervicis	L. capitis	S. capitis

INSERTIONS.   These various subdivisions of the muscle columns insert into the lumbar, thoracic, and cervical vertebrae, into the angles of the ribs and the mastoid process of the skull.

ACTION.   Extends the vertebral column and the head; if the muscle on one side contracts, it bends (extends) the vertebral column and head to the same side.

MUSCLES OF THE THORAX

The thoracic cavity consists of the bony and cartilaginous skeletal cage which is completed and made into a functional thoracic cavity by the muscles of the wall of the thorax and the diaphragm, which closes the cavity inferiorly. Through their actions, these muscles expand and contract the thoracic cavity, forcing air to be sucked into the lungs and then expelled in a rhythmic series of movements known as breathing. The *respiratory muscles* include the intercostals—external and internal, levatores costarum, transversus thoracis, and serratus posterior—superior and inferior, and the diaphragm.

Intercostals

The muscles that fill the intercostal spaces and complete the wall of the thoracic cavity are the external and internal intercostals.

External intercostals

The more superficial of the two; they consist of 11 paired muscle segments.

LOCATION.   Each muscle segment occupies an intercostal space. Each is muscular posteriorly, laterally, and anteriorly as far as the costal cartilages where the muscle is replaced by an aponeurosis.

FORM.   A thin layer of muscle fibers that posteriorly are directed obliquely downward and laterally; anteriorly, obliquely downward and medially.

ORIGIN.   Lower border of a rib.

INSERTION.   Upper border of the rib immediately below.

ACTION.   The external intercostals draw the ribs closer together. With the 1st rib fixed, they elevate the ribs thus increasing the capacity of the thoracic cavity.

NERVE SUPPLY.   Intercostal nerves.

Internal intercostals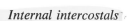

Lie deep to the external intercostals and consist of 11 paired muscle segments.

LOCATION.   Each muscle segment occupies an intercostal space. They are muscular anteriorly (starting at the sternum), laterally, and posteriorly as far as the angles of the ribs. Here they become aponeurotic for the remaining distance to the margins of the vertebrae.

FORM.   A thin layer of muscle fibers that posteriorly are directed obliquely downward and medially; anteriorly, obliquely downward and laterally.

ORIGIN.   The inner lower margin of a rib.

INSERTION.   Posterior edge of the upper border of the rib immediately below.

ACTION.   The internal intercostals draw the ribs together, and with the 12th rib fixed, decrease the capacity of the cavity by pulling the ribs down.

NERVE SUPPLY.   Intercostal nerves.

Levatores costarum

There are 12 pair of these muscles.

LOCATION.   Outer surface of the posterior thoracic cavity, lateral to the vertebral column and superficial to the external intercostals.

FORM.   Small, triangular-shaped muscles.

ORIGIN.   Tips of the transverse processes of the 7th cervical and the upper 11 thoracic vertebrae.

INSERTION.   Outer surface of the rib immediately below (between the tubercle and the angle of the rib).

ACTION.   Elevate the ribs, thus increasing the thoracic cavity. Extend the vertebral column in the thoracic area. When the muscles on one side contract, they extend and bend the vertebral column laterally, at the same time rotating it very slightly toward the opposite side.

NERVE SUPPLY.   Branches of the intercostal nerves.

Transversus thoracis

LOCATION.   Lies on the inner surface of the anterior chest wall (Fig. 122).

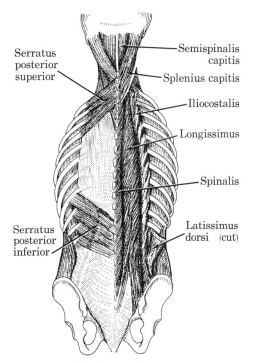

Serratus posterior superior

Semispinalis capitis

Splenius capitis

Iliocostalis

Longissimus

Spinalis

Serratus posterior inferior

Latissimus dorsi (cut)

Muscles of the back.

Transversus abdominis

A broad, flat, quadrangular muscle, the deepest of the three muscles forming the anterolateral wall of the abdomen (Fig. 124).

ORIGIN. Lower six costal cartilages, lumbodorsal fascia, anterior two thirds of the iliac crest, lateral one third of the inguinal ligament.

INSERTION. Xiphoid process of the sternum, linea alba, pubic tubercle.

NERVE SUPPLY. Intercostal nerves T_5 to T_{12}, iliohypogastric, ilioinguinal, and external spermatic nerves (T_5,T_{12},L_1L_2).

The precise method by which the broad aponeuroses of the anterolateral muscles of the abdominal wall reach the linea alba and interdigitate (merge) with the aponeuroses of attachment of the muscles of the opposite side requires explanation. At the lateral margin of the rectus abdominis in its upper two-thirds, the aponeurosis of the externus goes in front of the rectus along with the anterior layer of the aponeurosis of the internus which splits, half of it going in front and half going in back of the rectus. The aponeurosis of the transversus goes in back of the rectus with the posterior layer of the internus (Fig. 125A). In the lower third the aponeuroses of all three muscles go across in front of the rectus (Fig. 125B).

ACTIONS. With the thorax and pelvis fixed, the abdominal muscles compress the abdominal viscera.

With the pelvis and vertebral column fixed, these muscles compress the lower part of the thorax, assisting in expiration.

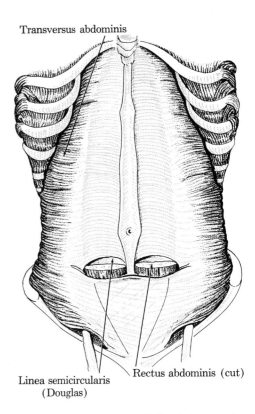

Fig. 124. Transversus abdominis muscle. The rectus abdominis muscle has been cut and its upper three fourths removed in order to expose the linea semicircularis.

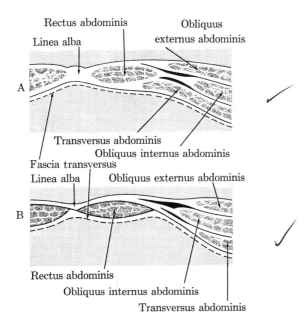

Fig. 125. Cross sections of the anterolateral abdominal wall to show the reflection of the aponeuroses of attachment of the anterolateral wall muscles around the rectus abdominis muscle. A. Section through the wall at a level above the linea semicircularis. B. Section through the wall at a level below the linea semicircularis.

With the pelvis fixed, the vertebral column is flexed if the muscles of both sides contract. If the muscles of one side contract, the body is bent toward the same side, and rotated toward the opposite side.

With the thorax fixed, the muscles draw the pelvis upward (as in climbing); muscles of one side contracting, pull the pelvis upward and bend the vertebral column to the same side.

The recti, with the pelvis fixed, depress the thorax and flex the vertebral column; with the thorax fixed, they flex the pelvis on the vertebral column.

MUSCLES OF THE PELVIC FLOOR

These muscles are the levator ani and coccygeus (Fig. 126).

Levator ani

The levator ani is paired and forms a thin, funnel-shaped floor for the pelvic cavity, which serves to support the pelvic structures. It allows passage of the anal canal and the urethra in both sexes, and the vagina in the female. It is reinforced below by the muscles and fascia of the urogenital diaphragm of the perineum. On contraction it raises the pelvic floor. It is supplied by branches of the pudendal plexus of nerves.

Coccygeus

These are two small muscles, one on either side of the pelvis, that extend from the spines of the ischium to the adjacent sides of the coccyx and sacrum. They complete the pelvic floor posteriorly. On contraction, they pull the coccyx forward and give additional support to the floor. They are supplied by branches of the pudendal plexus.

MUSCLES OF THE GLUTEAL REGION AND THE HIP

These muscles will be divided into three groups: the muscles of the buttocks, the six deep lateral rotators, and the two muscles that extend in front of the hip joint.

Muscles of the Buttocks and the Tensor Fasciae Latae

The gluteus maximus, gluteus medius, and gluteus minimus are the muscles of the buttocks, and the tensor fasciae latae is a superficial muscle of the hip.

Gluteus maximus

The superficial muscle of the buttock. It is a large, thick, very coarsely grained muscle that contributes considerably to the formation of the prominence of the buttock.

LOCATION.   Just under the skin of the buttock (Fig. 127).

FORM.   Very thick, flat, quadrangular muscle.

ORIGIN.   Posterolateral surface of the iliac blade, dorsal surface of the sacrum and coccyx, sacrotuberous ligament, and the lumbodorsal fascia.

INSERTION.   The iliotibial band of the fascia lata and the gluteal tuberosity of the femur.

ACTION.   Works over one joint—the hip. A powerful extensor of the thigh.

NERVE SUPPLY.   Inferior gluteal nerve ($L_5S_1S_2$).

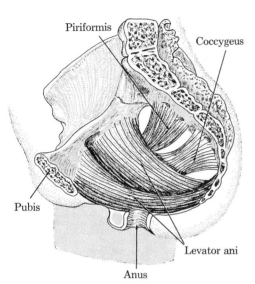

Fig. 126.   Pelvic muscles of the right side.

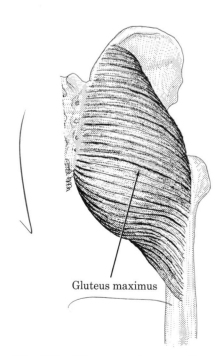

Fig. 127.   Gluteus maximus muscle.

Gluteus medius

LOCATION. Lateral side of the hip, where its upper and lateral portion is superficial (Fig. 128).

FORM. Thick, flat, triangular.

ORIGIN. Lateral surface of the iliac blade.

INSERTION. Lateral surface of the greater trochanter.

ACTION. Works over one joint—the hip. Abducts, extends and medially rotates the thigh.

NERVE SUPPLY. Superior gluteal nerve ($L_4L_5S_1$).

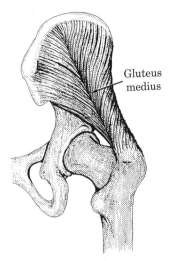

Fig. 128. Gluteus medius muscle.

Gluteus minimus   *underneath*

LOCATION. Lateral surface of the hip, just above the joint (Fig. 129).

FORM. Triangular.

ORIGIN. Lateral surface of the ilium.

INSERTION. Anterior surface of the greater trochanter.

ACTION. Works over one joint—the hip. Abducts and medially rotates the thigh, and aids in stabilizing the pelvis on the femur in walking. *Inward rotation*

NERVE SUPPLY. Superior gluteal nerve ($L_4L_5S_1$).

Tensor fascia latae

LOCATION. Superficial muscle on the lateral surface of the hip.

FORM. Thick, quadrangular muscle.

ORIGIN. Anterior superior spine of the ilium, the anterior part of the iliac crest, and the fascia lata.

INSERTION. Between the split layers of the fascia lata that fuse inferiorly to form the iliotibial band.

ACTION. Works over one joint—the hip. Flexes, abducts, and medially rotates the thigh. Tenses the fascia lata.

NERVE SUPPLY. Superior gluteal nerve ($L_4L_5S_1$).

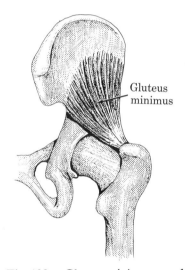

Fig. 129. Gluteus minimus muscle.

Deep Lateral Rotators of the Thigh (Fig. 130)

Piriformis	Gemellus inferior
Obturator internus	Quadratus femoris
Gemellus superior	Obturator externus

Piriformis

It arises from the front of the sacrum inside the pelvis and emerges from the pelvis through the greater sciatic foramen. (The greater sciatic notch is converted into a foramen by the sacrospinous ligament). It inserts into the upper border of the greater trochanter.

Obturator internus

It arises in the lesser pelvis from the fascia closing the obturator foramen and from the adjacent bony margin of the foramen. Its tendon leaves the pelvis by way of the lesser sciatic foramen. (The lesser sciatic notch is converted into a foramen by the sacrotuberous and sacrospinous ligaments). It inserts into the medial side of the greater trochanter above the trochanteric fossa.

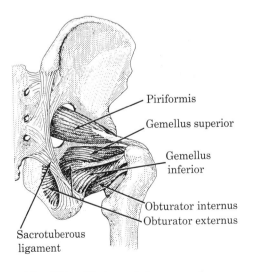

Fig. 130. Gluteus minimus muscle.

Gemelli (Twins)—superior and inferior

These muscles arise above and below the lesser sciatic notch, and their tendons merge with the tendon of the obturator internus. They insert into the medial surface of the greater trochanter.

Quadratus femoris

It arises from the outer border of the ischial tuberosity and inserts on the quadrate line of the femur.

Obturator externus

It arises from the outer surface of the fascia closing the obturator foramen and from the outer adjacent bony margins of the foramen. It inserts just below the intertrochanteric crest.

ACTIONS. These muscles all work over one joint—the hip. They all laterally rotate the thigh.

NERVE SUPPLY. Each muscle is innervated by an individual nerve from the sacral plexus.

Muscles That Extend in Front of the Hip

These are the psoas major and iliacus muscles which are often described as one muscle, called the iliopsoas, since they have a common tendon of insertion and produce the same action (Fig. 131). The psoas is the familiar tenderloin of beef or pork.

Psoas major (Fig. 132)

This is a long, thick, tapering muscle that arises from the transverse processes and the sides of the bodies of all five lumbar vertebrae. The tendon of the psoas merges with the tendon of the iliacus to insert on the lesser trochanter of the femur.

Iliacus

This is a triangular muscle that arises from the inner surface of the iliac blade (Fig. 132). The tendon of the iliacus merges with the tendon of the psoas to insert on the lesser trochanter of the femur.

ACTION. Both muscles act over the hip joint. They flex the thigh. The psoas also works over the intervertebral joints in the lumbar area. If the muscle on one side contracts, it bends the lumbar portion of the vertebral column forward toward its own side. If they both contract, they flex this portion of the column.

NERVE SUPPLY. Both are supplied by branches of the femoral nerve.

MUSCLES OF THE LOWER EXTREMITY

MUSCLES OF THE THIGH

Before entering into the description of the muscles of the thigh, it is desirable to discuss briefly the heavy, outer layer of investing fascia, called the *fascia lata,* that encloses the thigh muscles and helps to stabilize the hip joint. This fascia is drawn over the muscles of the thigh and fits closely much as a pair of tights would fit. It is firmly

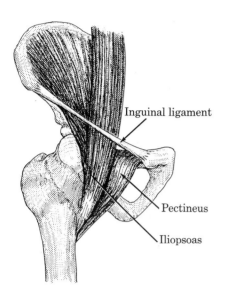

Fig. 131.   Iliopsoas and pectineus muscles.

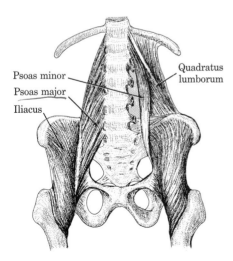

Fig. 132.   Psoas major, iliacus, and quadratus lumborum muscles.

attached to bone and ligaments at the knee below and to the pelvic girdle above. Beyond its bony and ligamentous attachments it merges with the fascia covering the external abdominal muscles and the lumbodorsal fascia above and the fascia of the leg below.

The fascia lata splits to enclose several superficial thigh muscles, including the sartorius, the gracilis, the gluteus maximus, and the tensor fascia latae. It also affords attachment for the tendinous insertion of the tensor fascia latae in its thickened lower lateral portion called the iliotibial tract or band.

From its deep surface, three septa extend down to attach to the linea aspera of the femur. These septa serve as partitions that divide the area of the thigh into compartments—anterior, medial, and posterior—that enclose and contain the anterior, medial or adductor, and posterior or hamstring muscles of the thigh.

Above the fascia lata is attached, in the following order, to the pubic tubercle, the inguinal ligament, the anterior superior spine of the ilium, the crest of the ilium, the posterior surface of the sacrum, the sacrospinous ligament, the ischial spine, the tuberosity of the ischium, the ischiopubic ramus, the body of the pubis, and back to the pubic tubercle. *Below* it is reinforced by and is attached to the tendons of insertion of the muscles of the thigh, and it is continuous with the fascia of the leg.

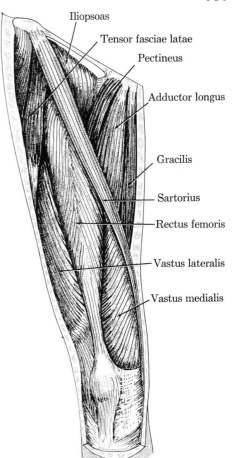

Fig. 133. Muscles of the anterior and medial aspect of the thigh.

Anterior Femoral Muscles of the Thigh

These muscles are the sartorius, quadriceps femoris (rectus femoris, vastus lateralis, vastus medialis, and vastus intermedius), and articularis genu (Fig. 133).

Sartorius

LOCATION. The sartorius is the most superficial muscle of the anterior femoral group (Figs. 133 and 134).

FORM. It is a long, narrow, flat, ribbon-like muscle, the longest muscle in the body. The fibers are arranged in parallel.

ORIGIN. It arises by a short tendon from the anterior superior spine of the ilium.

INSERTION. By a flat tendon on the proximal part of the medial side of the body of the tibia, medial to the tibial tuberosity and in front of the tendons of the gracilis and semitendinosus.

ACTION. Works over two joints—hip and knee. Flexes the thigh on the abdomen, abducts the thigh and rotates it laterally, and flexes the leg on the thigh.

NERVE SUPPLY. Femoral nerve (L_2 and L_3).

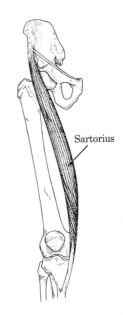

Fig. 134. Sartorius muscle.

Quadriceps femoris

LOCATION. In the anterior compartment of the thigh. It forms a large muscle mass that covers the front and sides of the femur (Figs. 133 and 135).

FORM. A "four-headed" muscle with each of the heads having separate origins but all joined into a common tendon for insertion.

COMPONENTS. *Rectus femoris.* A somewhat fuisform-shaped muscle with bipennate arrangement of fibers that arises on the anterior inferior spine of the ilium and the groove above the rim of the acetabulum (Fig. 135). It inserts by the common tibial tendon into

the tibial tuberosity. This is the only muscle of the group th
from the pelvic bone and works over two joints—hip an
flexes the thigh and extends the leg.

Vastus medialis. It arises from the lower half o
trochanteric line, medial lip of the linea aspera, and th
of the medial supracondylar ridge (Figs. 133 and 135). I
the tibial tuberosity by the common tendon. It works over
the knee. It extends the leg.

Vastus lateralis. It arises from the upper half o
trochanteric line, anterior and inferior borders of the greater trochanter,
lateral lip of the gluteal tuberosity, and the lateral lip of the linea
aspera (Figs. 133 and 135). It inserts into the tibial tuberosity by
common tendon. It works over one joint—the knee. It extends the
leg.

Vastus intermedius. It arises from the anterior surface of the
shaft of the femur and lies deep to the rectus femoris (Fig. 136). It
inserts by a thin, flat tendon that merges with the common tendon to
attach to the tibial tuberosity. It works over one joint—the knee. It
extends the leg.

NERVE SUPPLY. The components of the quadriceps femoris are
supplied by the femoral nerve (L_2,L_3,L_4).

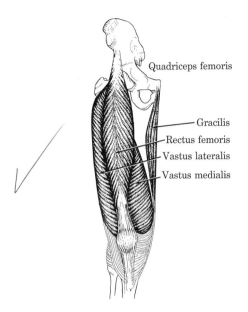

Fig. 135. Quadriceps femoris and gracilis muscles.

Articularis genu

A small muscle that lies beneath the vastus intermedius near the
knee joint.

ORIGIN. Anterior surface of the shaft of the femur in the lower
one-third.

INSERTION. Synovial membrane of the knee joint.

ACTION. Lifts the synovial membrane when the leg is extended.
This muscle does not act over any joint.

NERVE SUPPLY. Femoral nerve (L_2,L_3,L_4).

Medial Femoral Muscles of the Thigh

These muscles include the gracilis, pectineus, adductor longus,
adductor brevis, and adductor magnus.

Gracilis

LOCATION. The most superficial muscle of the medial femoral
muscles (Fig. 135).

FORM. A long, narrow, thin, and flat muscle. Fibers are arranged
in parallel.

ORIGIN. Arises from the inferior ramus of the pubis.

INSERTION. Into medial edge of the tibial tuberosity, below insertion of the sartorius.

ACTION. Involves two joints—the hip and the knee. Adducts
the thigh and flexes the leg.

NERVE SUPPLY. Anterior branch of the obturator nerve
(L_2,L_3,L_4).

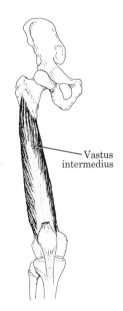

Fig. 136. Vastus intermedius muscle.

Pectineus

LOCATION. Upper medial part of the thigh, along the upper lateral margin of the adductor longus muscle.

FORM. Flat and quadrangular in shape.

ORIGIN. The pectineal line of the pelvic bone.

INSERTION. Into a narrow, roughened area between the lesser trochanter and the linea aspera of the femur.

ACTION. Works over one joint—the hip. Adducts and flexes the thigh and rotates it laterally.

NERVE SUPPLY. Femoral nerve (F_2, F_3, F_4).

Adductor longus

The most superficial of the three adductor muscles (Figs. 133 and 137).

LOCATION. Upper midportion of the medial part of the thigh.

FORM. Flat, thick, triangular in shape.

ORIGIN. Arises from the anterior surface of the superior ramus of the pubic bone.

INSERTION. Into the medial lip of the linea aspera.

ACTION. Involves one joint—the hip. Adducts and flexes the thigh.

NERVE SUPPLY. Anterior branch of the obturator nerve $(L_2$ and $L_3)$.

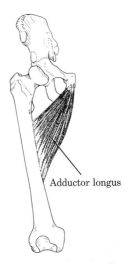

Fig. 137. Adductor longus muscle.

Adductor brevis

LOCATION. Medial and upper part of the thigh (Fig. 138).

FORM. Thick, triangular muscle.

ORIGIN. Arises from the anterior surface of the inferior ramus of the pubis.

INSERTION. Into a line leading from the lesser trochanter to the linea aspera and then along the upper third of the linea aspera.

ACTION. Works over one joint—the hip. Adducts and flexes the thigh, and rotates the thigh laterally.

NERVE SUPPLY. Anterior branch of the obturator nerve (L_2, L_3, L_4).

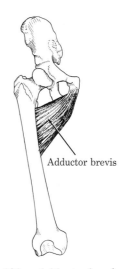

Fig. 138. Adductor brevis muscle.

Adductor magnus

LOCATION. Medial aspect of the thigh (Fig. 139).

FORM. Large, thick, triangular muscle.

ORIGIN. Arises from the inferior ramus of the ischium and the pubis, and from the ischial tuberosity.

INSERTION. By an aponeurosis into the medial lip of the linea aspera and the medial supracondylar ridge of the femur. In the lower part of the aponeurosis, next to the shaft of the femur, there is an opening in the aponeurosis called a *hiatus* that allows the passage of the femoral vessels to the posterior aspect of the knee.

ACTION. Works over one joint—the hip. Adducts and extends the thigh.

NERVE SUPPLY. Posterior branch of the obturator and the tibial nerves $(L_2, L_3, L_4, L_5, S_1)$.

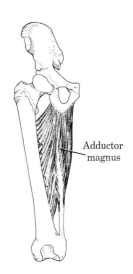

Fig. 139. Adductor magnus muscle.

Posterior Femoral Muscles of the Thigh

These muscles include the biceps femoris, semitendinosus, and semimembranosus (Fig. 140).

Biceps femoris

LOCATION. A superficial muscle on the posterior and lateral aspect of the thigh (Figs. 140, 141, and 142).

FORM. A "two-headed" muscle. The long head is fusiform in shape and the fibers have a modified parallel arrangement. The fibers forming the short head have unipennate arrangement.

ORIGIN. The long head and the semitendinosus arise by a common tendon from the ischial tuberosity. The short head arises from the lateral lip of the linea aspera.

INSERTION. Into the head of the fibula.

ACTION. Works over two joints—hip and knee. It extends the thigh, rotates it laterally, and adducts it. It flexes the knee.

NERVE SUPPLY. The long head by the tibial portion of the sciatic nerve (S_1, S_2, S_3); the short head by the peroneal portion of the sciatic nerve (L_4, L_5, S_1).

Semitendinosus

LOCATION. A superficial muscle on the posterior and medial aspect of the thigh (Figs. 140 and 143).

FORM. A fusiform-shaped muscle.

ORIGIN. Arises by common tendon (with the long head of the biceps femoris) from the ischial tuberosity.

INSERTION. Into the medial side of the tibia, immediately behind the insertion of the sartorius.

ACTION. Works over two joints—the hip and the knee. Extends and medially rotates the thigh; flexes the knee.

NERVE SUPPLY. Tibial portion of the sciatic nerve (L_5, S_1, S_2).

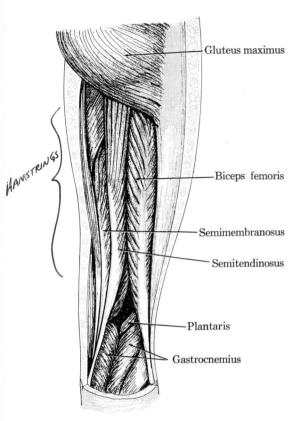

Gluteus maximus

Hamstrings

Biceps femoris

Semimembranosus

Semitendinosus

Plantaris

Gastrocnemius

Fig. 140. Muscles of the posterior aspect of the thigh.

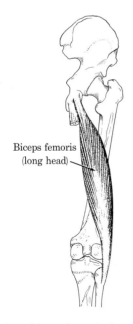

Biceps femoris (long head)

Fig. 141. Biceps femoris (long head).

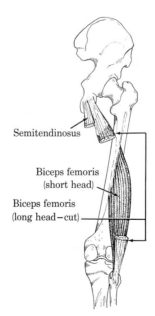

Semitendinosus

Biceps femoris (short head)

Biceps femoris (long head—cut)

Fig. 142. Biceps femoris (short head).

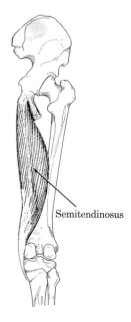

Semitendinosus

Fig. 143. Semitendinosus muscle.

Fig. 144.   Semimembranosus muscle.

Semimembranosus

LOCATION.   Lies deep to the semitendinosus on the posterior and medial aspect of the thigh (Figs. 140 and 144).

FORM.   Flat, quadrangular muscle.

ORIGIN.   Arises from the tuberosity of the ischium.

INSERTION.   Into a groove on the posterior surface of the medial epicondyle of the tibia.

ACTION.   Works over two joints—the hip and the knee. Extends and medially rotates the thigh; flexes the knee.

NERVE SUPPLY.   Tibial portion of the sciatic nerve (L_5, S_1, S_2).

MUSCLES OF THE LEG (CRURAL MUSCLES)

There are three groups of crural muscles—anterior, lateral, and posterior.

Anterior Crural Muscles

These muscles include the tibialis anterior, extensor hallucis longus, extensor digitorum longus, and peroneus tertius.

Tibialis anterior

LOCATION.   Superficial muscle of the front of the leg on the lateral side of the tibia (Fig. 145).

FORM.   Fibers have a bipennate arrangement.

ORIGIN.   Arises from the lateral surface of the upper half of the tibia.

INSERTION.   Into the medial and under surface of the first cuneiform, and the base of the first metatarsal.

ACTION.   Works over the ankle joint. Flexes and inverts the foot.

NERVE SUPPLY.   Common peroneal and deep peroneal nerves (L_4, L_5, S_1).

Extensor hallucis longus

LOCATION.   Lies deep to the anterior tibial muscle in the anterior part of the leg (Fig. 146).

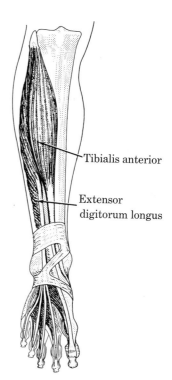

Fig. 145.   Tibalis anterior and extensor digitroum longus muscles.

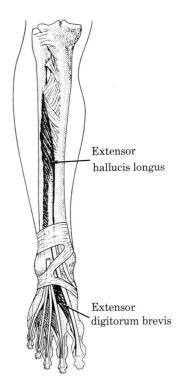

Fig. 146.   Extensors hallucis longus and brevis muscles.

FORM.   Thin, pennate muscle.

ORIGIN.   Arises from the middle half of the anterior surface of the fibula and in part from the interosseous membrane.

INSERTION.   Into the base of the distal phalanx of the great toe.

ACTION.   Works over several joints—ankle, metatarsophalangeal and interphalangeal joints of the great toe. Flexes the foot; extends the great toe.

NERVE SUPPLY.   Deep peroneal (anterior tibial) nerve (L_4,L_5, S_1).

Extensor digitorum longus

LOCATION.   Lies on the lateral side of the anterior part of the leg (Fig. 145).

FORM.   Flat, oblong muscle with pennate arrangement of muscle fibers.

ORIGIN.   Arises from the lateral condyle of the tibia, upper three fourths of the anterior surface of the fibula, and in part from the interosseous membrane.

INSERTION.   The tendon for insertion is long, and together with the tendon of the peroneus tertius, it passes beneath the transverse and cruciate ligaments at the ankle. The tendon of the extensor digitorum longus immediately splits into four tendinous slips which go to the second, third, fourth, and fifth toes. In the area of the metatarsophalangeal joints, these slips are reinforced by tendons of the intrinsic muscles of the foot (Fig. 147). These reinforced tendinous slips now flatten out to form a broad aponeurosis that covers the dorsum of the first phalanges of the second, third, fourth, and fifth toes. Just proximal to the first interphalangeal joint the aponeurosis for each toe splits into three slips. The middle slip extends forward to insert on the base of the middle phalanx; the two lateral slips continue distally and join to insert onto the base of the terminal phalanx.

ACTION.   Works over the interphalangeal, metatarsophalangeal, and ankle joints. It flexes the ankle and extends the toes.

NERVE SUPPLY.   Peroneus profundus (deep peroneal) nerve (L_4,L_5,S_1).

Peroneus Tertius

This muscle is generally considered to be a part of the extensor digitorum longus.

ORIGIN.   Arises from the lower third of the anterior surface of the fibula and the adjacent interosseous membrane.

INSERTION.   The tendon inserts into the dorsal surface of the base of the fifth metatarsal.

ACTION.   Works over the ankle joint. Flexes and assists in everting the foot.

NERVE SUPPLY.   Peroneus profundus (deep peroneal) nerve (L_4,L_5,S_1).

Lateral Crural Muscles

These muscles are the peroneus longus and peroneus brevis.

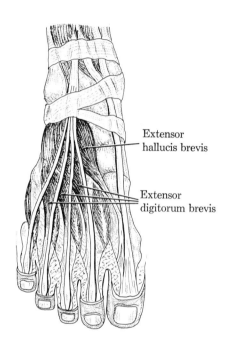

Extensor hallucis brevis

Extensor digitorum brevis

Fig. 147.   Extensor digitorum brevis and extensor hallucis brevis muscles.

Peroneus longus

LOCATION.   Occupies a superficial position on the lateral side of the leg, upper half (Fig. 148).

FORM.   Long and rather flat.

ORIGIN.   Arises from the upper two thirds of the lateral face of the fibula and the intermuscular septa.

INSERTION.   By a long tendon which passes behind the lateral malleolus, under the arch of the foot, to insert on the base of the first metatarsal, and the adjacent portion of the first cuneiform.

ACTION.   Works over the ankle joint. Extends and everts the foot.

NERVE SUPPLY.   Superficial peroneal nerve (L_4, L_5, S_1).

Peroneus brevis

LOCATION.   Lies deep to the peroneus longus on the lateral side of the leg. (Fig. 148).

FORM.   Flat, oblong, unipennate muscle.

ORIGIN.   Arises from the lower two thirds of the lateral face of the fibula and intermuscular septa.

INSERTION.   By long tendon that passes behind the lateral malleolus to insert on the tuberosity of the fifth metatarsal.

ACTION.   Works over the ankle joint. Extends and everts the foot.

NERVE SUPPLY.   Superficial peroneal nerve (L_4, L_5, S_1).

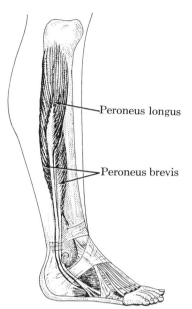

Fig. 148.   Peronei muscles.

Posterior Crural Muscles

These muscles include a superficial and a deep group.

Superficial Group. This group includes the gastrocnemius, soleus, and plantaris muscles.

Gastrocnemius

LOCATION.   A superficial muscle forming most of the calf of the leg (Fig. 149).

FORM.   A two-headed muscle; the medial head is larger than the lateral head.

ORIGIN.   Tendinous for both heads. The medial head arises from the back of the medial epicondyle and adjacent part of the femur; the lateral head arises from the side and back of the lateral epicondyle of the femur.

INSERTION.   By a large, long, tapered tendon called the tendo-calcaneus or Achilles tendon (common also to the soleus) into the posterior face of the calcaneus.

ACTION.   Works over two joints—the knee and ankle. Flexes the knee; extends the foot.

NERVE SUPPLY.   Tibial nerve (L_5, S_1, S_2).

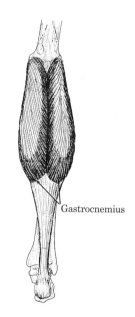

Fig. 149.   Gastrocnemius muscle.

Soleus

LOCATION.   Lies on the posterior side of the leg covered by the gastrocnemius (Fig. 150).

FORM.   Flat, broad, fusiform muscle.

ORIGIN.   Arises from the back of the head and upper one third of the posterior surface of the fibula, and the popliteal line and middle third of the medial margin of the tibia.

INSERTION.   By common tendon with the gastrocnemius into the posterior face of the calcaneus.

ACTION.   Works over one joint—the ankle. Extends the foot.

NERVE SUPPLY.   Tibial nerve (L_5, S_1, S_2).

Plantaris

LOCATION.   A small muscle on the upper lateral part of the back of the leg (Fig. 151).

FORM.   Very small, flat, fusiform muscle.

ORIGIN.   Arises from the lower part of the lateral supracondylar ridge of the femur.

INSERTION.   By a very long, slender tendon that inserts into the posterior face of the calcaneus (this tendon is often referred to as the "freshman's nerve" because freshmen medical students so often mistake it for a nerve).

ACTION.   A small, weak muscle that works over two joints— the knee and ankle. Assists in flexing the knee and extending the ankle.

NERVE SUPPLY.   Tibial nerve (L_5, S_1, S_2).

Deep Group.   This group of the posterior crural muscles includes the popliteus, flexor hallucis longus, flexor digitorum longus, and tibialis posterior.

Popliteus

LOCATION.   Lies behind the knee where it forms the lower part of the floor of the popliteal space (Fig. 152).

FORM.   Thin, flat, triangular muscle.

ORIGIN.   Arises from the lateral epicondyle of the femur.

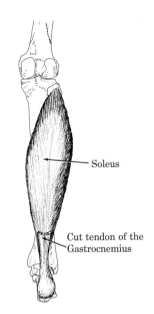

Fig. 150.   Soleus muscle.

— Soleus

Cut tendon of the
Gastrocnemius

Plantaris

Fig. 151.   Plantaris muscle.

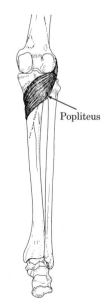

Popliteus

Fig. 152.   Popliteus muscle.

INSERTION.   Into the medial two thirds of the triangular space above the popliteal line of the tibia.

ACTION.   Works over one joint—the knee. Assists in flexing the knee, and rotates the tibia medially if the knee is flexed.

NERVE SUPPLY.   Tibial nerve (L_4,L_5,S_1).

Flexor hallucis longus

(Hallucis refers to the great toe).

LOCATION.   Lies on the fibular (lateral) side of the leg, deep to the soleus (Fig. 153).

FORM.   A penniform muscle.

ORIGIN.   Arises from the inferior two thirds of the posterior surface of the fibula.

INSERTION.   Into the base of the distal phalanx of the great toe by way of a long tendon which extends around the medial malleolus and under the sustentaculum tali to reach the great toe.

ACTION.   Works over several joints—ankle, tarsometatarsal, metatarsophalangeal, and the interphalangeal joints of the great toe. Extends and inverts the foot; flexes the great toe.

NERVE SUPPLY.   Tibial nerve (L_5,S_1,S_2).

Flexor digitorum longus

LOCATION.   Lies on the tibial (medial) side of the leg, deep to the soleus (Fig. 153).

FORM.   Flat, oblong, penniform muscle.

ORIGIN.   Arises from the middle third of the posterior surface of the body of the tibia.

INSERTION.   Into the base of the terminal phalanges of the second, third, fourth, and fifth toes. The tendon of the muscle extends around the medial malleolus, then obliquely forward and laterally into the area of the sole of the foot where it divides into four tendinous slips. These four slips insert into the bases of the terminal phalanges of the second, third, fourth, and fifth toes, after first passing through the split tendons of the flexor digitorum brevis which lie above them (Figs. 155 and 156).

ACTION.   Works over several joints—ankle, tarsometatarsal, metatarsophalangeal, and interphalangeal joints. Extends and inverts the foot; flexes the second, third, fourth, and fifth toes.

NERVE SUPPLY.   Tibial nerve (L_5,S_1).

Tibialis posterior

LOCATION.   Lies in the posterior part of the leg, directly on the interosseous membrane and adjacent portions of the tibia and fibula, and deep to the soleus (Fig. 154).

FORM.   Oblong, penniform muscle.

ORIGIN.   Arises from the posterior surface of the interosseous membrane and the adjacent surfaces of the upper two thirds of the tibia and the fibula.

INSERTION.   Into the tuberosity of the navicular bone primarily. It sends tendinous slips to the calcaneus and the three cuneiforms. This tendon also extends behind the medial malleolus.

ACTION.   Works over the ankle and tarsal joints. Extends and inverts the foot.

NERVE SUPPLY.   Tibial nerve (L_5,S_1).

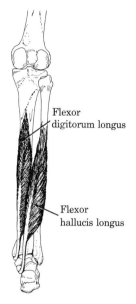

Fig. 153.   Flexor hallucis longus and flexor digitorum longus muscles.

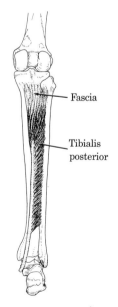

Fig. 154.   Tibialis posterior muscle.

MUSCLES OF THE FOOT

The details of the muscles of the foot are complex and are of interest primarily to the professional anatomist and the physician. Therefore, we shall confine our discussion to a general description of these muscles (Figs. 155 and 156). For more detailed information the student should consult a medical textbook of Anatomy.

GENERAL CONSIDERATIONS. The muscles of the foot and the hand have much in common.

1. Muscles of the foot and the hand include both extrinsic and intrinsic muscles.

2. The muscles of the plantar surface of the foot and the palmar surface of the hand are comparable in their arrangement. In both there are three groups of muscles:

Those associated with the great toe that correspond to the group associated with the thumb of the hand.

Comparable groups associated with the little toe and the little finger.

The muscles of the intermediate area in both the palm of the hand and the sole of the foot.

3. The way the tendons divide and insert is comparable for the following muscles:

Flexor digitorum brevis of the plantar surface of the foot and the flexor digitorum sublimis of the palmar surface of the hand.

Flexor digitorum longus of the foot and the flexor digitorum profundus of the hand.

Extensor digitorum longus of the foot and the extensor digitorum communis of the hand.

The differences in the hand and the foot are associated primarily with functional adaptations. The foot is a more compact, heavier, weight-bearing organ, designed for locomotion. Thus the great toe is aligned in parallel with the lesser toes, and they are all relatively short digits. The hand has been relieved of weight-bearing and has become adapted to grasping and manipulation of small objects. The thumb is attached at an angle and is so positioned that the ball of the thumb can be placed against the ball of each of the fingers, a morphological characteristic which facilitates the manipulation of tools and picking up of small objects and grasping.

The muscles of the plantar surface of the foot are arranged in four successive layers. In dissections, the order of their exposure from the superficial to the deep muscle layers is:

First layer
Abductor hallucis
Flexor digitorum brevis
Abductor digiti quinti
Second layer
Quadratus plantae
Lumbricales
Third layer
Flexor hallucis brevis
Adductor hallucis
Flexor digiti quinti brevis
Fourth layer
Interossei

These intrinsic muscles of the foot act, for the most part, on the toes and the actions of most of them are indicated in the muscle's name.

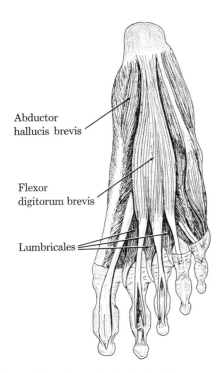

Abductor
hallucis brevis

Flexor
digitorum brevis

Lumbricales

Fig. 155. Flexor hallucis brevis, flexor digitorum brevis, and lumbricales muscles.

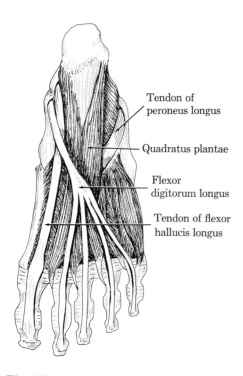

Tendon of
peroneus longus

Quadratus plantae

Flexor
digitorum longus

Tendon of flexor
hallucis longus

Fig. 156. Quadratus plantae muscle and tendons of flexors hallucis and digitorum longus and peroneous longus muscles.

6

THE BLOOD CIRCULATORY SYSTEM

At this time it should be recalled that the only living elements of the body are the cells, and there are literally billions of them throughout the body. To remain alive and to function, all of these cells must receive food and oxygen, regardless of their location. Moreover, these cells produce waste products as a result of their metabolic activities. In time, if these waste products were allowed to accumulate, they would destroy the very cells that produced them; they must be removed. Some cells produce secretions that are used by other cells in specific organs that may be located at some distance from the secretory cells.

Obviously, the body requires some form of transportation or delivery service and it must be widespread in its distribution, reaching all of the cells of the body. It must provide fast and efficient service if it is to be effective.

The circulatory system of the body is designed for such service. It consists of two divisions: the blood circulatory system which circulates blood throughout the body, and the lymph circulatory system which carries lymph from the periphery toward the heart. This chapter will deal with the blood vascular system. The lymph vascular system will be discussed in the following chapter (see p. 143).

The blood circulatory system represents part of the overall fluid transport system of the body. It includes the blood, which is a fluid tissue that serves as the transport vehicle, and the organs that distribute it: the blood vessels, which make up a closed, continuous system of tubes carrying the blood throughout the body, and the heart, a muscular pump whose contractions propel the blood through the blood vessels (Fig. 157).

THE BLOOD

DEFINITION. Blood is considered to be a form of connective tissue, consisting of cells, a fluid matrix (the plasma), and a potential for producing fibers (fibrin) under certain conditions, resulting in the formation of a blood clot.

DISTRIBUTION. Blood circulates to all parts of the body through a closed system of endothelial lined tubes, propelled by an endothelial lined pump, the heart.

FUNCTION. It serves as the fluid transport medium whereby oxygen and nutrient materials are delivered to all of the cells of the body, and the waste products of their metabolic activities are removed and ultimately eliminated from the body. It also transports cellular

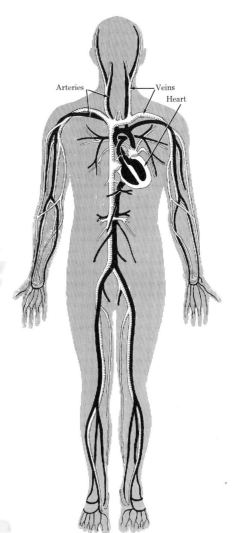

Fig. 157. The heart and major vessels of the blood circulatory system.

111

secretions (i.e., hormones) from their point of production to distant cells or organs that require and utilize these materials in their own metabolic activities.

THE FORMED ELEMENTS OF THE PERIPHERAL BLOOD

There are three formed elements of the peripheral blood—red blood corpuscles (erythrocytes), called corpuscles because they have no nuclei and are unable to divide and reproduce their own kind; white blood cells (leucocytes); and platelets, small fragments of the cytoplasm of megakaryocytes (Fig. 160).

Red Blood Corpuscles (ERYTHROCYTES)

The red blood corpuscles are small, round, anuclear, biconcave discs, measuring about 7.7 micra in diameter (Figs. 158 and 159). Single red corpuscles have a yellowish-red color; in large numbers they appear red. The red corpuscles are flexible and elastic. They can squeeze through spaces narrower than they are and then resume their usual shape. Red blood corpuscles contain a material called hemoglobin, which combines readily with oxygen to form oxyhemoglobin. It is oxyhemoglobin that gives the blood a bright red color. In the tissues the oxygen is released from oxyhemoglobin and carbon dioxide is taken up to be transported back to the lungs where it is released and expelled. Blood containing large amounts of carbon dioxide has a bluish red color (typical of most venous blood). The adult male has about 5,000,000 red blood corpuscles per cubic millimeter of blood, and the adult female has about 4,500,000 per cubic millimeter of blood. Red blood corpuscles have a life span of about 120 days.

White Blood Cells (LEUCOCYTES)

There are far fewer white blood cells than red blood corpuscles in the blood. Normally the white cell count per cubic millimeter of blood ranges between 5,000-9,000. There are two major classes of white cells in the peripheral circulation.

1. Cells without granules in their cytoplasm and a single nucleus (lymphocytes and monocytes) (Fig. 160).

2. Cells with granules in their cytoplasm and a nucleus that is lobulated—the granulocytes. Granulocytes are further subdivided on the basis of the way the granules stain, (neutrophils, basophils, and eosinophils) (Fig. 160).

Non-granular Leucocytes

LYMPHOCYTES.

NUMBER. These cells are the second most numerous white cell type in the blood and make up 20-25 per cent of the total number of leucocytes of normal peripheral blood.

DESCRIPTION. Lymphocytes vary in size, but the majority of them are small, slightly larger than red blood corpuscles. The nucleus is relatively large, practically filling the cell, and usually oval in shape, often with an indentation on one side. The scant cytoplasm these cells contain is free of granules (non-granular) (Fig. 160). The cells are mobile.

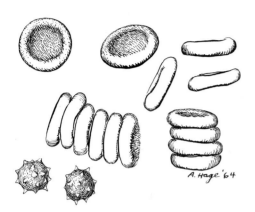

A. Hage '64

Fig. 158. Drawing of red blood corpuscles. Some of the corpuscles are seen in profile in rouleaux formation. The two in the lower right are crenated corpuscles.

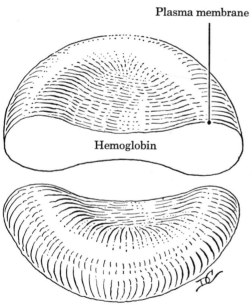

Plasma membrane

Hemoglobin

Fig. 159. Diagram of a red blood corpuscle that has been cut in half. (From Ham and Leeson. *Histology,* 4th ed. J. B. Lippincott Company.)

LOCATION.   The heart is located in the mediastinal space within the thoracic cavity. It lies between the lungs, in front of the trachea and thoracic aorta, and rests on the diaphragm (Fig. 161).

FUNCTION.   Contraction of the thick muscular walls of the heart pumps the blood through the vessels to all parts of the body.

SHAPE.   The heart is a cone-shaped organ.

POSITION.   It is obliquely placed in the lower part of the thoracic cavity. Its base is directed upward and to the right, and its apex to the left and downward. About two thirds of the heart lies to the left of the midline of the body (Fig. 161).

SIZE.   It is roughly the size of a man's clenched fist and weighs about 312 grams in the male, and 255 grams in the female. The size of the heart is closely correlated with physical effort. In athletes and people who do strenuous physical labor the heart is larger than average.

EXTERNAL APPEARANCE.   Externally, the heart presents for examination a base, an apex, two surfaces, two margins, and several grooves which mark the division of its cavity into four chambers.

The *base* of the organ is roughly quadrilateral in shape and is formed by the left atrium and a small portion of the right atrium. It is directed toward the right, upward and backward.

The *apex* is directed to the left, downward and forward. Most of the apex is formed by the left ventricle.

The *two surfaces* of the heart are the convex sternocostal surface that is directed forward, to the right, and upward, and the diaphragmatic surface which is flattened and rests on the diaphragm.

The *two margins* of the heart are the right and the left. The right margin is long and consists of a nearly vertical, rounded, upper portion, associated with the right atrium, and a thin, sharp, nearly horizontal, ventricular portion (sometimes called the inferior margin). The left margin is shorter, rounded, and formed mainly by the left ventricle. Only a small portion of this margin is associated with the left atrium.

The *four chambers* of the heart are formed by a division of the cavity into right and left halves by a median septum, and the division of each half into an upper chamber called an atrium (plural, atria) and a lower chamber called a ventricle (Fig. 162). Normally in the adult, there is no communication between the right and left halves of the heart. However, each atrium communicates with its corresponding ventricle by means of the atrioventricular orifice, which is guarded by a valve. The division of the heart into its four chambers is marked by grooves on the surface of the organ. In these grooves lie the blood vessels to the heart itself, lymph vessels and nerves, and some loose areolar connective tissue and fat.

THE RIGHT HALF OF THE HEART.   The right atrium and the right ventricle make up the right half of the heart.

The *right atrium* is thin-walled and consists of a main cavity and a small flap-like terminal free end called the auricle. This atrium is larger and its walls are thinner than the left atrium. Openings into the right atrium are the following.

Superior vena cava—returning blood from the upper half of the body.

Inferior vena cava—returning blood from the lower half of the body.

Coronary sinus—returning blood from the walls of the heart.

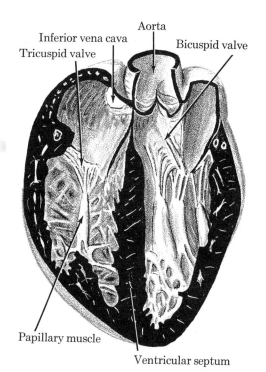

Fig. 162.   Heart cut open to show the four chambers and related structures.

Small foramina—marking the points at which small veins from the muscular layer of the heart empty.

Atrioventricular opening—a large opening between the right atrium and the right ventricle.

There are several other structures of interest in the right atrium.

1. The fossa ovale—an oval depression on the wall of the interatrial septum that marks the location of the fetal structure, the foramen ovale.

2. The crista terminalis—a vertical ridge of the lining membrane to the right of the superior and inferior vena caval orifices.

3. The musculi pectinati—small, parallel, muscular ridges in the auricle, extending for a short distance into the atrium, lateral to the crista terminalis.

The wall of the *right ventricle* is muscular and roughly a third as thick as the wall of the left ventricle (Fig. 163). This difference in thickness of the walls of the two ventricles is correlated with function. The right ventricle must force the blood through only the pulmonary circulation, which is a fairly restricted area and does not require the amount of work and pressure that is required for the left ventricle to force blood through the entire body (systemic circulation). The volume capacity of the two ventricles is equal, as might be expected. Openings into the right ventricle are the right atrioventricular opening and the orifice of the pulmonary artery.

There are several other structures of interest within the right ventricle.

1. The trabeculae carneae—rounded or irregular muscle columns of the heart wall that project into the cavity of the ventricle. Three types of trabeculae carneae are described: (a) ridges, that are attached along their entire extent on one side; (b) trabeculae, that are cord-like structures, attached at both ends and free in between; (c) papillary muscles, that are cone-shaped and attached at their bases only, the remainder of each papillary muscle being free and extending into the cavity of the ventricle.

2. The chordae tendineae—delicate, cord-like, tendinous structures that extend from the apex of the papillary muscle to the ventricular surface of the atrioventricular valve, preventing the valve from reversing itself when the ventricle contracts.

THE LEFT HALF OF THE HEART.   The left atrium and the left ventricle make up the left side of the heart.

The *left atrium* is similar in structure to the right atrium, but smaller in size. It presents a smooth surfaced main cavity and a flap-like auricle with its musculi pectinati. Inside the left atrium the following structures may be seen.

Openings for the four pulmonary veins.

Left atrioventricular opening.

Musculi pectinati—the inside of this atrium is smooth and the musculi pectinati are confined to the auricular portion of the left atrium.

The *left ventricle* is a conical chamber that is longer than the right ventricle. It forms most of the apical portion of the heart. Its muscular wall is about three times thicker than the wall of the right ventricle, the heavier wall being essential since this ventricle must generate enough pressure to force the blood throughout the entire body. The interior of the left ventricle presents two openings: the left atrioventricular orifice and the aortic opening—a circular opening

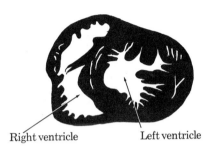

Fig. 163.   Cross section through the ventricles of the heart to show the relative thickness of the walls of the two ventricles.

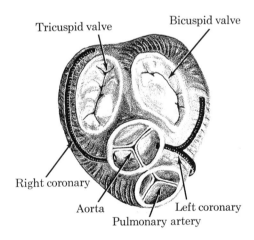

Fig. 164.   Base of the heart showing the two semilunar valves of the elastic arteries and the two atrioventricular valves—the tricuspid and the bicuspid.

portal circulation carries nutrients from the intestinal tract, through the liver, en route to the systemic circulation.

THE PULMONARY CIRCULATION

After circulating throughout the body the blood is depleted of its oxygen content and has a high concentration of carbon dioxide; it is returned to the right side of the heart. From there it is circulated through the lungs, where its carbon dioxide "load" is released and it takes on a new "load" of oxygen. From the lungs it is carried to the left atrium where it enters the systemic circulation.

Vessels of the Pulmonary System

Arteries

The pulmonary artery is a short, elastic artery about two inches long. It terminates just below the level of the arch of the aorta where it divides into the right and left branches. At the bifurcation, the ligamentum arteriosum, a very short, thick, cord-like structure, extends from the pulmonary artery to the anterior concave surface of the aortic arch. This cord is the fibrous remains of the fetal ductus arteriosus. The right branch of the pulmonary artery is directed horizontally below the arch of the aorta and in front of the right bronchus to enter the hilus of the right lung. This branch is larger and longer than the left branch. The left branch of the pulmonary artery is shorter, horizontally positioned, and extends in front of the left bronchus to the left lung. Within the lungs each vessel branches profusely and the branches tend to follow the branching of the bronchial tree. The terminal arterioles enter the capillaries.

Capillaries

Dense capillary networks surround the alveolae of the lung.

Veins

There are usually four pulmonary veins that carry oxygenated blood from the lungs to the left atrium of the heart. They start at the venous end of the capillary networks surrounding the alveolae, and through a successive merging of vessels, form ultimately two pulmonary veins that emerge from the hilus of each lung. The pulmonary veins empty into the left atrium of the heart.

THE SYSTEMIC CIRCULATION

The freshly oxygenated blood entering the left side of the heart from the pulmonary circulation is distributed throughout the entire body by the vessels of the systemic circulatory system. This system involves the left side of the heart and all of the vessels of the body except the pulmonary vessels.

Vessels of the Systemic Circulation

Arteries

AORTA.   The aorta is a large, long, elastic vessel that represents the main trunk from which ultimately all the systemic arteries arise,

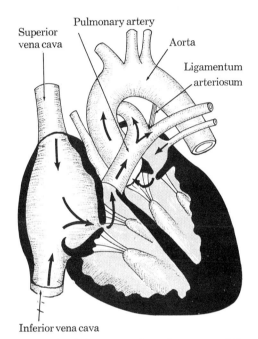

Fig. 175.   Diagram to show the course of the blood through the heart.

either directly as branches or indirectly as branches of branches (Fig. 176).

ORIGIN. The aorta arises from the left ventricle of the heart.

DIVISIONS. For descriptive purposes, the aorta is divided into an ascending portion, an arch, and a descending portion. This latter portion presents a thoracic and an abdominal segment.

COURSE. On leaving the left ventricle, the ascending aorta extends upward for about 2 inches, then turns backward and downward forming the aortic arch. It continues downward through the thoracic cavity (the thoracic segment of the descending aorta), lying in front of the bodies of the thoracic vertebrae. It continues through the aortic opening or hiatus in the diaphragm, into the abdomen (the abdominal segment of the descending aorta), lying in front of the lumbar vertebrae.

TERMINATION. At the level of the 4th lumbar vertebra, the aorta ends by dividing into right and left common iliac arteries.

BRANCHES.

    from the ascending aorta
        1. coronary arteries (right and left)
    from the arch of the aorta
        2. brachiocephalic (innominate) artery
        3. left common carotid artery
        4. left subclavian artery
    from the descending thoracic aorta
        5. pericardial arteries
        6. right and left bronchial arteries
        7. esophageal arteries
        8. mediastinal arteries
        9. intercostal arteries (9 pairs)
      10. subcostal arteries (paired)
      11. superior phrenic arteries (paired)
    from the descending abdominal aorta
      12. inferior phrenic arteries (paired)
      13. celiac trunk
      14. lumbar arteries (4 pairs)
      15. superior mesenteric artery
      16. middle suprarenal arteries (paired)
      17. renal arteries (paired)
      18. testicular (internal spermatic) arteries (paired in male) or ovarian arteries (paired in female)
      19. inferior mesenteric artery
      20. middle sacral artery
      21. right and left common iliac arteries (paired)—terminal branches

Branches of the Ascending Aorta. The two coronary arteries supply the muscular walls of the heart, anastomosing freely within the heart wall (Fig. 177).

The *right coronary* arises from the aorta (anterior aortic sinus) just after it leaves the left ventricle. It runs downward and to the right in the right atrioventricular sulcus (coronary sulcus), then turns to the left onto the diaphragmatic surface to the posterior longitudinal sulcus, as the posterior interventricular branch (posterior descending) to the apex of the heart where it anastomoses with the left coronary artery. It supplies the right atrium, the root of the aorta, and the root of the pulmonary artery. A branch, the marginal artery, supplies the right ventricle.

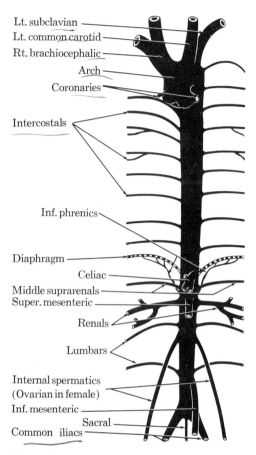

Lt. subclavian
Lt. common carotid
Rt. brachiocephalic
Arch
Coronaries
Intercostals
Inf. phrenics
Diaphragm
Celiac
Middle suprarenals
Super. mesenteric
Renals
Lumbars
Internal spermatics (Ovarian in female)
Inf. mesenteric
Sacral
Common iliacs

Fig. 176. The aorta and its branches.

The *left coronary* is larger than the right coronary and arises from the aorta (posterior aortic sinus) just after it leaves the left ventricle. A short distance from its origin it divides into the anterior interventricular artery (anterior descending branch) and a circumflex branch. The anterior interventricular artery lies in the anterior interventricular sulcus and extends to the apex of the heart. It supplies both ventricles. The circumflex artery follows the left extension of the right atrioventricular sulcus (coronary sulcus) and reaches nearly to the posterior longitudinal sulcus. It supplies the left atrium and ventricle.

Branches of the Arch of the Aorta. These branches supply the head, neck, and upper extremities (Fig. 177).

The *brachiocephalic (innominate) artery* is a wide, short (about 3.75 to 5 centimeters long) artery that carries blood for distribution to the right side of the head and neck and right upper extremity. It arises from the first part of the aortic arch. It extends upward and toward the right, and terminates behind the right sternoclavicular joint by dividing into the right common carotid and right subclavian arteries. These branches will be discussed with the comparable arteries of the opposite side.

The *left common carotid artery* arises from the arch of the aorta between the brachiocephalic (innominate) and left subclavian arteries.

The *left subclavian artery* arises from the arch of the aorta beyond the left common carotid. For discussion of the subclavian arteries, see page 130.

The Common Carotid Arteries (Right and Left). These two arteries differ in their origin and therefore their length. The left common carotid arises from the peak of the arch of the aorta and is longer than the right common carotid. It extends upward and enters the root of the neck behind the left sternoclavicular joint. The right common carotid begins behind the right sternoclavicular joint as one of the terminal branches of the brachiocephalic (innominate) artery. In the neck, the two common carotid arteries are so similar one description will serve for both.

Course. In the neck, both common carotids extend upward and laterally, behind the sternocleidomastoid muscle.

Termination. At the level of the upper border of the thyroid cartilage, the common carotids terminate by dividing into two branches —the external and internal carotid arteries.

Branches. In the adult, the *external carotid artery,* at its origin, is about the size of the internal carotid. However it gives off so many and such large branches, it quickly decreases in size as it extends up the neck. The artery arises as a branch of the common carotid artery at the level of the upper border of the thyroid cartilage. Throughout most of its course it is fairly superficial. It ascends in the neck and passes behind the angle of the mandible. Opposite the neck of the mandible, the artery terminates by dividing into its two terminal branches—the superficial temporal and the internal maxillary arteries.

Throughout its course the external carotid gives off eight major branches (Fig. 178). Listed in order, from its origin upward, they are:

1. Superior thyroid artery which supplies the thyroid gland and sends small branches to adjacent muscles and to the larynx.

2. Ascending pharyngeal artery which supplies the area of the pharynx.

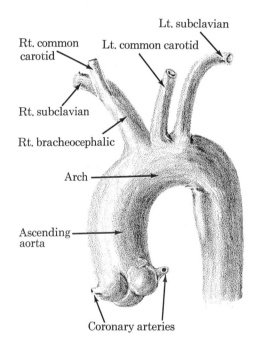

Fig. 177. Branches of the ascending aorta and the arch of the aorta.

3. Lingual artery which sends branches to the tongue and the sublingual gland.

4. Facial artery (external maxillary artery). This vessel is at first below and deep to the ramus of the mandible. It curves forward and upward over the lower edge of the body of the mandible and extends obliquely across the cheek to the side of the nose. It branches profusely to supply the structures of the face, neck, ear, scalp, soft palate, palatine glands, and tonsils.

5. Occipital artery which supplies the posterior part of the scalp and adjacent structures.

6. Posterior auricular artery which supplies structures of the ear and the adjacent scalp area.

7. Superficial temporal artery which supplies the scalp and region of the temple. It is one of the two terminal branches of the external carotid.

8. Maxillary (internal maxillary) artery is the other terminal branch of the external carotid; it supplies the deeper structures of the head, including the teeth.

The *internal carotid artery* is larger than the external carotid in the child; in the adult the two vessels are about equal. In the neck this vessel gives off no branches (Fig. 178). On entering the skull the internal carotid gives off branches which supply the brain, the eye, the various accessory structures of the eye, and some branches to the nose and forehead. At its origin from the common carotid, the internal carotid artery presents a slight sausage-shaped dilatation of its wall, called the *carotid sinus*. The walls of the vessel forming this sinus are modified and contain specialized nerve endings that respond to blood pressure changes within the vessel. When these nerve endings are stimulated, a reflex is set off that conveys an impulse to the medulla and results in a compensating increase or decrease in the rate of the heart beat.

ARTERIES OF THE BRAIN. Most of the blood to the brain arrives by way of the internal carotid arteries, and a smaller amount is delivered by the basilar artery which is formed by the union of the two vertebral arteries. From these vessels, branches are given off which form a vascular circle, called the circle of Willis, around the base of the brain. The student should consult the diagrammatic representation of the vascular circle, Figure 179, to more clearly visualize its components.

THE CIRCLE OF WILLIS (FIG. 179). From each internal carotid artery, two vessels are given off: an anterior cerebral and a posterior communicating branch. To form the vascular circle of Willis, the two anterior cerebral arteries (right and left sides) extend forward and medially, and are joined together anteriorly by a short anterior communicating branch. The posterior communicating branches on either side extend posteriorly and are continuous with the posterior cerebral branches of the basilar artery, thus completing the circle posteriorly. The cerebral vessels of the circle of Willis supply the cerebrum.

THE ANTERIOR, POSTERIOR, AND MIDDLE CEREBRAL ARTERIES. From the circle of Willis the anterior and posterior cerebral arteries, along with the middle cerebral artery (one of the terminal branches of the internal carotid artery), continue on beyond the circle to supply the cerebral hemisphere. These vessels give off numerous branches both to the surface and to deeper substance of the brain. The arteries on the surface of the brain anastomose freely, but within the brain, anastomoses between vessels are rare.

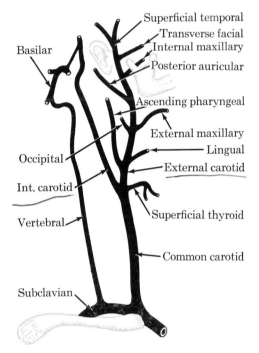

Fig. 178.   Arteries of the head and neck.

Branches. These arteries give off small, unnamed branches to the esophagus and the bronchial lymph nodes.

ESOPHAGEAL ARTERIES. These four or five small arteries arise at intervals from the front of the aorta and supply the esophagus.

MEDIASTINAL ARTERIES. These are small branches that arise from the aorta and supply the pleura and structures in the posterior mediastinum.

INTERCOSTAL ARTERIES. Nine pairs of intercostal arteries arise from the back of the aorta and extend laterally under each rib to supply the lower ten intercostal areas of the thoracic cavity.

SUBCOSTAL ARTERIES. These are a pair of arteries that arise below the last rib, from the back of the aorta, to supply the body wall.

SUPERIOR PHRENIC ARTERIES. These are two small vessels that arise from the aorta above the diaphragm, and supply the upper surface of the diaphragm.

ARTERIES TO THE WALLS AND VISCERA OF THE ABDOMEN AND PELVIS. These arteries arise from the abdominal portion of the descending aorta (Fig. 176) and include the

1. Inferior phrenics
2. Celiac trunk
3. Lumbars
4. Superior mesenteric
5. Middle surprarenals
6. Renals
7. Testiculars (internal spermatics) in the male
8. Ovarians in the female
9. Inferior mesenteric
10. Middle sacral
11. Common iliacs

INFERIOR PHRENIC ARTERIES. These are the first pair of arteries that arise from the abdominal aorta. They supply the inferior surface of the diaphragm. The right and left phrenics give off the right and left superior suprarenal arteries, respectively, to supply the adrenal gland of the same side.

CELIAC TRUNK. This is a very short (1.25 centimeters long), thick vessel that arises from the front of the aorta. It almost immediately divides into three branches—the left gastric, the common hepatic, and the splenic arteries.

The *left gastric* artery is the smallest branch of the celiac trunk. It ascends toward the left to the cardiac end of the stomach, then turns sharply downward and to the right along the lesser curvature of the stomach to anastomose with the right gastric branch of the common hepatic artery.

The *common hepatic* artery is larger than the left gastric, but smaller than the splenic branch. It takes a wide looped course downward and to the right, to enter the liver at its porta. In its course it gives off three branches—the right gastric, the gastroduodenal, and the proper hepatic artery (cystic). The common hepatic and its branches supply the stomach, duodenum, pancreas, liver, and gallbladder.

The *splenic* artery from its origin passes horizontally to the left, along the upper margin of the pancreas, to the spleen. It supplies the spleen and sends branches to the body and tail of the pancreas.

LUMBAR ARTERIES. These are four pairs of arteries that arise from the descending abdominal aorta. They extend around the abdominal walls, parallel to the intercostal vessels. They supply the walls of the abdominal cavity.

SUPERIOR MESENTERIC ARTERY (FIGS. 176 AND 181). This is a large vessel that supplies the small intestine and the first half of the large intestine.

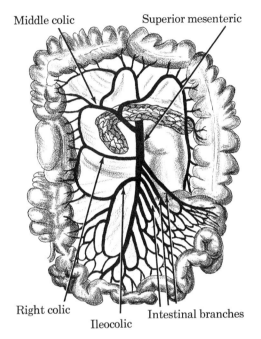

Middle colic   Superior mesenteric

Right colic   Intestinal branches
          Ileocolic

Fig. 181. Superior mesenteric artery and its branches.

Origin. It arises from the abdominal aorta about 1.25 centimeters below the celiac trunk.

Course. It extends downward, behind the splenic vein and the neck of the pancreas, then forward between the layers of the mesentery to the lower right quadrant of the abdomen. In its course it arches gently to the right.

Termination. This artery terminates by anastomosing with the ileocolic artery, one of its own branches.

Branches. The superior mesenteric gives rise to the following five branches.

The *inferior pancreaticoduodenal* artery supplies branches to the head of the pancreas and to the duodenum.

The *intestinal branches* are usually 12 to 15 vessels that arise from the convex (left) side of the superior mesenteric arch. These vessels form a series of anastomosing arches, with their convexities directed toward the intestines. Branches from the arches supply the jejunum and ileum.

The *ileocolic* is the lowest branch from the concave side of the superior mesenteric artery. It branches and anastomoses with adjacent vessels to supply the lower part of the ileum, the appendix, cecum, and first part of the ascending colon.

The *right colic* branch arises from the concave side of the superior mesenteric artery about midway between its origin and termination. It forms arterial loops from which vessels arise to supply the ascending colon.

The *middle colic* branch arises from the upper part of the superior mesenteric artery. Its two branches give rise to vessels which form anastomosing arterial loops supplying the transverse colon. Numerous terminal vessels arise from the convexities of the arterial loops to supply the walls of the intestines.

MIDDLE SUPRARENAL ARTERIES. These are two small vessels that arise, one on either side of the aorta, opposite the superior mesenteric artery. They extend laterally to supply the corresponding suprarenal (adrenal) glands.

RENAL ARTERIES (FIG. LEFT). These are two large arteries that deliver blood to the kidneys. The right renal artery is longer than the left.

Origin. They arise one from either side of the aorta just below the superior mesenteric artery.

Course. Each is directed laterally to the hilus of the corresponding kidney. The right renal artery passes behind the inferior vena cava and the corresponding renal vein. The left renal artery is placed a bit higher than the right and lies behind the left renal vein.

Termination. On entering the hilus each renal artery usually divides into three branches. As they cross the renal sinus to reach the substance of the kidney, these renal branches in turn branch to form the interlobar arteries that enter the substance of the kidney to supply the upper, middle, and lower portions of the organ.

Branches. The inferior suprarenal arteries are given off, one from each renal artery, to supply the suprarenal gland and the ureter of the respective side.

TESTICULAR (INTERNAL SPERMATIC) ARTERIES. These are two, long, slender vessels that supply the testes (Fig. left).

Origin. They arise from the abdominal aorta just below the renal arteries.

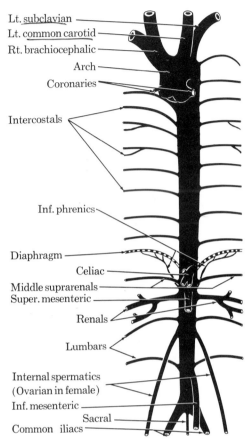

Lt. subclavian
Lt. common carotid
Rt. brachiocephalic
Arch
Coronaries
Intercostals
Inf. phrenics
Diaphragm
Celiac
Middle suprarenals
Super. mesenteric
Renals
Lumbars
Internal spermatics (Ovarian in female)
Inf. mesenteric
Sacral
Common iliacs

The aorta and its branches.

Course. Each artery passes downward and laterally on the posterior abdominal wall, behind the peritoneum to the abdominal inguinal ring. Here each joins other structures forming the spermatic cord, and passes through the inguinal canal to the testes.

Termination. It divides into small vessels which supply the testes.

Branches. Throughout its course small vessels are given off which supply the ureter, the cremasteric muscle of the spermatic cord, the epididymus, and the testes.

OVARIAN ARTERIES. These are two arteries in the female comparable to the testicular arteries in the male. They stay within the abdominal cavity and are, therefore, shorter than their counterparts in the male. They supply the ovaries.

Origin. They arise from the abdominal aorta just below the renal arteries.

Course. Each artery passes downward and laterally on the posterior abdominal wall, behind the peritoneum. At the upper pelvic margin these arteries enter the broad ligament of their respective side to be distributed to the corresponding ovary.

Branches. Small branches are given off the artery to supply the ureters, uterine tubes, and the uterus. Some follow the round ligament to supply the labia majora.

INFERIOR MESENTERIC ARTERY (FIGS. 176 AND 182). This is a single vessel that branches repeatedly to supply the terminal half of the colon and most of the rectum.

Origin. It arises from the abdominal aorta about 3.75 centimeters above its termination.

Course. It extends downward, in front of, and then to the left side of the aorta and behind the peritoneum.

Termination. This artery terminates where it crosses the left common iliac artery and becomes the superior hemorrhoidal artery.

Branches. The inferior mesenteric artery gives rise to the following three branches.

The *left colic* artery, whose branches supply the transverse colon and descending colon.

The two or three *sigmoid* arteries whose branches supply the sigmoid colon.

The *superior hemorrhoidal* artery, a continuation of the inferior mesentric artery, which branches to supply the rectum.

MIDDLE SACRAL ARTERY (FIG. 176). This is a small artery that arises from the posterior surface of the aorta at its point of division into the two common iliac arteries. It extends downward on the anterior surface of the sacrum and coccyx. It branches to form a pair of lumbar (5th) arteries, four lateral sacral branches, and branches to the rectum.

COMMON ILIAC ARTERIES (FIG. 176). These are the two, short, terminal branches of the abdominal aorta.

Origin. They arise at the bifurcation of the aorta at the level of the body of the 4th lumbar vertebra.

Course. They extend laterally and downward.

Termination. At the level of the lumbosacral articulation the arteries divide into their terminal branches—the external iliacs that distribute blood to the lower extremity, and the internal iliac (hypogastric) arteries that distribute blood to the organs and walls of the pelvis.

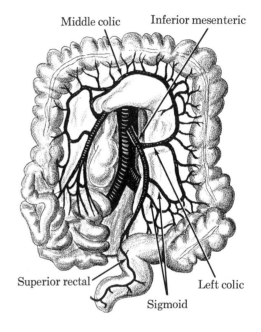

Fig. 182. Inferior mesenteric artery and its branches.

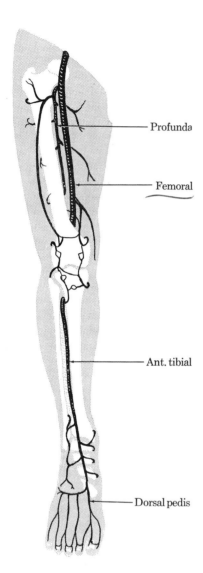

Branches.   The common iliac arteries give rise to the following two branches.

The internal iliac (hypogastric) artery. This is a short, wide vessel, smaller than the external iliac. It enters the pelvis, where it gives off twelve branches which supply the walls of the pelvis and the viscera of the region—the rectum, urinary bladder, prostate gland (in the male), and the uterus and vagina (in the female).

The *external iliac* artery. This vessel is larger than the internal iliac (hypogastric) artery. It extends laterally and downward along the pelvic brim to the midpoint of the inguinal ligament. Here it passes under the ligament and becomes the femoral artery. This artery gives off several small vessels and two branches (inferior epigastric and deep circumflex iliac), of considerable size.

ARTERIES OF THE LOWER EXTREMITY.   Blood is distributed to the lower extremity by a large vessel, the femoral artery, which is a continuation of the external iliac.

FEMORAL ARTERY.   *Origin.*   This artery arises as a continuation of the external iliac from the level of the inguinal ligament downward (Fig. 183).

Course.   It extends obliquely downward and medially through the region of the thigh.

In its upper 3.75 centimeters it runs in the lateral compartment of a short, funnel-shaped fibrous sheath, the femoral sheath, along with the femoral vein; it continues obliquely downward and medially in the adductor canal (Hunter's canal), a fascial structure covered by the sartorius muscle.

The *femoral sheath* is a short, funnel-shaped fibrous sheath, composed of abdominal fascia. Its wide, open end is directed upward and it is divided by fascial septa into three compartments. These are a lateral compartment containing the first part of the femoral artery, a middle compartment containing the femoral vein, and a small, medial compartment called the femoral canal which contains fat, lymph vessels, and a lymph node.

Termination.   The artery passes through the hiatus of the tendon of the adductor magnus muscle, to enter the posterior region of the knee, where it becomes the popliteal artery.

Branches.   The femoral artery gives rise to the following seven branches.

The *superficial epigastric* is a long, thin vessel that supplies the superficial structures of the anterior abdominal wall.

The *superficial iliac circumflex* is a small vessel supplying the superficial area of the groin.

The *superficial external pudendal* extends medially to supply the skin of the lower part of the abdomen, the penis and scrotum of the male, and the labium majus in the female.

The *deep external pudendal* vessel extends medially under the fascia lata to supply the skin of the scrotum and perineum in the male, and the labium majus of the female.

The *muscular branches* are given off to the muscles of the medial half of the thigh.

The *profunda femoris* is a large vessel that goes deep and medial to the femur. It extends onto the back of the thigh to supply the muscles of that area. Its branches (medial and lateral femoral circumflex, perforating, and muscular arteries) supply the structures in the

Fig. 183.   Major artery of the lower extremity and its branches. Anterior aspect.

Profunda

Femoral

Ant. tibial

Dorsal pedis

area of the hip joint and the gluteal region, and the lateral region of the thigh as far as the knee.

The *supreme genicular* vessel supplies the knee joint and is given off the femoral artery just before it becomes the popliteal.

POPLITEAL ARTERY. This vessel is the continuation of the femoral artery on the posterior aspect of the knee (Fig. 184).

Origin. It begins at the level of the hiatus in the adductor magnus muscle tendon.

Course. At first it is directed laterally and downward, then vertically downward to the lower border of the popliteus muscle where it ends.

Termination. It terminates below the knee joint, where it divides into the anterior and posterior tibial arteries.

Branches. The popliteal artery gives off a number of small muscular branches, branches to the skin, and vessels forming anastomoses around the knee joint. Its two terminal branches, the anterior and posterior tibial arteries, are large and supply the leg, ankle, and foot.

The *anterior tibial* vessel reaches the anterior surface of the leg between the upper portions of the tibia and fibula. It extends nearly vertically down the front of the leg. In front of the ankle it becomes the dorsal pedis artery which gives off a number of branches to the dorsal surface of the foot and toes.

The *posterior tibial* vessel extends down the posterior aspect of the leg, around the medial malleolus to the sole of the foot where one of its terminal branches, the lateral plantar, forms the deep plantar arch. From the convex side of the arch, smaller branches are given off to the toes (Figs. 184 and 185).

Veins

FORMATION OF THE VENOUS SYSTEM. The veins, which return blood to the heart, commence as minute vessels called venules that receive blood from capillary beds. Venules join to form veins, which in turn merge to form vessels of gradually increasing size.

PULMONARY AND SYSTEMIC VEINS. The veins are arranged in two sets—pulmonary and systemic. The four pulmonary veins carry oxygenated (arterial) blood from the lungs to the left atrium of the heart; the systemic veins return deoxygenated (venous) blood from the remainder of the body to the right atrium of the heart. The systemic venous channels include the superficial and deep veins, and the venous sinuses of the cranium.

Superficial veins are found in the tissue under the skin; they return blood from superficial areas. These veins are mostly unnamed vessels whose patterns are extremely variable (compare the venous patterns on the back of your two hands). They communicate with the deep vessels.

Deep veins accompany arteries and usually have the same name as the vessel they accompany. With the smaller arteries, there are usually two veins (called venae comitantes), one on either side of the artery; the larger vessels have only one accompanying vein.

Venous sinuses are venous channels located between the dura mater, within the cranial cavity. They are lined by endothelium continuous with that lining the vessels with which they are associated.

The systemic veins return blood to the heart by *three major routes.*

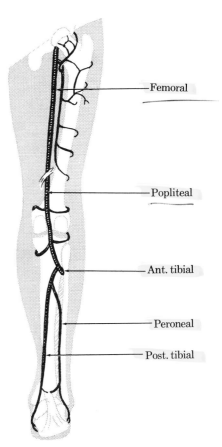

Fig. 184. Major arteries of the lower extremity. Posterior aspect.

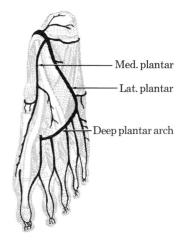

Fig. 185. Arteries of the sole of the foot.

1. Blood is returned from the heart itself by way of the veins of the heart that empty into the coronary sinus.

2. Blood from the head, neck, upper extremities, and the thorax is returned by veins that are tributaries of the superior vena cava.

3. Blood from the lower extremities, pelvis, and abdominal area, is returned by way of the tributaries of the inferior vena cava.

VEINS OF THE HEART. The venous drainage of the heart has been discussed under blood supply of the heart (see p. 118).

VEINS OF THE CRANIAL CAVITY. These are the veins of the brain, sinuses of the dura mater, emissary and diploic veins.

VEINS OF THE BRAIN. The veins that return blood from the brain are peculiar in that their walls are extremely thin and devoid of any muscular layer. They have no valves. These vessels accompany the arteries of the brain and have the same names as the vessels they accompany. They empty into the venous sinuses of the cranium and ultimately into the internal jugular veins.

VENOUS SINUSES OF THE DURA MATER (Figs. 186 and 187). These endothelial-lined venous channels lie between layers of the dura mater. There are ten of these sinuses, five in the upper and back part of the skull forming a posterosuperior group, and five at the base of the skull forming an antero-inferior group of sinuses.

Posterosuperior group

    1. Superior sagittal
    2. Inferior sagittal
    3. Two transverse
    4. Straight
    5. Occipital

Antero-inferior group

    1. Two cavernous
    2. Two intercavernous
    3. Two superior petrosal
    4. Two inferior petrosal
    5. Basilar plexus

The blood from the sinuses drains directly or indirectly into the internal jugular vein.

EMISSARY VEINS. This is a variable group of veins that extend between the venous sinuses of the dura within the cranium and veins outside of the cranial cavity. They are without valves. Blood in these veins can flow in either direction depending on the pressure within the sinuses as compared to the pressure within the veins outside the cranial cavity. Because of this, infections may at times enter the sinuses from outside the cranium and cause a meningitis (inflammation of the meninges) or a brain abscess.

DIPLOIC VEINS. These are venous channels that lie in the diploë between the plates of bones of the cranium.

VEINS OF THE EXTERIOR OF THE HEAD AND FACE, AND THE NECK (Fig. 188).

    1. External jugular
    2. Posterior external jugular
    3. Anterior jugular
    4. Internal jugular
    5. Vertebral

The *external jugular* vein and its tributaries return blood from the deep structures of the face and outside of the cranial cavity, and empty into the large brachiocephalic vein.

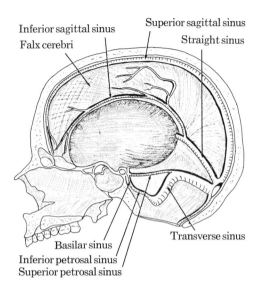

Fig. 186. Venous sinuses of the cranial dura viewed from the side.

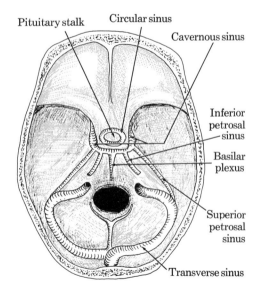

Fig. 187. Venous sinuses of the cranial dura viewed from above.

The *posterior external jugular* vein returns blood from the skin and superficial muscles of the back of the neck. It empties into the external jugular vein.

The *anterior jugular* vein returns blood from the larynx and thyroid gland in the anterior part of the neck. It empties into the internal jugular vein. This vein is without valves.

The *internal jugular* vein is a deep vein. Its tributaries return blood from the brain, superficial structures of the face, and the neck. Besides receiving venous tributaries, this vessel at its junction with the subclavian veins receives as tributaries the terminal vessels of the lymph system. The left internal jugular vein receives the thoracic duct. The right internal jugular vein receives the right lymphatic ducts.

The *vertebral* vein and its tributaries return blood from the muscles of the upper posterior part of the neck and from the venous plexuses of the cervical portion of the spinal canal. The vertebral veins empty into the brachiocephalic veins near their origins.

VEINS OF THE UPPER EXTREMITY. Blood is returned from the upper extremities by two sets of veins, a *superficial* set which is located just beneath the skin, and a *deep* set, the venae comitantes, which accompany the arteries. Valves are present in both sets of veins but are less numerous in the superficial veins. These two sets of veins frequently communicate with one another.

There are three named superficial veins of the upper extremity (Fig. 189).

The *cephalic* begins near the lateral side of the base of the thumb. It is formed from the dorsal venous network of veins. The cephalic vein extends up the lateral side of the forearm in front of the elbow and along the lateral border of the biceps brachii muscle. It empties into the axillary vein just below the clavicle. Throughout its course it receives numerous tributaries. At the elbow it gives off the mediana cubiti which joins the basilic vein.

The *basilic* arises on the back of the hand from the dorsal venous network. It extends upward, curves around the medial edge of the forearm just below the elbow to reach the anteromedial surface of the arm. About halfway up the arm, it goes deep to enter the brachial vein. The mediana cubiti vein from the cephalic enters the basilic at the elbow.

The *mediana cubiti* is a relatively short vessel extending diagonally upward and medially across the front of the elbow. It serves as a communicating vessel between the cephalic and basilic veins.

The deep veins of the upper extremities follow and have the same names as the arteries of the upper extremities.

The *ulnar* vein returns blood from tributaries of the superficial volar arch, and in the forearm receives tributaries from the posterior surface.

The *radial* vein returns blood from tributaries of the deep volar arch, and in the forearm it receives tributaries from the anterior and posterior surfaces. At the elbow it receives the mediana cubiti.

The ulnar and radial vessels join to form the brachial vein.

The *brachial* vein receives tributaries comparable to branches given off by the brachial artery it accompanies. It also receives the superficial basilic vein as a tributary. As the brachial vein enters the axillary space, it becomes the axillary vein.

The *axillary* vein and its tributaries (including the superficial vein, the cephalic) continues as the subclavian vein at the outer border of the first rib.

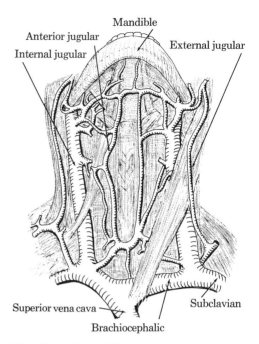

Fig. 188. Veins of the neck. Anterior aspect.

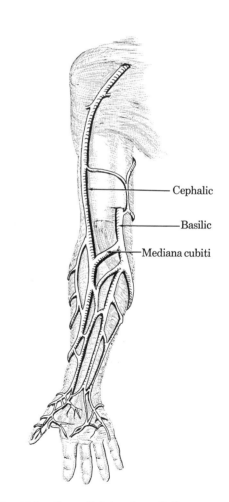

Fig. 189. Superficial veins of the upper extremity.

The *subclavian* vein starts at the outer border of the first rib as the continuation of the axillary vein. Behind the sternoclavicular joint it joins the internal jugular vein to form the brachiocephalic vein (innominate vein). Tributaries of importance are the external jugular vein and the terminal lymphatic vessels which empty at the point of junction of this vessel with the internal jugular. On the right side, the lymphatic vessels (usually two) are called the right lymphatic ducts; on the left is a single lymphatic vessel, the thoracic duct.

VEINS OF THE THORAX. The brachiocephalic (innominate) veins are two large vessels, right and left, that are formed by the union of the subclavian and internal jugular veins of their respective sides. These two large vessels are without valves.

The *right brachiocephalic (innominate)* is a short, wide vessel, about 2.5 centimeters long, directed almost vertically downward from its origin to its union with the left brachiocephalic vein to form the superior vena cava. It receives as tributaries the right vertebral vein, the right internal mammary, and often the first intercostal.

The *left brachiocephalic (innominate)* is about two and a half times as long as the right brachiocephalic. It extends obliquely downward and to the right in front of the three large vessels branching from the arch of the aorta, and joins with the right brachiocephalic to form the superior vena cava. It receives as tributaries the left internal mammary vein, left inferior thyroid, and the left highest intercostal.

The *superior vena cava* is a large, short (about 7 centimeters long) vein that receives the blood from the upper half of the body. It is formed by the union of the two brachiocephalic veins. It descends almost vertically and empties into the right atrium of the heart. Its tributaries are the azygos vein, the hemiazygos, accessory hemiazygos, and the bronchial. These vessels return blood from the thoracic cavity and its contained organs.

VEINS OF THE LOWER EXTREMITY. In the lower extremity there are two sets of veins returning blood to the heart, a *superficial* and *deep* set, comparable to those found in the upper extremity. Because of the distance the blood must travel against the force of gravity, there are numerous valves in these veins.

There are two named superficial veins of the lower extremity— the great and small saphenous. These two veins and their tributaries make up the superficial set of vessels (Figs. 190 and 191).

The *great saphenous* is the longest vein of the entire body. It begins on the medial side of the dorsum of the foot, ascends along the medial aspect of the leg and thigh, and empties into the femoral vein a short distance below the inguinal ligament. It receives many small unnamed tributaries as it extends up the leg, and larger named tributaries that include the accessory saphenous, superficial epigastric, superficial iliac circumflex, and superficial external pudendal. The larger tributaries enter the great saphenous vein very near its termination in the femoral vein.

The *small saphenous* vein is a smaller, shorter vessel than the great saphenous. It starts along the lateral margin of the foot, extends behind the lateral malleolus, and follows a straight course up the back of the leg to the middle of the back of the knee, where it empties into the popliteal vein. It communicates with the deep veins of the area and with the great saphenous.

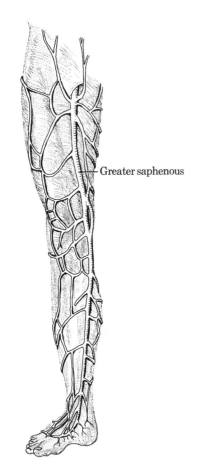

Greater saphenous

Fig. 190. Superficial veins of the lower extremity. Anterior aspect.

The deep veins of the lower extremity accompany the arteries and have comparable names.

The *anterior tibial* vein is formed by tributaries returning blood from the dorsal, medial, and plantar portions of the foot. It accompanies the anterior tibial artery as its venae comitantes. In its upper extent the anterior tibial vein runs between the fibula and the tibia to the back of the leg. It unites with the posterior tibial vein to form the popliteal vein.

The *posterior tibial* vein is formed by tributaries returning blood from the lateral and dorsal portions of the foot. It extends up the posterior aspect of the leg, receives the peroneal vein as a tributary, and ends just below the knee where it joins the anterior tibial to form the popliteal.

The *popliteal* vein is a relatively short vein that starts at the junction of the anterior and posterior tibial veins. It extends upward through the popliteal space, behind the knee, then curves medially to the hiatus of the adductor magnus muscle at the medial border of the femur. It goes through the hiatus and becomes the femoral vein.

The *femoral* vein is the continuation of the popliteal vein at the hiatus of the adductor magnus muscle. It accompanies the femoral artery through the thigh. It terminates at the level of the inguinal ligament where, as the external iliac vein, it enters the abdominal cavity. The tributaries entering the femoral vein correspond in name and distribution to the arterial branches given off by the femoral artery with the exception of the superficial great saphenous vein.

Veins of the Abdomen and Pelvis. The *external iliac* vein starts at the level of the inguinal ligament as a continuation of the femoral vein. It extends along the pelvic brim to its junction with the hypogastric vein to form the common iliac vein.

The *hypogastric* vein is formed in the pelvis by tributaries which return blood from the perineum, pelvic area, and the pelvic organs. It follows the course of the hypogastric artery and joins the external iliac to form the common iliac vein.

The *common iliac* veins are relatively short vessels that are formed by the union of the external iliac and hypogastric veins. These veins extend upward and medially. They unite at the level of the 5th lumbar vertebra to form the inferior vena cava.

The *inferior vena cava* is a large vessel that returns blood from the body below the level of the diaphragm. It begins at the level of the 5th lumbar vertebra by the union of the right and left common iliac veins. It extends vertically upward on the posterior abdominal wall in front of the vertebral column, and to the right of the aorta, to the liver. It continues upward, behind the liver, perforates the diaphragm, then turns forward and medially to empty into the lower posterior part of the right atrium. The inferior vena cava receives the following veins as tributaries: four pairs of lumbar veins, the right testicular or the right ovarian (the left testicular or the left ovarian empties into the left renal vein), the two renal veins, the suprarenal veins, the inferior phrenics, and the several hepatic veins.

The *portal* vein is a major vessel of the portal circulation of blood through the liver. Three abdominal veins—the splenic, superior mesenteric, and inferior mesenteric—which do not accompany their

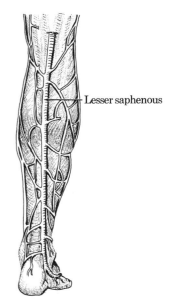

Lesser saphenous

Fig. 191. Superficial veins of the lower extremity. Posterior aspect.

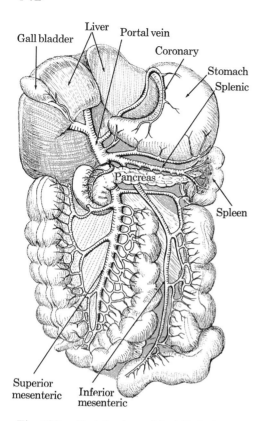

Fig. 192.   Portal vein and its tributaries.

arteries in returning blood in the systemic system, merge to form the portal vein (Fig. 192). Blood delivered to the liver by way of the portal vein passes through the hepatic sinuses where it is mixed with the blood from the hepatic artery, and leaves the liver by way of several short hepatic veins which empty into the inferior vena cava as it passes behind the liver.

Portal Circulation

This is a subdivision of the systemic circulation. It consists of veins that convey blood from the spleen and the gastrointestinal tract. These vessels converge to form the portal vein to the liver. In the liver, the portal vein "branches" like an artery and finally ends in capillary-like, thin-walled sinusoids. From the sinusoids, small venous vessels carry the blood through a series of vessels of increasing size, the hepatic veins, which empty into the inferior vena cava. The tributaries forming the portal vein are the superior mesenteric, the inferior mesenteric, and the splenic veins.

An interesting situation in the portal circulation should be called to the attention of the student. The blood carried through the portal circulation passes through two sets of capillaries. The first set of capillaries is in the spleen, pancreas, and walls of the digestive tract. From these capillaries, veins arise and merge, ultimately forming the portal vein that conveys the blood to the liver. This is venous blood containing dissolved food substances absorbed from the digestive tract. The second set of capillaries is in the liver, and consists of capillary-like sinusoids between the cords of hepatic cells. The terminal branchings of the portal vein, and the terminal arterioles of the hepatic artery carrying oxygenated blood, open into these sinusoids. From the hepatic sinusoids the blood is conveyed by veins which empty into the hepatic veins and then into the inferior vena cava.

7

THE LYMPHATIC SYSTEM AND LYMPHOID ORGANS

THE LYMPHATIC SYSTEM

The lymphatic system consists of a network of anastomosing lymphatic capillaries, lymph vessels, the two large terminal lymph ducts which carry the lymph, and lymph nodes located at intervals along the course of the vessels.

The lymph circulatory system differs from the blood circulatory system in two ways.

1. The lymphatic system has no pumping apparatus and does not form a complete circuit, but starts as blind end capillaries in the peripheral tissues, carries lymph toward the heart, and delivers it into the veins of the neck.

2. It has an "open" system of vessels, for in the lymph nodes the continuity of the vessels is interrupted, and the lymph is not confined to the endothelial-lined lymph vessels, but continues its course through lymphoid sinuses and is filtered through the parenchyma of the lymph nodes.

Lymph

The tissue fluid that diffuses through the walls of the lymph capillaries is called *lymph,* and is similar in composition to blood plasma. It is a clear, colorless or slightly straw-colored fluid, formed from tissue fluid by filtration. Comparing the two circulating fluids of the body—lymph and blood—it is found that lymph has a slightly lower specific gravity than blood; lymph normally contains lymphocytes and a few granular leucocytes, but no red blood corpuscles, platelets, or fibrinogen; it will clot (coagulate), but much more slowly than blood. Both fluids contain enzymes and antibodies. The lymph in the capillaries of the small intestine, during and after a meal containing fat, has a milky appearance due to the absorbed fat it contains. This "milky" lymph is called *chyle*. The capillaries containing chyle also appear creamy in color (milky), and for this reason such capillaries are always referred to as lacteals.

Lymphatic Capillaries (Fig. 193)

Lymphatic capillaries arise peripherally as blind-end capillary networks. These capillaries are endothelial-lined, very thin walled

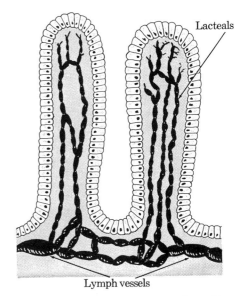

Fig. 193.   Drawing to show lymph capillaries, lacteals, and lymph vessels of the wall of the small intestine.

143

tubes of irregular diameter, and are somewhat larger than blood capillaries. They do not have valves. Lymphatic capillaries have not been found in the following places:

1. The central nervous system, the meninges, and the peripheral nerves.

2. The orbit of the eye and the eyeball, except the conjunctiva, which is the mucous membrane covering the anterior surface of the eyeball.

3. The internal ear.

4. The endomysium of striated muscle.

5. The interior of the lobules of the liver.

6. The parenchyma of the spleen and kidney.

Lymphatic Vessels (Fig. 193). Lymphatic capillaries unite to form small lymphatic vessels. These in turn join to form successively larger and larger vessels. The walls of lymphatic vessels, like those of blood vessels, consist of three layers: intima, media and an adventitia. However, particularly in the smaller lymphatic vessels, the layers are not as well defined as they are in blood vessels. Lymphatic vessels have valves, and these lymphatic valves are more numerous than in the veins. The valves, by preventing backward flow, are indirect aids to the movement of lymph.

The lymphatic vessels are distributed so as to form a superficial and a deep set of vessels. The superficial vessels drain the superficial or surface areas of the body or the surfaces of organs. The deep set of vessels, which are larger but less numerous, accompany the deep blood vessels of the area. Non-vascular structures such as cartilage, nails, and the like, have no lymphatic vessels. All the lymph is ultimately carried into either the right lymphatic duct or the thoracic duct.

LYMPH DUCTS

The terminal lymphatic vessels are the *thoracic duct* and the *right lymphatic duct.*

The thoracic duct is the larger of the two terminal lymphatic ducts (Fig. 194). It begins in the abdominal cavity in front of the second lumbar vertebra as a dilated saccular structure called the *cisterna chyli,* which extends upward to the eleventh thoracic vertebra. The thoracic duct continues to ascend nearly vertically, lying at first to the right and behind the aorta. It passes through the aortic hiatus of the diaphragm, ascending along the thoracic aorta, and then curves to the left behind the aortic arch. It empties into the blood circulation at the junction of the left internal jugular and subclavian veins. At its termination it has valves to prevent the blood from the veins entering it. The thoracic duct carries the lymph and the chyle from all parts of the body except those drained by the right lymphatic duct and its tributaries (see below) (Fig. 194).

The right lymphatic duct is a short duct formed by several tributaries (Fig. 194). It enters the right subclavian vein at its junction with the right internal jugular vein. It receives lymph from the right side of the head, neck and thorax, the right upper extremity, the right lung, the right side of the heart, and the right upper convex surface of the diaphragm (Fig. 194). However, it is more common for these tributaries to empty directly into the right subclavian vein without uniting to form the right lymphatic duct.

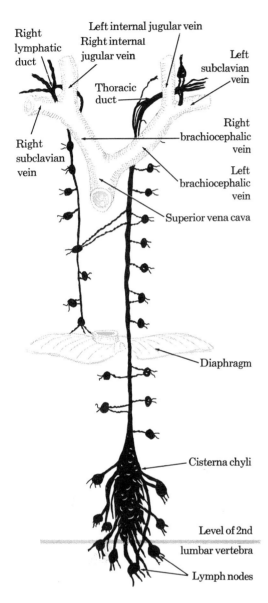

Fig. 194. Right lymph duct and the thoracic duct.

Right lymphatic duct
Left internal jugular vein
Right internal jugular vein
Left subclavian vein
Thoracic duct
Right subclavian vein
Right brachiocephalic vein
Left brachiocephalic vein
Superior vena cava
Diaphragm
Cisterna chyli
Level of 2nd lumbar vertebra
Lymph nodes

Lymph Nodes (Lymph Glands) (Fig. 195)

Lymph nodes are small, flattened, round to bean-shaped organs of variable sizes that are interposed at various points along the course of the lymph vessels. A lymph node is composed of lymphoid tissue which forms the *parenchyma* of the organ and is supported by a reticular tissue *stroma*. A fibrous connective tissue *capsule* encloses the node, and *septa* or *trabeculae* extend from its inner surface into the parenchyma. The parenchyma is divided into two parts: an *outer portion,* the *cortex* and an *inner portion,* the *medulla.* The cortex contains lymph nodules surrounded by diffuse lymphoid tissue. In the medulla, diffuse tissue is arranged in anastomosing cords that are continuous with the diffuse lymphoid tissue of the cortex.

In each *nodule* in the cortex, the lymphocytes are organized into a spherical, closely packed mass. Many nodules will show a less densely packed central area, called a *germinal center,* consisting of large lymphocytes and less differentiated cells that may give rise to new lymphocytes.

Lymph vessels (afferent vessels) enter each lymph node along its convex border, opposite the hilus. They penetrate the capsule and open into the *subcapsular* and *trabecular sinuses.* These sinuses are continuous with sinuses which extend throughout the parenchyma of the node. The lymph brought by the afferent vessels circulates freely through the sinuses, where it is filtered, and new lymphocytes are added. Near the hilus of the node, the sinuses give rise to the efferent lymph vessels that leave the node at the hilus. At the hilus, blood vessels also enter and leave the node.

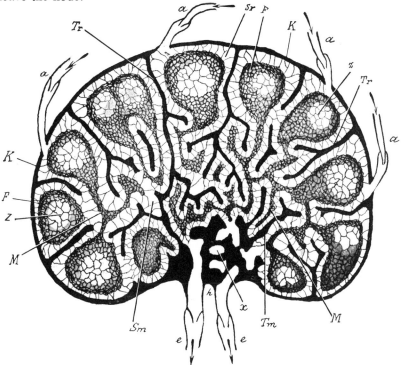

Fig. 195.   Diagram of lymph node. a, afferent and, e, efferent lymphatic vessels with valves; the arrows indicate the direction of lymph flow; F, cortical tissue; K, capsule; M, medullary cords; Sm, medullary and, Sr, cortical sinuses; Tm, medullary trabeculae, continuous with those of the cortex; Tr, trabeculae originating in the capsule and dividing the cortex into ampullae; x, lymphatic vessels in the dense connective tissue of the hilum, h; Z, nodules. (From Bloom and Fawcett. *A Textbook of Histology,* 8th ed. W. B. Saunders Company.)

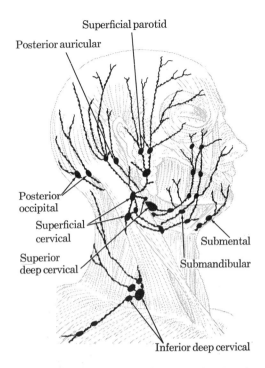

Fig. 196. Lymph drainage of the head and neck.

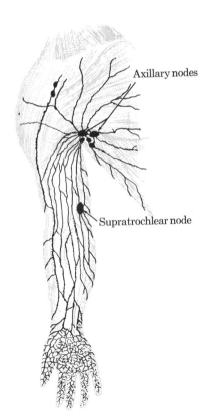

Fig. 197. Lymph drainage of the right upper extremity.

FUNCTION.   Lymph nodes carry out two major functions.

1.   They produce blood lymphocytes and monocytes and tissue plasma cells and macrophages.

2.   They filter out bacteria and foreign particles carried by the lymph.

DISTRIBUTION.   Lymph nodes are scattered throughout the body, sometimes singly, but more commonly in groups that vary both in the number and size of nodes they contain. These groups of nodes are usually arranged into two sets, superficial and deep. Because of the large number of lymph nodes present in the body, it would be impractical to discuss them in detail in this book. Locations of groups of nodes will be given, however, and the general area they drain will be indicated. Lymph nodes that filter the lymph from an infected area may become swollen and painful. Therefore, knowledge of the areas drained by particular nodes can be helpful in determining the sites of an acute infection.

LYMPH NODES OF THE HEAD AND NECK.   These nodes are arranged in two sets, superficial and deep (Fig. 196).

The superficial cervical nodes form a chain lying along the course of the external jugular vein in the neck. These nodes receive afferent vessels draining lymph from the skin and superficial structures of the head and neck. A second set of nodes, the deep superficial nodes, is associated with the carotid sheath enclosing the carotid arteries and the internal jugular vein. These nodes receive afferent vessels draining lymph from the mucous membranes of the upper portion of the alimentary and respiratory tracts, and the thyroid gland. In this deeper set of superficial nodes are the following groups.

1.   The occipital nodes.
2.   The posterior auricular nodes.
3.   The anterior auricular nodes.
4.   The parotid nodes.
5.   The submaxillary and facial nodes.
6.   The submental nodes.

The deep cervical nodes form a long chain of 15 to 30 nodes that extend from the base of the skull to the root of the neck. They lie along the course of the carotid artery and the internal jugular vein. Afferent vessels to these nodes drain lymph from the mucous membranes of the alimentary and respiratory tracts in the head and neck regions, and from the superficial nodes. The chain of deep cervical nodes is divided into a superior and inferior group, marked by the point at which the omohyoid muscles cross the common carotid artery. Above the muscle are the superior deep cervical nodes, and below, the inferior deep cervical nodes.

LYMPH NODES OF THE UPPER EXTREMITY (Fig. 197).   Most of the lymph nodes of the arm lie in the axilla where they form part of the axillary group of nodes that receive afferent vessels that drain lymph from the upper extremity and the wall of the thorax (including the mammary glands). A more distal group of nodes is located in the region of the elbow, and include the superficial and deep cubital nodes, whose afferent vessels drain lymph from the hand, wrist, forearm, and elbow regions. The groups of nodes in the upper extremity are as follows:

1.   The antibrachial nodes.
2.   The superficial cubital nodes.

3. The deep cubital nodes.
4. The deltopectoral nodes.
5. The axillary nodes.

LYMPH NODES OF THE THORAX.   The lymph drainage of the superficial area of the thorax goes to the axillary nodes (Fig. 198). The thoracic nodes are deep nodes within the thoracic cavity. Their afferent vessels drain lymph from thoracic organs and the inner portion of the wall of the thorax. These nodes are divided into parietal (draining the wall of the thorax) and visceral (draining the organs) groups.

Parietal groups
    1. Intercostal nodes.
    2. Internal mammary (sternal) nodes.
Visceral groups
    1. Anterior mediastinal nodes.
    2. Tracheal nodes.
    3. Posterior mediastinal nodes.

LYMPH NODES OF THE ABDOMEN.   The lymph nodes of the abdomen form chains along the course of the aorta. Afferent vessels of the *right* and *left lumbar nodes* bring lymph from the regions of the lower extremities, external genitalia, abdominal wall, kidneys, suprarenals, and reproductive organs within the pelvis. Their terminal vessels converge to form the right and left lumbar trunks, which empty into the thoracic duct. The afferent vessels to the *preaortic nodes* carry lymph drained from the stomach, part of the duodenum, spleen, pancreas, and liver. Lymph filtered through these nodes ultimately reaches the thoracic duct. They are arranged into three subgroups as follows.

1. Celiac nodes that receive lymph from the stomach, spleen, and part of the duodenum, pancreas, and liver.

2. Superior mesenteric nodes that receive lymph from the rest of the small intestine, the first half of the large intestine, and the pancreas.

3. Inferior mesenteric nodes that drain the lower half of the colon and the rectum.

The *postaortic nodes* receive lymph from the lumbar and preaortic chain of nodes, and their efferent vessels open into the cisterna chyli.

LYMPH NODES OF THE PELVIC AREA.   Along the course of the common iliac, the external iliac, and the hypogastric arteries are groups of nodes bearing the same names as the arteries. The *common iliac nodes* receive afferent vessels bringing lymph from the external iliac and hypogastric nodes, thus mixing the lymph from the pelvic organs and abdominal wall with lymph returned from the lower extremity and perineum. From the common iliac nodes the lymph is carried to the lumbar chain of nodes. The *external iliac nodes* receive lymph from the superficial and deep inguinal nodes and the vessels draining the lower part of the anterior abdominal wall and the bladder. In the male, afferent vessels also return lymph from the prostate, seminal vesicles, ductus deferens, prostatic and membranous urethra, and in the female from the cervix of the uterus and vagina. The *hypogastric nodes* receive lymph from all the pelvic organs, the perineum, the gluteal region, and from the thigh. The *sacral nodes* receive lymph from the rectum and posterior wall of the pelvis.

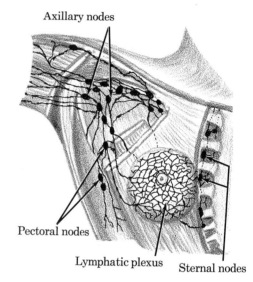

Axillary nodes

Pectoral nodes

Lymphatic plexus   Sternal nodes

Fig. 198.   Lymph drainage of the right breast and thorax.

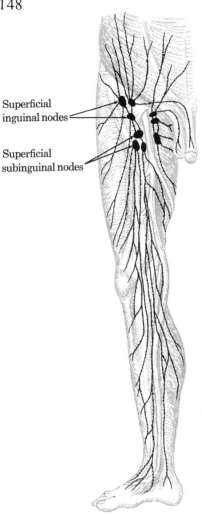

Fig. 199. Lymph drainage of the right lower extremity.

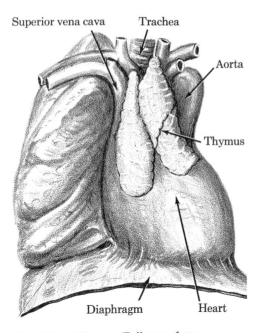

Fig. 200. Thymus. Full-term fetus.

LYMPH NODES OF THE LOWER EXTREMITY (Fig. 199). The arrangement of lymph nodes draining the lower extremity is similar to the axillary group of nodes draining the upper extremity, in that a large group of nodes, the *inguinal nodes,* is located in the region where the extremity joins the body. These nodes are divided into a superficial and a deep set, each of which is further subdivided into upper (inguinal) and lower (subinguinal) groups of nodes. *Superficial inguinal nodes* receive lymph from the skin of the anterior and lateral abdominal walls, the gluteal region, external genitalia and perineum. The lymph is carried into the external iliac nodes. The *superficial subinguinal nodes* receive lymph from the skin of the anterior and medial aspect of the leg and the dorsum of the foot. Some lymph is also received from the gluteal region and the perineum. Efferent vessels carry lymph from these nodes to the deep subinguinal and the external iliac nodes. The *deep inguinal node* is a single node located in the femoral ring. The *deep subinguinal nodes* receive lymph from the deep structures of the lower extremity and from the glans penis or clitoris. They drain into the external iliac nodes.

Another small group of nodes, a *popliteal* group, is located in the popliteal space behind the knee. They receive lymph from the posterolateral part of the leg, the lateral part of the foot and the knee joint. After it leaves the popliteal nodes, lymph is carried by the lymph vessels to the deep inguinal nodes.

THE LYMPHOID ORGANS

There are four so-called lymphoid organs in man: lymph nodes, which are discussed above with the lymphatic system, page 145; the tonsils, which are discussed with the pharynx, and tongue; the thymus; and the spleen.

THE THYMUS GLAND (FIG. 200)

DERIVATION. The thymus, derived from endoderm, arises as paired outgrowths from the pharynx.

LOCATION. It lies partly in the upper part of the thorax (in the superior mediastinum) and partly in the root of the neck.

SHAPE AND SIZE. Its shape is irregular and its size changes with age. The thymus grows most rapidly up to two years of age, and from then until puberty it grows at a slightly slower rate. After puberty it starts to degenerate (involute) and the parenchymal tissue is gradually replaced by connective tissue and fat. The normal thymus gland in the newborn weighs from 10 to 15 grams; its weight increases to a maximum of about 35 grams at puberty.

DESCRIPTION. The thymus gland consists of two somewhat flattened lateral *lobes,* joined together in the midline by connective tissue. Each lobe is enclosed by a fibrous connective tissue *capsule* from which trabeculae extend into the lobes subdividing them into *lobules.* Each lobule presents a deeply staining peripheral *cortex* and a lighter staining central *medulla* (Fig. 201). The cortex contains numerous small cells, the *thymocytes,* that appear to be identical with small lymphocytes. The medulla is a much lighter staining, more loosely arranged mass of cells, resembling the germinal centers of large lymph nodules. The most characteristic structures of the thymus, the *thymic (Hassal's) corpuscles,* are round or ovoid bodies that occur only in the medulla. They consist of hyalinized, concentrically arranged epitheloid cells. The significance of these structures is unknown.

FUNCTION. Recent work on the thymus has shown that it stimulates the formation of lymphocytes in other lymphoid organs, particularly during late fetal and early postnatal life. It also exerts control over immunological reactions of the body.

BLOOD SUPPLY. The thymus gland is supplied by branches of the internal mammary and the superior and inferior thyroid arteries. Blood is drained by veins that empty into the left brachiocephalic and the thyroid veins.

LYMPHATICS. The lymphatic vessels of the thymus are restricted to the trabeculae and the capsular area. They empty into the anterior mediastinal, tracheobronchial and sternal nodes.

NERVE SUPPLY. In the thymus gland small fibers are derived from the thoracic sympathetic and the vagus nerves. They end in the walls of the blood vessels and in the thymic medulla.

THE SPLEEN

This organ more nearly resembles an overgrown hemolymph node found in lower forms than it does a lymph gland. Unlike lymph nodes, it has no afferent lymph vessels. It is comparable to hemolymph nodes in that its sinusoidal spaces are filled with blood, not lymph.

LOCATION. It lies in the left upper quadrant of the abdominal cavity, to the left of and a little behind the stomach.

SHAPE AND SIZE. The spleen is an elongated, flattened organ about 10 to 14 centimeters long, 6 to 10 centimeters wide, and 3 to 4 centimeters thick. The size of the spleen varies in different individuals and in the same individual under different conditions (Fig. 202).

DESCRIPTION. The organ has a deep purplish red color because of its extreme vascularity. Its posterolateral (diaphragmatic)

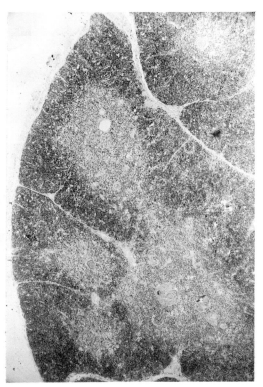

Fig. 201. Photomicrograph of the thymus. Note the darker stained outer cortical portion and the more lightly stained inner medullary portion of the organ.

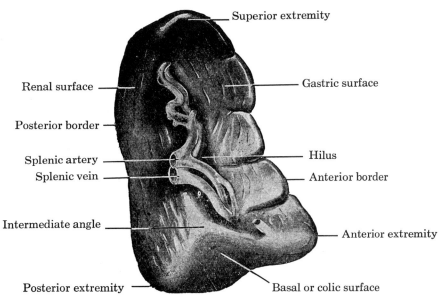

Fig. 202. Tetrahedral spleen, visceral surface. (From Morris' *Human Anatomy,* 11th ed. J. P. Schaeffer, ed. Blakiston Division, McGraw-Hill Book Company.)

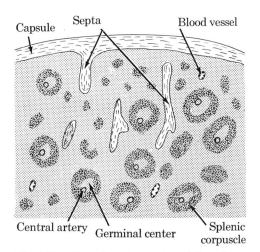

Capsule   Septa   Blood vessel

Central artery   Germinal center   Splenic
                                        corpuscle

Fig. 203.   Drawing of a section of the spleen.

surface is smoothly convex and fits the under surface of the diaphragm. Its anteromedial (visceral) surface is irregularly concave, marked by depressions produced by adjacent organs, the stomach, pancreas, kidney, and the splenic flexure of the colon. Near the center of the medial side of the spleen is a fissure, the hilus, where the splenic blood and lymph vessels and nerves enter and leave the substance of the organ.

MICROSCOPIC STRUCTURE (Fig. 203). Examined histologically, the spleen is seen to be enclosed in a relatively heavy fibrous connective tissue *capsule* containing scattered elastic and smooth muscle fibers. From the capsule, *septa* or *trabeculae* extend into the substance of the gland where they branch and anastomose, incompletely dividing the parenchymal tissue. The capsule and trabeculae contain a relatively high percentage of elastic and some smooth muscle fibers which facilitate the frequent changes in size, e.g., after meals, to which the spleen is subject.

The parenchyma of the gland is not uniform in appearance. It contains areas of *red* and *white pulp*. The areas of white pulp are scattered throughout the organ and are accumulations of lymphocytes, predominantly small lymphocytes that surround small blood vessels and form the *splenic (Malpighian) corpuscles*. The central artery, around which the corpuscles are arranged, is usually eccentrically positioned, despite its name. The remainder of the parenchyma of the spleen forms the red pulp. This consists of numerous anastomosing cords of lymphoid cells (with other connective tissue cells) separated by relatively wide, blood-filled sinuses.

FUNCTION. In the adult, the spleen stores blood and releases it when needed. It serves as the graveyard for old, wornout, red blood corpuscles, salvaging and returning to the blood iron and other materials essential in the formation of new hemoglobin. Like any lymphoid organ, it produces cells of the lymphoid (non-granular) series of white blood cells. Many of its cells are actively phagocytic, ingesting bacteria and other minute bits of foreign particulate matter.

BLOOD SUPPLY. Blood is brought to the spleen by the splenic artery, which is a branch of the celiac trunk. Numerous small anastomosing veins within the organ converge and empty into the splenic vein, which contributes to the formation of the portal vein.

LYMPHATICS. Superficial and deep sets of vessels drain the spleen and empty into the nearby pancreaticosplenic nodes.

NERVE SUPPLY. The nerves are chiefly non-myelinated and arise from the celiac plexus. They supply the walls of the splenic artery, which carries them into the gland; they are also distributed to the smooth muscle fibers in the capsule and trabeculae.

8

THE NERVOUS SYSTEM

The study of the nervous system depends in part on gross observations, but most of it must be approached from the microscopic and functional study of the organs involved. The information that has been compiled, particularly in recent years, is so enormous that the study of the morphology of the nervous system, Neuroanatomy, has developed into an independent subdivision of Anatomy. Under such circumstances, it is obviously impractical to include the whole field of Neuroanatomy in a book designed as a basic Gross Anatomy text. It therefore becomes necessary to limit the discussion of the nervous system to a more or less introductory approach. It is hoped that the student may become interested in pursuing the subject in greater detail by reference to standard medical textbooks on Neuro-anatomy.

Irritability and conductivity are properties of all living proto-plasm, but in the cells of the nervous system these two properties reach their highest degree of development and refinement. Another property found only in the cells of this system is the capacity to cor-relate all of the impulses that are being constantly transmitted to the nervous system from our environment, both external and internal (from within our own bodies). Some of the signals reaching the nervous system are simple and can be handled in a more or less routine manner (instinctive or unconditioned reflex reaction) by neurons in the cord. These cells send out messages (impulses) to effector organs that respond promptly.

In more complicated situations, incoming impulses are directed to higher levels for evaluation, correlation, and return directives. An impulse that involves survival of the organism usually receives prior-ity. The ability to evaluate situations depends on the cells of the brain having some means of storing previous "messages" (memory) so as to utilize previously gained experience (learning). It means developing and using a great network of intercommunicating path-ways in the brain so that previous experience can be utilized quickly and surely. Man's entire existence and his every reaction to his environment is under the control of the nervous system. Injury to any segment or organ of this system results in temporary or permanent interference with his ability to adjust quickly to the ever changing environment in which he lives, and may endanger his very existence.

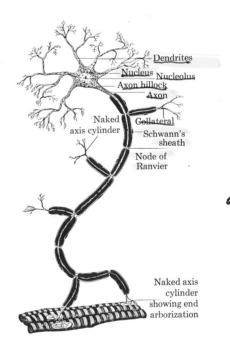

Dendrites
Nucleus Nucleolus
Axon hillock
Axon
Naked axis cylinder
Collateral
Schwann's sheath
Node of Ranvier

Naked axis cylinder showing end arborization

Nerve cell.

NERVE TISSUE

DEFINITION.   This is the most highly differentiated and specialized of the four fundamental tissues of the body.

DERIVATION.   It is derived from ectoderm.

COMPONENTS.   The components of nerve tissue are neurons (the specialized conducting cells), and neuroglia (interstitial elements that serve as supportive tissue).

FUNCTION.   The neurons conduct impulses; neuroglia is primarily supportive.

THE NEURON (NERVE CELL)

DEFINITION.   The nerve cell (neuron) is the structural and functional unit of the nervous system.

PARTS.   Each neuron consists of a cell body and its processes—an axon and dendrites (Fig. 204).

CELL BODIES OF NERVE CELLS.   *Distribution.*   The cells bodies of nerve cells are found only in the gray matter of the brain and spinal cord (central nervous system) and in sensory and autonomic ganglia outside the central nervous system.

Shape.   The cell bodies of nerve cells vary markedly in shape, depending on the type of the nerve cell, its location, and specific function. Their shapes may be stellate (star-shaped), spindle shaped, triangular, or round (Fig. 204).

Size.   They also show a remarkable range in size, the smallest being about half the size of a red blood corpuscle and the largest about 17 times the size of a red blood corpuscle.

Structure.   The cell body of a neuron is fairly abundant in cytoplasm and has a relatively large nucleus. The cytoplasm of nerve cells is often referred to as the neuroplasm. Besides the nucleus, the cytoplasm contains neurofibrils, chromophil substance (Nissl bodies), mitochondria, and a Golgi apparatus; in addition, certain inclusions are present.

The *neurofibrils* are fine, threadlike fibers which form a closely meshed, branching network within the body of the cell and extend through the entire length of the processes (Fig. 205). In the processes, the neurofibrils are arranged parallel to each other and to the long axis of the process.

Chromophil substance (Nissl bodies) is a prominent component of the cytoplasm of nerve cells. It usually appears in the form of flattened, irregular clumps of chromidial material that stains intensely with basic dyes. Chromidial substance is found in the cytoplasm of the cell body and extends into the dendritic processes (Fig. 206). There is no chromidial substance in the axon hillock or in the axon. The function of this material is not clearly understood, but from recent research it appears that the chromidial substance is concerned with the synthesis of cytoplasmic protein material. If the cell body or its axon is severely injured the chromidial substance undergoes dissolution or chromatolysis.

Mitochondria are similar to mitochondria of other cells of the body (Fig. 207).

Golgi apparatus varies in location with the type of cell, but it normally surrounds the nucleus. When properly stained, it appears as

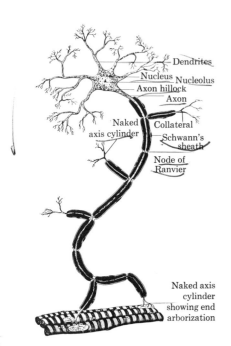

Fig. 204.   Nerve cell. Drawing.

Dendrites
Nucleus Nucleolus
Axon hillock
Axon
Naked
axis cylinder
Collateral
Schwann's
sheath
Node of
Ranvier

Naked axis
cylinder
showing end
arborization

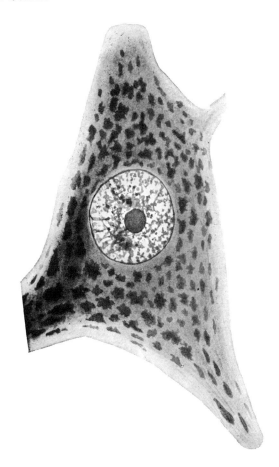

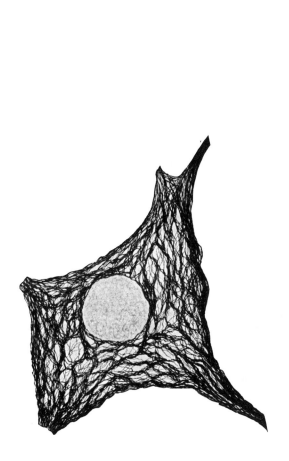

Fig. 205. Motor cell of the ventral gray column of spinal cord of rabbit; the net of neurofibrils in the perkaryon continues into the processes; the nucleus appears as a pale disk. Bielschowsky method. 500 X. (A.A.M.). (From Bloom and Fawcett. *A Textbook of Histology,* 8th ed., W. B. Saunders Company.)

Fig. 206. Motor cell from the gray substance of the ventral horn of the spinal cord of a cat, showing granular chromophile substance. Ax, Axon hillock. 670 X. (A.A.M.) (From Bloom and Fawcett. *A Textbook of Histology,* 8th ed., W. B. Saunders Company.)

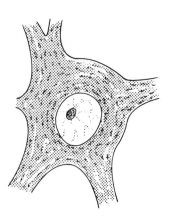

Fig. 207. Mitochondria in the body of a nerve cell.

a network of coarse, irregular fibers. The Golgi apparatus breaks up if the axon is cut off (Fig. 208).

Inclusions are fat droplets, pigment granules, and mineral deposits.

The nucleus is relatively large, usually round or oval, has a well defined nuclear membrane, and contains a large nucleolus. While the nuclei of many nerve cells are in the center of the cell body, in certain types of neurons they are eccentrically placed.

CELL PROCESSES OF NERVE CELLS.   The most distinguishing feature of a nerve cell is its processes. The length of these cytoplasmic extensions varies markedly and depends in part on the kind and location of the cell. The longest of the processes may measure approximately a meter in length, and the shortest may be less than a micron. There are two kinds of nerve cell processes—axons and dendrites. A single nerve cell has only one axon but it may have several dendrites.

Dendrites are processes that are fairly broad where they leave the cell body; almost immediately they send out many branches, much as a tree does (Fig. 209). An exception occurs in the dendrites of peripheral nerves, which so closely resemble axons that they are called axo-dendrites. Dendrites convey impulses (sensory) toward the cell body, and for this reason they are often referred to as afferent fibers or sensory fibers. A nerve cell may have a number of dendritic processes. Dendrites are intimately associated with a variety of specialized sensory end organs.

Axons (or axis cylinder), one for each cell body, arise from a cone-shaped prominence of the cell body called the axon hillock (Fig. 209). The axon hillock and the axon itself are without any chromidial substance. Axons are usually characterized by having a fairly uniform and constant diameter throughout their entire extent. They give off collaterals or branches at intervals that leave the main axis cylinder at right angles.

Axons vary in diameter in different fibers, but the diameter is relatively constant for a single neuron, tapering just slightly from its beginning at the hillock to its termination in a specialized type of motor ending. In the central nervous system axons may terminate in contact with the dendrites or the cell bodies of other neurons; in the periphery of the body these endings are associated with muscle or gland cells. The thicker axons conduct at a faster rate than the finer axons. Axons conduct impulses away from the cell body, and for this reason they are said to conduct efferent or motor impulses.

All of the axons and axo-dendrites of the peripheral system are enclosed through most of their extent by a thin cytoplasmic sheath of the Schwann cells, called the neurilemma or sheath of Schwann. In some neurons a relatively thick layer of fatty material called myelin lies between the axis cylinder and the Schwann cell layer. Such fibers are called myelinated fibers. Other fibers were formerly thought to have no myelin layer and were therefore called unmyelinated fibers. From observations made with the electron microscope, however, it appears that in nearly all fibers there is at least a very thin layer of myelin, even though it cannot be seen in light microscope preparations. Fibers in which no myelin has been histologically demonstrated, called Remak's fibers, are few. In myelinated fibers the myelin does not form a continuous layer along the axis cylinder; it forms a string of uniform, sausage-like, or bead-like segments along the axis cylinder. Between the segments of myelin, the neurilemma dips down to

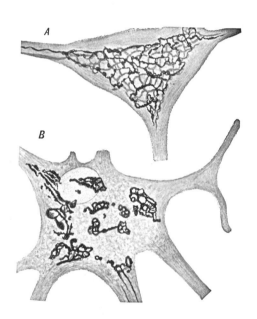

Fig. 208.   A, normal cell of the nucleus of the sublingual nerve of rabbit, showing the intracellular reticular apparatus (Golgi apparatus); B, similar cell four days after cutting the nerve. (Redrawn after Marcora.) (From Bloom and Fawcett. *A Textbook of Histology,* 8th ed., W. B. Saunders Company.)

contact the axis cylinder. These "constrictions" are called the nodes of Ranvier (Fig. 209).

The axons of the central nervous system, on the other hand, have no neurilemma sheath or Schwann cells. The supportive tissue for the axon in the cord and brain is furnished by glia cells, specifically the oligodendrocytes. The absence of a neurilemma sheath around fibers in the central nervous system is a factor in their inability to regenerate when cut or destroyed.

Schwann cells give rise to both the neurilemma and the myelin. In fact, these structures are actually components of the Schwann cells (its outer membrane and part of its cytoplasm). Schwann cells are derived from ectoderm and are thought to be involved in the metabolism of the axon and in the maintenance of the myelin sheath. They are essential in the regeneration of the peripheral nerves. There are no Schwann cells in the brain or cord, where their place and function is assumed by the oligodendrocytes.

While *myelin* is now considered to be a derivative of the cytoplasm of the Schwann cell, its precise origin is still unknown. It serves as an insulating material for the axis cylinder, and its thickness is correlated with the rate of impulse conduction. Fibers with thick myelin sheaths conduct most rapidly. Degeneration of an axis cylinder always results in degeneration of its myelin covering, but an axis cylinder can still be functional even if its myelin sheath has degenerated.

The *neurilemma sheath* is a thin, continuous, structureless membrane that encloses the axis cylinder of every neuron of the peripheral system. It is derived from the Schwann cells and is essential in regeneration of peripheral nerve fibers. It is not present as covering for nerve fibers of the brain and cord.

GENERAL CONSIDERATIONS REGARDING NEURONS. The nerve cell (neuron) is a highly specialized cell designed to receive stimuli, conduct impulses, correlate reactions and effect motor responses. In order to carry out these functions effectively, the nerve cell is greatly modified and differs from all other cells of the body in having long cytoplasmic processes extending from the body of the cell. Other important features of neurons are the following:

1. The total complement of neurons is present at birth; no new ones are formed later by any precursor cells or by division of the neurons.

2. The neuron is a fully differentiated, nerve cell.

3. Neurons differ in form and internal structure from all other cells of the body. The most important distinguishing features of their internal structure are the neurofibrils and the chromophil substance in the cytoplasm.

4. Neurons appear in a wide variety of forms, determined partly by their location and partly by their function. They exhibit both physiological and functional specificity.

5. Neurons may be classified according to the number of their processes as unipolar, bipolar, or multipolar. Neurons of the sympathetic ganglia are usually multipolar (having many processes), while those of the dorsal root ganglia are unipolar.

6. While neurons are morphologically discrete and separate cells, they do not function singly. In their simplest functional group they are linked together in a chain to form a "reflex arc." The short-

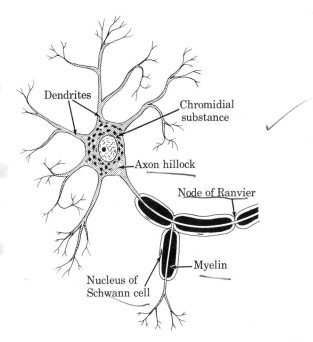

Fig. 209. Drawing of a nerve cell showing axon hillock, part of the axon with one collateral, sheath of Schwann cell, and nodes of Ranvier.

est, simplest chain consists of only two neurons, while the most complicated chains involve literally hundreds of neurons.

7. If sensory impulses brought to the central nervous system involve, for instance, three separate neurons from the periphery to their destination in the central nervous system, these afferent neurons are referred to as the neuron of the first order, neuron of the second order, and neuron of the third order, as a means of precise identification and location.

8. At the junction between two neurons there is no fusion or protoplasmic continuity of the neurons. It is a "contact" junction. As two or more persons might clasp hands to make a human chain, the processes of neurons also "make contact" with other neurons in order to transmit or conduct impulses. These points of contact are known as *synapses*.

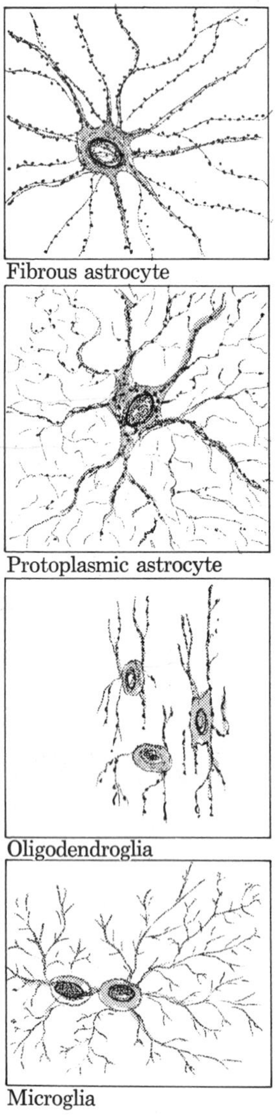

INTERSTITIAL ELEMENTS OF NERVE TISSUE

These elements are all the components of the nervous system other than the neuron and blood vessels. They include:

Neuroglia cells

The ependyma

Satellite or capsular cells of peripheral ganglia

Schwann cells of peripheral fibers (peripheral neuroglia). See page 154.

Neuroglia Cells

There are three types of "glia" cells: astrocytes, oligodendrocytes, and microglia.

Astrocytes are derived from ectoderm. They are stellate or star-shaped cells with processes; their large, oval nuclei have scant chromatin material. Their main function is supportive. There are two kinds of astrocytes, *protoplasmic* and *fibrous*.

Protoplasmic astrocytes (Fig. 210) are located primarily in the gray matter of the central nervous system. They have many branching processes that project from all over the cell. Many of the processes end in relation to blood vessels, which they contact by structures on the ends of the processes called *perivascular feet*. These cells form the supportive framework for the cell bodies of the neurons in the gray matter, and anchor them to adjacent blood vessels.

Fibrous astrocytes (Fig. 210) are found in the white matter of the brain and cord. Their processes contain fibers and are longer and straighter than the processes of the protoplasmic astrocytes. These cells lie between the myelinated fibers. They bind the fibers together and to adjacent blood vessels to which they are attached by perivascular feet.

Oligodendrocytes are also derived from ectoderm. Their nuclei are round to oval and smaller than the nuclei of the astrocytes. These cells are found in both the grey and white matter of the brain and cord. They are smaller and have fewer processes than the astrocytes. They have no perivascular feet. In the gray matter the oligodendrocytes lie close to the cell bodies of the nerve cells and are called the perineural satellite cells. In the white matter they are arranged in rows between the myelinated fibers, where their processes form an incomplete covering (sheath) for the fiber. They also serve to bind the nerve fibers together. In both the gray and the white matter these

Fibrous astrocyte

Protoplasmic astrocyte

Oligodendroglia

Microglia

Fig. 210. Neuroglia cells of the central nervous system.

cells lie close to blood vessels, and in this relationship they are called perivascular satellite cells.

Microglia (Fig. 210) are derived from mesoderm and probably developed from cells of the pia mater during the embryonal development of the nervous system. (The pia mater is a vascular membrane derived from mesoderm, which covers the brain and spinal cord.) The microglia have small nuclei which are irregular in shape. They do not have perivascular feet. These cells are more numerous in the gray than in the white matter of the brain and cord. In the gray matter they form perineural satellite cells about the bodies of the neurons, and perivascular satellite cells in relation to blood vessels. They are present, but not numerous, in the white matter, where they lie between the myelinated fibers. These cells are phagocytic and as such belong to the reticulo-endothelial system of cells.

The Ependyma

In the adult the term ependyma is more or less restricted to the cells lining the central canal of the spinal cord and the cells lining the ventricles of the brain. The ependyma is reflected over the capillaries of the choroid plexuses of the ventricles; however, in its relation to the capillaries, it is called choroid plexus epithelium, not ependyma. The ependyma in the adult is derived from and is a remnant of the original epithelium lining the neural tube.

Satellite or Capsular Cells of Peripheral Ganglia

These are flattened cells with rather prominent nuclei that form a capsule around the cell bodies of neurons of peripheral ganglia. They are derived from ectoderm of the neural crest.

ORGANS OF THE NERVOUS SYSTEM

The nervous system is a highly integrated group of organs and structures. It receives, correlates, and integrates incoming impulses and initiates the responses of the organism to environmental (external and internal) stimuli.

The structural and functional unit of this system is the nerve cell, or neuron. The organs of the nervous system include the *brain* and *spinal cord, peripheral nerves* (Fig. 211), *ganglia,* and *sensory* and *motor end organs.* The division of the organs of the nervous system can be done on a topographic (regional) basis as follows:

The central nervous system—brain and spinal cord

The peripheral nervous system—cranial and spinal nerves and their peripheral end organs

The autonomic nervous system

THE CENTRAL NERVOUS SYSTEM (BRAIN AND SPINAL CORD)

The student seeing for the first time the neural tube of a developing embryo and the fully developed central nervous system, the brain and spinal cord, would find it hard to believe that they are related structures, and that the latter evolves from the former. The remarkable change in appearance of the two structures is brought about by

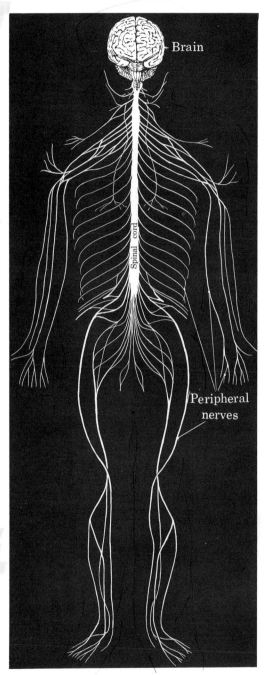

Fig. 211. Organs of the central nervous system. Brain, spinal cord, and peripheral spinal nerves. The nerves of the autonomic system are not included.

the unequal growth rates of the cells in the walls of the embryonic neural tube, and by the folding of the neural tube at its anterior end.

DEVELOPMENT OF THE BRAIN. At the anterior end of the neural tube (the portion of the tube that develops to become the brain), the first change that results from the unequal rates of growth is the formation of three enlargements called *vesicles,* separated by two constrictions. The vesicles represent the *forebrain, midbrain,* and *hindbrain* (Fig. 212). Due to the rapid growth of the neural tube and its confinement within the cranial cavity, it becomes folded on itself, forming two flexures in what had been a straight tubular structure. The most anterior folding (*cephalic flexure*) bends the forebrain forward and downward against the midbrain. The second flexure, the *pontine flexure,* is in the opposite direction and folds the hindbrain upward against the midbrain, forming a roughly N-shaped, enlarged anterior end to the developing neural tube.

The growth rate within the *forebrain* is not uniform. The anterior part of the forebrain grows and develops very rapidly and gives rise to the two relatively immense masses called the *cerebral hemispheres.* The central canal of this portion of the forebrain becomes the lateral ventricle of each hemisphere. The posterior part of the forebrain grows more slowly, and with less distortion of the basic tubular configuration. This area gives rise to the thalamus, hypothalamus, and the subthalamus, and the central canal enlarges to form the third ventricle. The third ventricle communicates with the lateral ventricles through the interventricular foramina.

In the *midbrain* the rates of growth are more uniform, with the result that much of the basic tubular structure is retained in the adult brain. The thickening of the walls reduces the central canal to a relatively narrow lumen called the *aqueduct.* The aqueduct affords communication between the third ventricle of the posterior forebrain and the fourth ventricle of the hindbrain.

Through thickening of the floor of the neural tube, the anterior part of the *hindbrain* forms the *pons* (a bridge of tissue); the lateral walls undergo marked growth and form ultimately the *cerebellar hemispheres.* The posterior part of the hindbrain is continuous distally with the spinal cord, and gives rise to the *medulla oblongata.* The lumen of the central canal in the hindbrain gives rise to the fourth ventricle, which opens distally into the small central canal of the spinal cord.

In summary, we can say that the three swellings of the neural tube give rise to the following subdivisions of the brain (Fig. 213):

Forebrain — $\begin{cases}\text{cerebral hemispheres, thalamus, hypothalamus, and}\\ \text{subthalamus}\end{cases}$

Midbrain — midbrain

Hindbrain — pons, cerebellar hemispheres, medulla oblongata

The central canal forms:

Lateral ventricles — located in the cerebral hemispheres

Interventricular foramina — $\begin{cases}\text{connecting each lateral ventricle}\\ \text{to the third ventricle}\end{cases}$

Third ventricle — $\begin{cases}\text{located between and below the}\\ \text{cerebral hemispheres in relation}\\ \text{to the thalamus}\end{cases}$

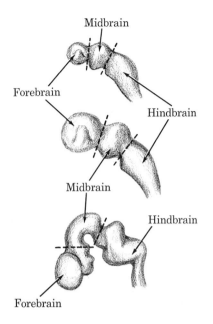

Fig. 212. Diagrams showing changes occurring in the early stages of the developing brain.

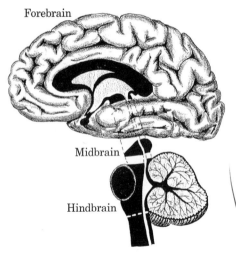

Fig. 213. Division of the adult brain into forebrain, midbrain, and hindbrain areas.

Aqueduct — { in the midbrain, connecting the third ventricle to the fourth ventricle.

Fourth ventricle — { in the hindbrain, opens distally into the central canal of the spinal cord

DEVELOPMENT OF THE SPINAL CORD.   The spinal cord is the least modified part of the embryonic neural tube, and the spinal nerves which arise from the cord still clearly mirror the segmental pattern which is seen in the primitive nervous systems of lower forms (Fig. 214). During the growth and development of the embryonic nervous system, the lateral walls of the neural tube become markedly thickened due to increase of the neuro-ectodermal cells in the area. The cells of the ventral and dorsal walls of the neural tube show very little activity and these areas form the *floor plate* (ventral wall) and the *roof* (dorsal wall) of the developing cord (Fig. 215). In the lateral thickening, however, there is disparity in the rates of growth of the dorsal and ventral portions of the lateral walls (Fig. 215). The two dorsal thickenings form the *alar plates,* which give rise to cells that synapse with the incoming sensory (afferent) neurons. The two ventral thickenings, the *basal plates,* give rise to cells of efferent neurons. A longitudinal sulcus (the *sulcus limitans*) separates the dorsal and ventral segments of the cord. The lumen of the neural tube ultimately becomes the very small tubular structure of the adult cord, the *central canal* (Fig. 215).

ORGANIZATION OF THE GRAY AND WHITE MATTER OF THE CENTRAL NERVOUS SYSTEM. The changes that occur in the development of the central nervous system, between the cord and the brain, are both structural and functional. They involve the gray and white matter, its amount and distribution, the central canal, and the external appearance of the structures that develop from the vesicles of the developing neural tube. These will now be considered.

The gray and white matter of the brain presents a very complicated arrangement compared to that of the spinal cord. This change in structure, however, is not abrupt. The lower part of the brain, the brain stem, which is continuous with the spinal cord below, in a sense serves as a transitional zone. The gray matter of the cord continues into the lower segment of the brain stem, the medulla oblongata, in the same pattern and position it held in the cord. Very shortly, in the cerebellum, the gray matter becomes broken up into small clumps of cell bodies of neurons, called nuclei, separated by bundles of myelinated fibers (white matter) which cross from one side of the medulla to the other. This crossing forms the so-called *decussation* in the brain. An additional outer layer of gray matter, covering the cerebellar and cerebral hemispheres, is the result of cells of the middle layer of the neural tube migrating out to the periphery, so that the white matter becomes sandwiched in between two layers of gray matter. The outer layer of gray matter covering the cortices (plural of cortex) consists of cell bodies of neurons, glia cells, unmyelinated nerve fibers, and in some areas, myelineated fibers are to be found. Rearrangement also occurs in the white matter of the medulla and the brain. With the increased number of neurons involved in connecting various nuclei, associating cranial elements and neurons of the higher levels of the brain, the architecture of the brain becomes extremely complex.

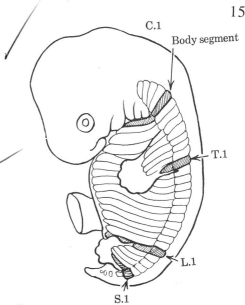

Fig. 214.   Segmentation of body and nervous system. C, diagram of body of early human embryo showing segmentation in terms of mesodermal somites or myotomes (After Patten); certain segments have been emphasized for purposes of correlation with adjacent figure. (From Hausman. *Illustrations of the Nervous System,* Charles C Thomas, Publisher.)

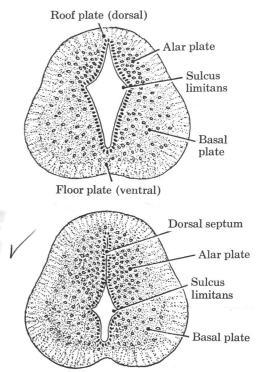

Fig. 215.   Diagrams of cross sections of neural tube developing into spinal cord. (From Ham and Leeson. *Histology,* 4th ed., J. B. Lippincott Co.)

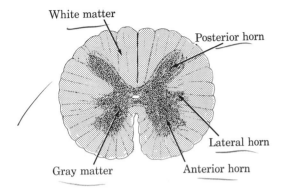

Fig. 216. Cross section of the spinal cord.

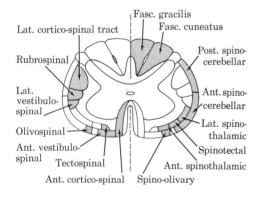

Fig. 217.   Diagram indicating the location of some of the fiber tracts of the spinal cord. The major descending tracts are shown on the left side; the ascending tracts, on the right side.

The gray matter of the cord is arranged in the form of two large, symmetrical, lateral, longitudinal masses called *horns* or *columns,* joined by a transverse bar of gray matter, the *transverse commissure.* In cross section of the cord, the gray matter appears roughly H-shaped (Fig. 216). The posterior or dorsal horns (columns) are longer and narrower than the ventral horns (columns) and are directed backward and somewhat laterally. Only a narrow rim of white matter extends between their terminal margins and the surface of the cord. The ventral horns are broad and short, and are separated from the surface of the cord by a moderately wide band of white matter. A relatively inconspicuous lateral horn of gray matter is present in the thoracic and upper lumbar segments of the cord.

The gray matter is composed primarily of the cell bodies of neurons. Those in the anterior horns are large; they are small in the posterior horns, and intermediate in size in the lateral horns. The cell bodies of neurons in the ventral horns are those of motor neurons; the dorsal column contains the cell bodies of sensory neurons. In the lateral columns are cells whose axons go to the autonomic ganglia. The neuron cell bodies are not distributed uniformly through the entire extent of the cord. In the upper thoracic and lumbosacral regions, for example, there are areas of concentration of neuron cell bodies whose processes form nerves of the brachial and lumbosacral plexuses and supply the upper and lower extremities.

The white substance of the cord lies superficial to the gray matter. It consists primarily of myelinated nerve fibers with some supporting connective tissue. These fibers are dendritic processes of the sensory neurons carrying impulses up the cord and axons of motor neurons going down the cord. A few bundles of fibers extend across the cord to the opposite side. In the cord there is a marked tendency for nerve fibers transmitting the same type of impulse (sensory, motor) and going to the same general area, to travel together in bundles called *tracts* (Fig. 217). These tracts are subdivided further into groups of fibers carrying specific types of impulses, such as pain, touch, and pressure, to mention just a few. The longest fibers (those going the greatest distance) are arranged nearer the periphery of the cord, while the shortest fibers usually lie nearest the gray matter. Some fibers may leave a bundle, cross to the other side of the cord, and continue their course by joining a group of the opposite side. Others may go only part way up the cord, cross and terminate in the substance of the cord. A great variety of pathways, junctions, and terminals levels are utilized by neurons forming this extremely complex communications system.

The name given a tract of fibers often indicates where it starts and what its immediate destination will be. For example, the name, "spinothalamic" tract, tells us that the fibers of this tract start in the cord and end in the thalamus of the brain; they carry afferent impulses. The name, "rubro-spinal," on the other hand, indicates that the tract starts in the red (rubro) nucleus of the midbrain, ends in the cord, and conducts motor impulses. The names of some fiber tracts, however, are not so helpful in analyzing the origin and destination of the contained fibers. The short axons of posterior column neurons that cross the cord to the opposite side to synapse with motor neurons at the same or nearly the same level are called *intersegmental* or *association fibers.* The names of the major ascending tracts (sensory) in the cords are:

1. Fasciculus gracilis
2. Fasciculus cuneatus
3. Tractus dorsolateralis
4. Tractus spinocerebellaris posterior
5. Tractus spinocerebellaris anterior
6. Tractus spinotectalis
7. Tractus spinothalamicus lateral ⎫
8. Tractus spinothalamicus anterior ⎬ spinal lemniscus
9. Tractus spino-olivaris ⎭

The names of the major descending tracts (motor) in the cord are:

1. Tractus corticospinalis
2. Tractus rubrospinalis
3. Tractus olivospinalis
4. Tractus tectospinalis
5. Tractus vestibulospinalis

The fasciculi proprii (ground bundles) are mostly short ascending or descending fibers of neurons of the gray matter of the cord that carry impulses from one level to another without crossing (decussating) the midline of the cord.

The Brain

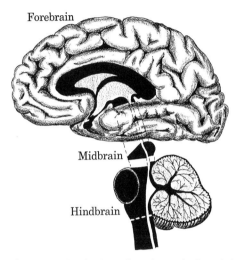

Fig. 218. Sagittal section through the adult brain showing the structures derived from the fetal forebrain, midbrain, and hindbrain.

The student should be reminded once again that the brain develops from a simple cylindrical, tubular structure. This simple structure however, is tremendously distorted in the adult brain, due in part to the different rates of growth of the nerve cells of the walls of the developing neural tube and in part to the folding which occurs along its longitudinal axis. But if the adult brain could be stretched out to eliminate the folds, the continuity of the various segments and the original tubular derivation and relationships would become obvious.

DEFINITION.   The brain is the part of the central nervous system contained within the cranial cavity. It is morphologically and functionally continuous with the spinal cord.

SHAPE.   When examined from above, the brain appears ovoid in shape and is broader behind than in front.

WEIGHT.   In the adult male, the average weight of the brain is about 1,380 grams; for the adult female, about 1,250 grams. It reaches its maximum weight by about the twentieth year, then decreases in weight very slowly with aging.

DIVISIONS.   The brain is divided into three areas (Fig. 218).
  Hindbrain—the medulla oblongata (a continuation upward of the spinal cord), pons, and cerebellum
  Midbrain
  Forebrain —thalamus, hypothalamus and subthalamus, cerebrum

THE HINDBRAIN.   *The Medulla Oblongata (Fig. 218).*   Definition. The medulla is the most inferior and least modified portion of the brain and serves as a transitional segment between the cord and the brain.

Location.   Its anterior surface rests against the basilar portion of the occipital bone. Its posterior surface is covered by the cerebellar hemispheres.

Shape.   The medulla is a bilaterally symmetrical, cone-shaped segment, with its broad base directed upward and its apical portion continuous with the spinal cord.

Length.   It measures a little over 2.5 centimeters long in the adult.

General Structure.   The structures of the spinal cord continue into and through the medulla. However, in their upward course through the medulla there is a rearrangement of structures. One major change involves the marked enlargement and widening of the central canal to form the fourth ventricle. The lower half of the fourth ventricle is in the medulla but its upper half is in the substance of the pons. The roof of the fourth ventricle is a thin membrane devoid of neurons. A vascular plexus, the choroid plexus of the fourth ventricle, is associated with the outer surface of the roof. The central gray matter of the cord, as it extends into the medulla, is broken up and rearranged to form a number of discrete and separate clumps of cell bodies of neurons called nuclei. (The reader must not confuse cell nuclei with the term "nuclei" as it is used in neuroanatomy to specify groups of cell bodies of neurons within the substance of the gray matter of the brain). The various sensory and motor tracts of the spinal cord forming the white matter continue into the medulla. Many of these ascending and descending fibers cross (decussate) from one side to the other. The major crossing of these fibers occurs over a relatively short distance and forms the *pyramidal decussation* or crossing of fibers.

The Pons (Fig. left). This is the segment of the brain stem between the medulla oblongata below and the midbrain above. The name "pons," from the Latin word meaning bridge, was chosen because of the presence on its ventral surface of a large, transverse band of fibers (the oblique fasciculus of the pons) which "bridges" the deeper structures and enters the substance of the cerebellum on either side. The anterior (ventral) surface of the pons is relatively smooth and markedly convex from side to side. Its curved, bulging surface marks its junction below with the medulla. The posterior or dorsal surface is roughly triangular in shape and is well hidden by the cerebellum. Anteriorly, the pons rests against the lower part of the body of the sphenoid bone near its articulation with the occipital. The pons contains approximately the upper half of the fourth ventricle of the medulla oblongata.

The Cerebellum (Fig. left). This uppermost segment of the hindbrain is folded back so that it lies above and behind the medulla and the pons. It occupies the posterior fossa of the cranium and is separated from the cerebral hemispheres above by the tentorium cerebelli. The tentorium is actually a fold of the dura which forms the membranous roof of the posterior fossa. The cerebellum is a large, oval organ, flattened from above downward and constricted in the midline. Its surface has a laminated or layered appearance due to the presence of many long curved sulci and fissures that are arranged more or less parallel to each other. The sulci extend across the width of the cerebellum and are quite close together. Several deeper fissures divide the organ into lobes. The cerebellum is connected to the underlying nerve tissue called the *brain stem* (the medulla, pons, and midbrain) by three pairs of bundles of fibers, the *superior, middle,* and *inferior* peduncles. The cerebellum is connected with the medulla by the inferior peduncles, with the pons by the middle peduncles, and the

Forebrain

Midbrain

Hindbrain

Sagittal section through adult brain.

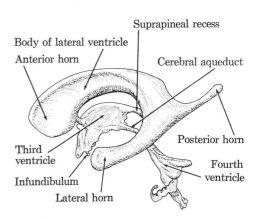

Fig. 224. Ventricles of the brain viewed from the side.

The area of the motor cortex (pyramidal area) contains a particular type of neuron, the large pyramidal or Betz cells that conduct motor impulses from the cortex to the cord. The axons of these cells form the large, descending pyramidal tracts (corticospinal tracts). One important feature concerning the course of these fiber tracts is the decussation or crossing of roughly 90 per cent of these fibers to the opposite side (forming the lateral corticospinal tracts); the decussation occurs in the medulla oblongata. The remaining 10 per cent of the fibers continue downward, uncrossed, as the ventral corticospinal tracts (Fig. 223). The fibers of the corticospinal tracts terminate by synapsing with anterior horn cells of the spinal cord.

Since the cerebral cortex usually exerts an inhibitory effect over the motor neurons of the cord, injury or destruction of the cortical cells results in a spastic type of paralysis of the body segments upon stimulation of the motor neurons of the cord (anterior horn cells). Injury to the anterior horn cells, on the other hand, results in a flaccid paralysis of the involved body segments.

THE VENTRICLES OF THE BRAIN. Within the brain there are a series of spaces called ventricles that are connected by narrow tubular structures (Figs. 224 and 225). The largest of the ventricles, the paired lateral ventricles, lie within the substance of the cerebral hemispheres. Each lateral ventricle consists of a central portion which gives off three extensions or horns. The largest, the anterior horns, extend into the substance of the frontal lobes; the inferior horns are directed downward, forward, and laterally into the temporal lobes; and the posterior horns extend horizontally backward into the posterior lobes. The lateral ventricles communicate with the third ventricle by way of the *interventricular foramen (foramen of Monroe)*. The third ventricle is a small, midline structure. It opens into a tubular structure, the *aqueduct,* through which it communicates with the fourth ventricle. The fourth ventricle is formed in part by the pons and in part by the medulla. The cerebellar hemispheres rest on its roof. It communicates below with the upward extension of the central canal of the spinal cord.

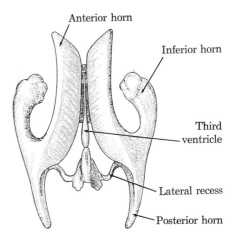

Fig. 225. Ventricles of the brain viewed from above.

The Spinal Cord

The spinal cord is the least changed of the structures derived from the embryonic neural tube.

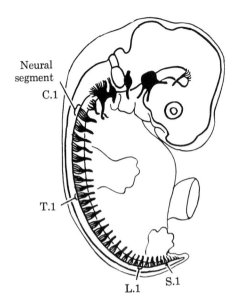

Neural
segment
C.1

T.1

L.1   S.1

Fig. 226.   D, diagram of nervous system of early human embryo, showing segmentation in terms of peripheral nerves (after Streeter). (From Hausman. *Illustrations of the Nervous System,* Charles C Thomas, Publisher.)

LOCATION.   It occupies roughly the upper two thirds of the bony vertebral canal.

ORIGIN.   It starts at the level of the foramen magnum, where it is continuous with the medulla oblongata of the brain.

TERMINATION.   In the adult, the spinal cord terminates below at the level of the 1st lumbar vertebra in a cone-shaped structure, the *conus terminalis;* from the apex of the cone, a fine filament, the *filum terminale,* continues downward to attach to the first segment of the coccyx.

RELATIONSHIP OF CORD STRUCTURES TO VERTEBRAL CANAL. In the young embryo the spinal cord extends the full length of the vertebral canal (Fig. 226), but because the bony vertebral column and the cord have different growth rates, the cord in the newborn ends at the level of the 3rd and 4th lumbar vertebra (Fig. 227), and in the adult still higher, at the level of the 1st lumbar vertebra (Fig. 228). This disparity in growth rates also involves the spinal nerves which attach to the cord. In the early embryo the spinal nerves leave the cord and are directed nearly horizontally to the intervertebral foramina through which they emerge. In the adult, the upper cervical nerves are still directed nearly horizontally, but the lower nerves become directed more and more obliquely downward toward their intervertebral foramina. The sacral and coccygeal nerves are so arranged in relation to one another, and their direction has become so nearly vertical, that they resemble somewhat the hairs of a horse's tail, and are called the *cauda equina* (Fig. 229).

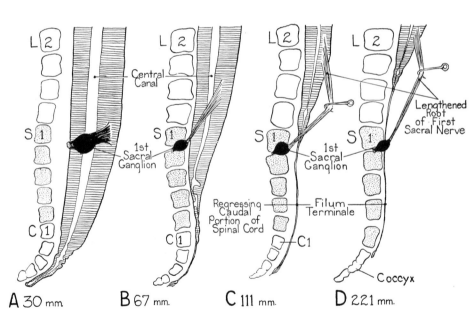

A 30 mm.   B 67 mm.   C 111 mm.   D 221 mm.

Fig. 227.   Diagrams showing changes in relations of caudal end of spinal column and spinal cord due to differential growth. A-D, relations of the first sacral nerve and ganglion at different ages used as an indicator of the changing position of the spinal cord within the spinal canal. (After Streeter. *Am. J. Anat.,* Vol. 25, 1919.) (From Patten. *Human Embryology,* 2nd ed., Blakiston Div., McGraw-Hill Book Co.)

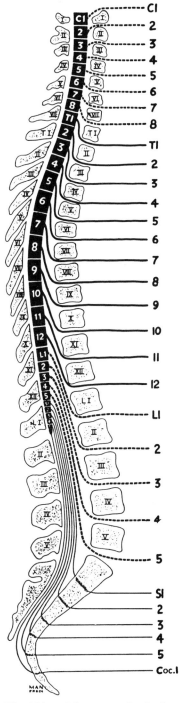

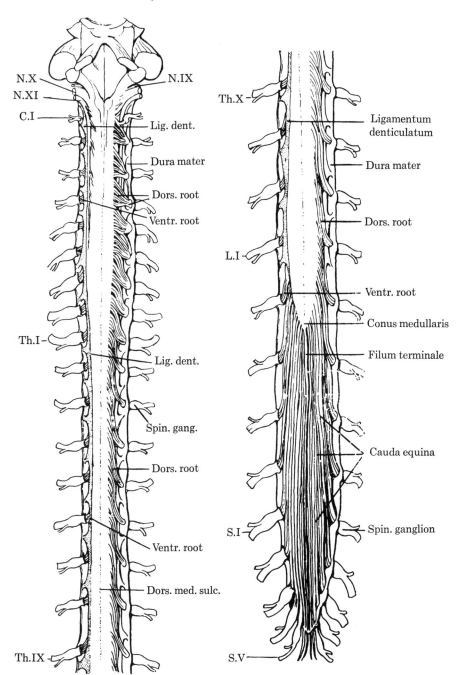

Fig. 228. Alignment of spinal segments with vertebrae. The bodies and spinous processes of the vertebrae are indicated by Roman numerals; spinal segments and their respective roots by Arabic numerals. Note that the cervical roots (except C8) take exit through intervertebral foramina ABOVE their respective vertebral bodies and that the other nerves issue BELOW these bodies. (From Haymaker and Woodhall. *Peripheral Nerve Injuries,* W. B. Saunders Co.) (From Hausman. *Illustrations of the Nervous System,* Charles C Thomas, Publisher.)

Fig. 229. Dorsal view of spinal cord with ganglia and nerve roots. The dorsal portion of the dura mater has been removed to show the contents of the dural sac. On the left side the dorsal roots have been cut to expose the denticulate ligament (Lig. dent.) and the ventral roots. Note that in the spinal cord each pair of spinal roots marks off the corresponding neural segment. The corresponding spinal ganglia lie in the intervertebral foramina and accordingly are more distally placed in relation to the pertinent spinal segment. This distance increases caudalward. The spinal nerves are indicated by Roman numerals. C, cervical; Th, thoracic; L, lumbar; S, sacral. (From Strong and Elwyn. *Human Neuroanatomy,* 3rd ed., Williams & Wilkins Co.) (From Hausman. *Illustrations of the Nervous System,* Charles C Thomas, Publisher.)

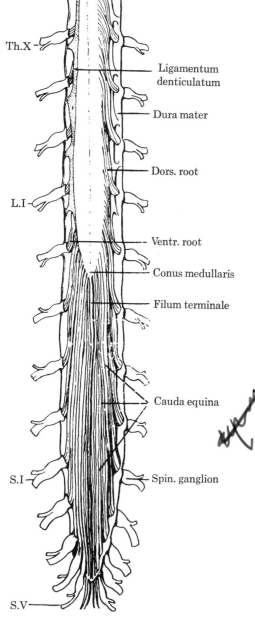

Th.X

Ligamentum denticulatum

Dura mater

Dors. root

L.I

Ventr. root

Conus medullaris

Filum terminale

Cauda equina

S.I

Spin. ganglion

S.V

(From Hausman. *Illustrations of the Nervous System,* Charles C Thomas, Publishers.)

LENGTH. The average length of the spinal cord of the adult male is about 45 centimeters, and for the adult female about 42.5 centimeters.

FORM. Compared to the neural tube, the shape of the adult spinal cord has changed very little. It is a round to oval-shaped, long tubular structure with two fusiform swellings. One swelling between the 3rd cervical and 2nd thoracic vertebrae gives rise to the spinal nerves for the upper extremity; a second swelling between the 9th thoracic and 1st lumbar vertebrae gives rise to the spinal nerves for the lower extremity. **The termination of the spinal cord is cone-shaped (Fig. left).**

GROSS APPEARANCE. The spinal cord has a relatively smooth surface marked by a *posterior median sulcus* and an *anterior median fissure,* which extend nearly to the central canal and divide the cord into two symmetrical halves joined only by a relatively narrow strip of nerve tissue called the *commisural band.* A short distance lateral to the posterior median sulcus is a vertical furrow, the *posterolateral sulcus,* where the rootlets of the dorsal root enter the cord. The portion of cord which lies between the posterior median sulcus and the posterolateral sulcus is called the *posterior funiculus.* In the cervical and upper thoracic portion of the cord, the posterior funiculus is subdivided by a relatively short vertical (longitudinal) septum, the *posterointermediate septum,* that divides it into a medial fasciculus gracilis and a lateral fasciculus cuneatus. The remainder of the cord forms the anterolateral region and is subdivided into anterior and lateral funiculi by the emerging rootlets of the ventral roots.

The Meninges (The Coverings of the Brain and Spinal Cord)

Both the brain and cord are enclosed by three membranes affording protection and nourishment, which together are called the meninges. In order, from the outside inward they are: the dura mater, the arachnoid, and the pia mater.

THE DURA MATER (FIG. 230). The dura mater covering the brain is a two-layered, thick, tough, fibrous connective tissue layer. It is predominantly collagenous tissue with some elastic fibers intermixed. The outer of the two layers covering the brain is actually the internal periosteum of the cranial bones. The inner layer of dura is continuous with and comparable to the single layer of dura covering the spinal cord. The inner layer of the dura is less vascular than the outer layer.

Two *dural septa* are formed, one between the right and left cerebral hemispheres and one between the cerbral and cerebellar hemispheres. The inner layer of the dura, extending into the longitudinal fissure between the right and left cerebral hemispheres, forms a double fold (partition) of tissue called the *falx cerebri.* A second septum, the *tentorium cerebelli,* or dural fold, extends between the cerebrum and the cerebellum, separating the two and forming a roof covering the posterior cranial fossa.

Between the layers of the dura are endothelial-lined spaces, the *venous sinuses* of the dura, which drain the blood from areas of the brain. One of the major sinuses of this group is the triangular-shaped *superior sagittal sinus,* formed in the midline at the point where the inner layer of the dura leaves the outer layer to form the falx cerebri.

The cranial nerves are varied in their composition; some are motor only, some sensory, while still others consist of somatic and visceral afferent (sensory) and somatic and visceral efferent (motor) components. Within the cranial nerves, also, are the nerves of special sense—smell, sight, hearing, equilibrium, and taste.

ORIGINS OF CRANIAL NERVES. Deep origin refers to the nucleus composed of the cell bodies within the substance of the brain. Superficial origin is the place at which the nerve emerges from the brain. In the following discussion of cranial nerves, we shall limit our description by using the superficial origin and leaving the intricate and detailed discussion of the deep origins (except for the nerves associated with the organs of special sense) to the textbooks of Neuroanatomy.

Olfactory (1st Cranial) Nerve (Fig. 233)

The sensory nerve for smell.

COMPONENTS. This nerve contains special visceral afferents and special somatic afferents.

The first order neurons are bipolar ganglion cells of the olfactory epithelium lining the roof and upper parts of the sides of the nasal fossae. The axons of these unmyelinated cells pass through small openings in the cribriform plate (lamina cribrosa) of the ethmoid to enter the cranial cavity. After entering the cranium, these filaments end in the olfactory bulb where they synapse with the second order neurons. The cell bodies of the second order neurons (mitral cells) lie in the olfactory bulb, a slightly enlarged terminal end of the olfactory tract. The axons extend posteriorly forming the olfactory tract (a narrow band of myelinated fibers on the inferior surface of the frontal lobe of the brain) and its three striae, to end in the cortex of the anterior end of the hippocampal gyrus (uncus).

Optic (2nd Cranial) Nerve (Fig. 234)

The sensory nerve for vision.

COMPONENTS. This nerve contains special somatic afferents.

The first order neurons consist of a chain of three neurons in the retina starting with the neuroepithelial cells, the rods and cones, that synapse with the bipolar cells which in turn synapse with the ganglion cells. All of the cells are located in the layers of the pars optica of the retina lining the posterior segment of the eye. The axons of the ganglion cells leave the posterior segment of the optic disc and form the optic nerve. It extends backward and medially, through the optic foramen to enter the middle cranial fossa. Here it joins the optic nerve of the other eye to form the *optic chiasma,* where crossing of some of the fibers (decussation) takes place. At the decussation, axons from the left half of each eye enter the left optic tract, from the right half of each eye they enter the right optic tract. The fibers then regroup to form the optic tracts that continue posteriorly to terminate in the thalamus and midbrain (lateral geniculate bodies).

The second order neurons have cell bodies in three separate locations. Those for vision are located in the lateral geniculate body. Some of the fibers of the optic tract concerned with reflex adjust-

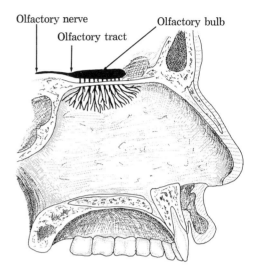

Fig. 233. Olfactory nerve.

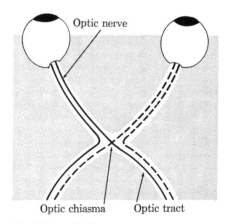

Fig. 234. Optic nerve.

ments of the pupils to varying intensities of light end in the pretectal region where the cell bodies of these neurons are located. The third area where the second order neurons are to be found is in the superior quadrigeminal body. Neurons of this area are associated with eye moving responses.

Oculomotor (3rd Cranial) Nerve

The motor nerve for the ocular muscles.

COMPONENTS.   This nerve contains somatic efferent fibers, some proprioceptive (sensory) fibers, and parasympathetic fibers. The somatic efferent (motor) fibers supply the voluntary ocular muscles. The parasympathetic motor fibers supply the involuntary ocular muscles.

COURSE.   This nerve leaves the ventral aspect of the midbrain and extends forward, entering the orbit by way of the superior orbital fissure and is distributed to the following muscles.

Striated muscles
1. Levator palpebrae superioris of the eyelid
2. Superior rectus
3. Medial rectus
4. Inferior rectus
5. Inferior oblique

Smooth muscle
1. Sphincter of the iris
2. Ciliary muscle

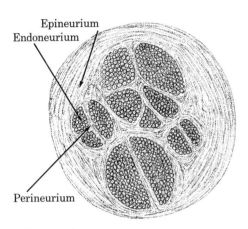

Epineurium
Endoneurium

Perineurium

Cross section of a small peripheral nerve.

Trochlear (4th Cranial) Nerve

A motor nerve; the smallest cranial nerve.

COMPONENTS.   This nerve contains somatic efferent (motor) fibers to the superior oblique muscle of the eye for movement of the eyeball, and proprioceptive fibers from this muscle.

COURSE.   Fibers of this nerve leave the midbrain, extend forward, and enter the orbit through the superior orbital fissure.

Trigeminal (5th Cranial) Nerve

A motor and sensory nerve; the largest cranial nerve. This is the sensory nerve to the head and face, and the motor nerve to the muscles of mastication and other head and neck muscles.

COMPONENTS.   This nerve contains general somatic afferents, special visceral efferents, and proprioceptive fibers of muscles of mastication.

COURSE.   The trigeminal emerges from the side of the pons by two roots, a small motor and a large sensory root. The nerve extends forward and laterally into the middle cranial fossa, where a large semilunar (Gasserian) ganglion is found on the sensory root. At the anterior margin of the ganglion, the nerve divides into three sensory branches.

1. The ophthalmic, conveying sensory impulses from the front half of the scalp and skin of the forehead and nose bridge, upper eyelids, and orbits.

2. The maxillary, conveying sensory impulses from the lower eyelids, nose, cheeks, upper lip, palate, upper teeth, lining of the nasal cavity, and temporal regions.

3. The mandibular, which is both sensory and motor. The sensory portion conveys sensory impulses (for temperature, pain, and touch, but not for taste) from the lower lip, lower jaw, tongue, sides and floor of the mouth and lower teeth. The motor root lies medial to the sensory root and extends forward beneath the semilunar ganglion. It leaves the skull with the mandibular nerve through the foramen ovale, then merges with the mandibular nerve. These motor fibers supply the muscles of mastication—internal pterygoid, external pterygoid, masseter, and temporal muscles—as well as the mylohyoid, the digastric (anterior belly), tensor tympani, and the tensor veli palatini.

Abducens (6th Cranial) Nerve

A motor nerve that supplies the rectus lateralis muscle of the eye.

COMPONENTS. This nerve contains both somatic efferent and proprioceptive fibers.

COURSE. The abducens emerges from the brain between the pons and the medulla oblongata. It extends upward and forward to enter the orbit through the superior orbital fissure.

Facial (7th Cranial) Nerve

A motor and sensory nerve with some parasympathetic fibers. It supplies motor fibers to the muscles of facial expression and sensory fibers for taste.

COMPONENTS. This nerve contains special and general visceral efferents, special visceral afferents for taste, general visceral afferents, and general somatic afferents (skin).

COURSE. The facial nerve emerges from the brain at the lower border of the pons, lateral to the abducens nerve and very close to the point of emergence of the acoustic nerve. The facial nerve extends to and enters the internal acoustic meatus accompanied by the acoustic nerve. Within the petrous portion of the temporal bone, the facial nerve enters the facial canal, and its course through the temporal bone becomes quite complicated. The canal terminates at the stylomastoid foramen, and the facial nerve leaves the cranium at this point. From the stylomastoid foramen, the nerve (consisting of motor fibers) extends forward through the parotid gland, to be distributed to the muscles of facial expression (mimetic muscles), and to the posterior belly of the digastric and to the stylohyoid muscles. Within the facial canal, the nerve gives off a small branch to the stapedius muscle. A short distance above the point where it leaves the cranium, the facial nerve receives the chorda tympani nerve which crosses the tympanic cavity of the middle ear, lying on the inner surface of the ear-drum. The chorda tympani contains sensory fibers for taste from the anterior two thirds of the tongue and secretory (motor) fibers to the submandibular (submaxillary) and sublingual glands. The chorda tympani fibers terminate in the geniculate ganglion. The fibers extending from the geniculate ganglion to the brain form the nervus intermedius which has always been considered as a component of the facial nerve.

Acoustic (8th Cranial) Nerve

A sensory nerve which is the nerve of hearing.

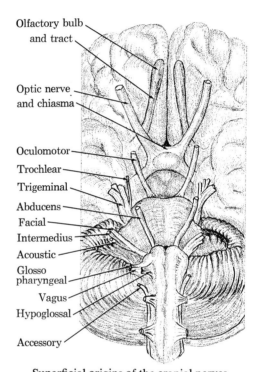

Superficial origins of the cranial nerves.

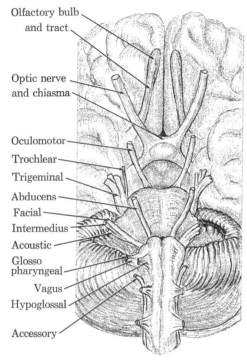

Olfactory bulb and tract

Optic nerve and chiasma

Oculomotor

Trochlear

Trigeminal

Abducens

Facial

Intermedius

Acoustic

Glosso pharyngeal

Vagus

Hypoglossal

Accessory

Superficial origins of the cranial nerves.

DIVISIONS. This nerve has two divisions—cochlear and vestibular.

COMPONENTS. The vestibular division contains special proprioceptor fibers for equilibrium and static sense; the cochlear division contains special somatic afferent fibers for auditory impulses.

COURSE. The acoustic nerve emerges from the brain stem behind the pons and lateral to the facial nerve. It then extends to and enters the internal acoustic meatus, where it divides, forming the vestibular and cochlear nerves to be distributed to the structures of the inner ear. The vestibular fibers are distributed to cells of the neuroepithelial structures to the christae of the ampulla of the semicircular canals and the membranous maculae of the utricle and saccule. This division of the nerve responds to stimuli that results in maintenance of body equilibrium and in the recognition of the position and movement of the head. The cochlear division enters the modiolus (central core) of the cochlea to be distributed to the organ of Corti for reception and transmission of auditory impulses (sound waves).

Glossopharyngeal (9th Cranial) Nerve

A motor and sensory nerve, containing parasympathetic fibers. It supplies sensory fibers to the pharynx and posterior third of the tongue, and motor fibers to muscles for swallowing.

COMPONENTS. This nerve contains general somatic afferent fibers distributed to the skin of the mastoid area and back of the ear, general visceral afferent fibers distributed to the mucosa of part of the tongue and the mucosa of the pharynx, special visceral afferent fibers distributed to the posterior third of the tongue for taste, general visceral efferent fibers (parasympathetic) distributed to the parotid gland.

COURSE. This nerve emerges from the side of the medulla and extends laterally. It leaves the cranium together with the vagus and the accessory through the central part of the jugular foramen. It descends into the neck, giving a branch to the stylopharyngeus muscle, and enters the area of the pharynx between the superior and middle constrictor muscles. It is distributed to the mucosa of the pharynx and back of the tongue. Parasympathetic fibers (preganglionic) of this nerve synapse in the otic ganglion with cells whose axons (postganglionic) go to the parotid gland. The glossopharyngeal also contain sensory fibers from the carotid body and carotid sinus that form reflexes for the control of blood pressure.

Vagus (10th Cranial) Nerve (Fig. 235)

A motor and sensory nerve, containing parasympathetic fibers. This nerve supplies motor fibers for the muscles of the larynx; its destruction would paralyze the laryngeal muscles and the voice would be lost.

COMPONENTS. This nerve contains general somatic and visceral afferent fibers, special visceral afferent fibers, and general and special visceral efferent fibers.

COURSE. The vagus emerges from the side of the medulla below the glossopharyngeal nerve and leaves the cranium by way of the jugular foramen with the glossopharyngeal and the accessory

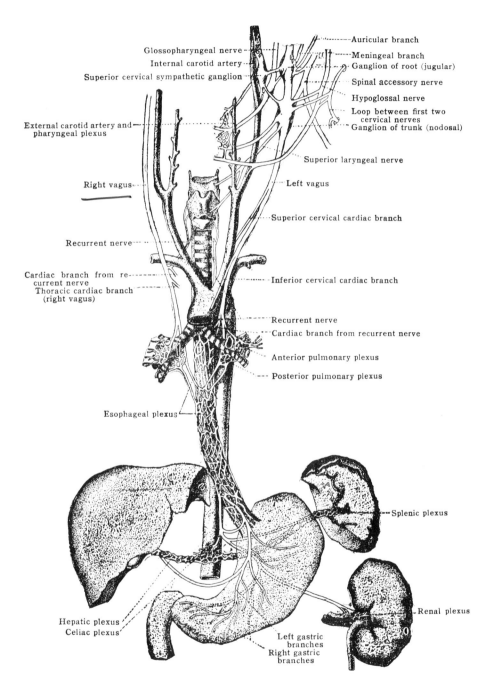

Fig. 235.   Diagram of the branches of the vagus nerves. (From Morris' *Human Anatomy*, 11th ed., Schaeffer, Ed., Blakiston Div., McGraw-Hill Book Co.)

nerves. It extends down the neck in the carotid sheath between the internal carotid artery and the internal jugular vein into the thorax. In the thorax the vagi give off the recurrent laryngeal nerves which ascend into the neck in the groove between the trachea and the esophagus. At the root of the lung the vagi of the two sides form the pulmonary plexuses. From the lower parts of the pulmonary plexuses several cords continue downward to form the esophageal plexus on the wall of the esophagus. From this plexus the gastric nerves form; they are distributed to the smooth muscle of the stomach wall, blood vessels, and gastric glands, and branches are sent to the duodenum, pancreas, liver, spleen. and kidneys. Vagal fibers leaving the esophageal plexus also enter the celiac plexus and other preaortic abdominal plexuses (hepatic and splenic) where they become intermingled with sympathetic fibers.

Accessory (11th Cranial) Nerve

A motor nerve, peculiar in that it contains both cranial and spinal components.

COMPONENTS.   This nerve contains general and special visceral efferent fibers.

COURSE.   The cranial portion emerges from the medulla below the vagus. The spinal portion arises from the upper four or five cervical nerves which form a nerve that extends upward through the foramen magnum to join the cranial (bulbar) portion of the nerve. The accessory leaves the cranium by way of the jugular foramen. The spinal part of the nerve descends in the neck as the accessory nerve to supply the sternocleidomastoid and trapezius muscles. The cranial portion joins the vagus and is distributed to the muscles of the pharynx, larynx, and soft palate.

Hypoglossal (12th Cranial) Nerve

A motor nerve to the muscles of the tongue.

COMPONENTS.   This nerve contains general somatic efferent fibers, and proprioceptor fibers from the muscles of the tongue.

COURSE.   The nerve emerges from the ventral aspect of the medulla below the accessory nerve and leaves the cranium by way of the hypoglossal canal. The nerve descends in the neck to a point about opposite the angle of the mandible, where it turns forward and upward to enter the substance of the tongue.

The Spinal Nerves

The spinal nerves are those peripheral nerves that are attached to the spinal cord. They leave the bony vertebral canal enclosing the cord through the intervertebral foramina between adjacent vertebrae. There are 31 pairs of spinal nerves grouped as follows.

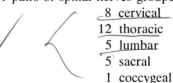

8 cervical
12 thoracic
5 lumbar
5 sacral
1 coccygeal

(Note: The first cervical nerve, usually referred to as the sub-occipital nerve, leaves the vertebral canal between the base of the skull and the first cervical vertebra and accounts for there being eight cervical nerves and only seven cervical vertebrae. The remainder of

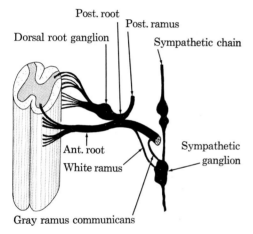

Fig. 236.   Drawing to show the structure of a typical spinal nerve.

Branches.

	in the forearm	supply flexor carpi ulnaris and flexor digitorum profundus
Muscular branches	in the hand	supply palmaris brevis, intrinsic muscles of little finger, interossei, 3rd and 4th lumbricales, adductores pollicis, and medial head of flexor pollicis brevis
Cutaneous branches		supply sensory fibers to medial side of hand, little finger, and ulnar (medial) half of 4th finger
Articular branches		supply elbow

The Median Nerve. Origin. The terminal portions of the medial and lateral cords of the brachial plexus merge to form the median nerve.

Spinal Components. C6, C7, and C8, and T1.

Course (Fig. 240). Near its origin, it lies lateral to the brachial artery; about a third of the way down the arm it crosses in front of the artery to the medial side at the elbow. It extends down the middle of the forearm to the wrist where it becomes quite superficial. It enters the palm of the hand by passing under the transverse carpal ligament and terminates in the hand and fingers.

Branches. The median nerve gives off two branches in the arm.

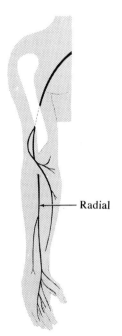

Fig. 241. Radial nerve. Dorsal aspect of forearm and hand.

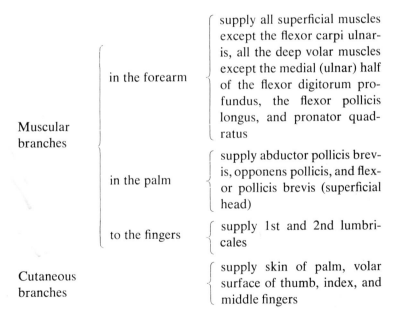

	in the forearm	supply all superficial muscles except the flexor carpi ulnaris, all the deep volar muscles except the medial (ulnar) half of the flexor digitorum profundus, the flexor pollicis longus, and pronator quadratus
Muscular branches	in the palm	supply abductor pollicis brevis, opponens pollicis, and flexor pollicis brevis (superficial head)
	to the fingers	supply 1st and 2nd lumbricales
Cutaneous branches		supply skin of palm, volar surface of thumb, index, and middle fingers

The Radial Nerve.   This is the largest nerve of the brachial plexus.

Origin.   It is a continuation of the posterior cord.

Components.   C5, C6, C7, and C8, and T1.

Course (Fig. 240 and 241).   At its origin the radial nerve lies behind the axillary artery. It extends downward and then obliquely laterally behind the humerus (in the radial groove on that bone) and deep to the triceps muscle (lateral head). At the elbow the radial nerve lies in front of the lateral epicondyle. It extends down the forearm along its lateral (radial) volar surface to the area of the wrist. Near the wrist the nerve curves around the lateral side of the forearm to its dorsal surface to terminate on the dorsal aspect of the hand (lateral half).

Branches.   The radial nerve is the great "extensor muscle" nerve.

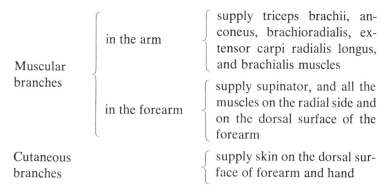

Muscular branches	in the arm	supply triceps brachii, anconeus, brachioradialis, extensor carpi radialis longus, and brachialis muscles
	in the forearm	supply supinator, and all the muscles on the radial side and on the dorsal surface of the forearm
Cutaneous branches		supply skin on the dorsal surface of forearm and hand

Nerve-Bone Relationship (Fig. 241).   Where the radial nerve lies in the radial groove on the back of the humerus, it presents an important nerve-bone relationship. Fracture of the humerus at its midpoint can seriously injure or even sever the nerve. It may also become seriously damaged if it is caught between the jagged end of the bones when they are "set" following fracture.

(Note: For convenience and brevity, the lumbar and sacral plexuses will be treated as a single plexus.)

LUMBOSACRAL PLEXUS (FIG. 242).   COMPONENTS.   The lumbosacral plexus is formed by the anterior rami of the lumbar, sacral, and coccygeal spinal nerves.

LOCATION.   The lumbosacral plexus lies on the posterior abdominal and pelvic wall, just lateral to the spinal column. The origin of the lumbar segment is hidden by the psoas muscle. The origin of the sacral segment is covered by pelvic fascia. The nerve fibers converge toward the greater sciatic foramen.

FORMATION OF PLEXUS.   Lumbar Segment—The anterior rami of all the lumbar nerves receive gray rami communicantes near their origins from lumbar sympathetic chain ganglia. L1 and L2 are joined (also sometimes L3 and L4) to the sympathetic chain by white rami communicantes.

Sacral and Coccygeal Segment—The anterior rami of all the sacral nerves receive gray rami communicantes from sacral sympathetic chain ganglia. From S3 (sometimes S2 and S4) a white ramus communicans extends to the pelvic sympathetic plexus. The S5 and coccygeal nerves will not be considered; since Man does not possess a "functional" tail, this part of the plexus becomes relatively unimportant.

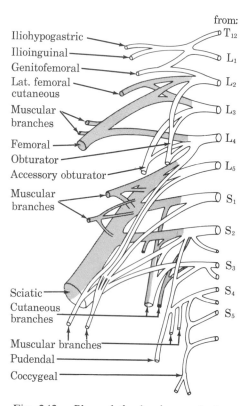

Fig. 242.   Plan of the lumbosacral plexus.

The lumbar portion of L1 splits into an upper and lower branch. A branch from T12 joins the upper branch of L1. This nerve then splits to form the iliohypogastric and the ilioinguinal nerves. The lower branch of L1 joins with the branch of L2 to form the genitofemoral nerve. The remainder of L2, L3 and L4, S1 and S2, divide into the ventral and dorsal divisions. The ventral divisions of L2, L3, and L4 unite to form the obturator. Small branches are given off from the ventral divisions of L3 and L4 that join to form the accessory obturator. The dorsal divisions of L2 and L3 divide into two branches. One branch of L2 and one branch of L3 unite to form the lateral femoral cutaneous nerve. The remaining branches of L2 and L3 join, and this branch merges with the dorsal division of L4 to form the femoral nerve.

Lumbosacral Trunk—This trunk connects the lumbar and sacral plexuses and consists of the major portion of the anterior rami of L4, all of the ventral divisions of L5 and S1, and parts of the ventral division of S2 and the anterior rami of S3. The lumbosacral trunk joins with a short nerve segment formed by the dorsal divisions of L5 (reinforced by a branch from L4) and S1 and S2, to form the sciatic nerve.

Branches from the ventral divisions of L4 and L5 and S1 form the nerve to the quadratus femoris and gemellus inferior muscles. Branches from the ventral divisions of L5 and S1 and S2 form the nerve to the obturator internus and gemellus superior muscles. Branches of the ventral division of S2 and S3 and the anterior rami of S4 join to form the pudenal nerve.

Posterior branches of the anterior rami of S2 and S3 join to form the perforating cutaneous nerve. Branches of the ventral divisions of S2 and S3 join with branches of the dorsal division of S1 and S2 to form the posterior femoral cutaneous nerve.

Branches of the dorsal divisions of L5 and S1 with a posterior branch of the anterior rami of L4 form the superior gluteal nerve. Branches of the dorsal divisions of L5, S1 and S2, join to form the inferior gluteal nerve.

Visceral branches are given off the anterior rami of S2, S3, and S4.

BRANCHES.   The branches of the lumbosacral plexus are formed within the abdomen and pelvis, close to the point of emergence of the spinal nerves from the intervertebral foramina and their division into posterior and anterior rami. All branches of this plexus will be listed and their destinations indicated. Two main branches, the femoral and sciatic, will be discussed in some detail.

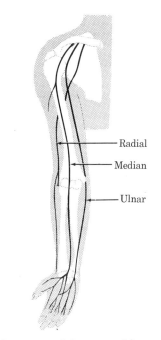

Major nerves of the upper right extremity.

Iliohypogastric	supplies skin of the gluteal region and skin of hypogastric region
Ilioinguinal	supplies obliquus internus muscle, skin of upper and medial thigh region, skin over root of penis and upper part of male scrotum, and skin over mons pubis and labium majus in female
Genitofemoral	supplies cremaster muscle, skin of male scrotum, accompanies round ligament of female, and supplies skin of anterior surface of upper thigh
Femoral	(will be discussed later)

(As the obturator nerve enters the thigh, it splits into an anterior and posterior branch)

Obturator (anterior branch)	supplies articular branch to hip joint, muscular branches to adductor longus, gracilis, adductor brevis, rarely the pectineus, cutaneous branches to skin of upper half of the medial side of the leg
Obturator (posterior branch)	supplies obturator externus and adductor magnus muscles, and articular branch to knee joint
Accessory obturator	supplies articular branch to hip joint, muscular branches to pectineus, quadratus femoris, gemellus inferior, obturator internus, gemellus superior, and piriformis muscles
Superior gluteal	supplies gluteus minimus, gluteus medius, and tensor fasciae latae muscles
Inferior gluteal	supplies gluteus maximus muscle
Posterior femoral cutaneous	supplies skin of the gluteal region, perineum, and posterior surface of thigh and leg
Sciatic	(will be discussed later)

The Femoral Nerve. This is the largest nerve of the lumbar portion of the lumbosacral plexus.

Origin. It originates by a merging of the dorsal divisions of the 2nd, 3rd, and 4th lumbar nerves.

Course (Fig. 243). In the abdominal cavity, the femoral nerve lies at first under the psoas muscle, then extends downward between the psoas and the iliacus muscles (covered by iliac fascia). It passes under the inguinal ligament and enters the anterior region of the thigh. It then splits into an anterior and posterior division.

The anterior division gives off muscular and cutaneous branches which are restricted to the anterior thigh region. The posterior division gives off muscular branches to the anterior thigh muscles and a branch to the saphenous nerve, which is a long cutaneous nerve that extends obliquely downward and medially under cover of the sartorious muscle, and becomes subcutaneous at the medial side of the knee. The saphenous nerve extends downward along the medial side of the leg to its lower third where it divides into two terminal cutaneous branches —one, distributed to the skin of the ankle; the other, supplying the skin on the medial side of the foot and great toe.

Fig. 243.   Femoral nerve. Anterior thigh.

Branches.

Muscular	in the abdomen	supply iliacus muscle
	in the thigh	supply pectineus, sartorius, and all four heads of the quadriceps femoris muscles
Cutaneous		supply skin of front of thigh, medial side of leg, ankle, and foot
Articular		supply both hip joint and knee joint

9

THE DIGESTIVE SYSTEM

All living cells of the body must be supplied with nutritional material for growth, replacement, and repair. These materials also furnish energy for the cells to carry out the work they are designed to perform. Most foods cannot be utilized as they are taken into the body, but must be subjected to both mechanical and chemical treatment which will convert them into substances that can be absorbed and utilized by the cells.

It is important to realize that, in a sense, material in the lumen of the alimentary tract is outside the body, even though the tract itself is contained within the body cavity. The epithelium lining the entire tract is continuous at either end with the epithelium covering the body surface. In other words, it would be possible, theoretically at least, for food to go through the entire alimentary tract without reaching or benefiting a single body cell. To become available for cell use, the food must be in a form that can be absorbed through the protective epithelial lining of the tract, and enter the blood or lymphatic vessels for transportation and distribution to individual cells throughout the body. Material which cannot be put into a form that can be absorbed remains within the lumen as waste material (*feces*), and is ultimately eliminated from the body.

The process by which food is converted for absorption from the alimentary tract and later assimilation by the cells of the body is known as *digestion;* it takes place in the lumen of the tract. The organs responsible for carrying out the work of digestion belong to the *digestive system*. The digestive or alimentary system consists of the *digestive* or *alimentary tract* and *accessory organs* and *glands* that lie outside the wall of the tract itself, but communicate with it by means of ducts.

Before starting the discussion of the digestive tract, it seems wise to describe a mucous membrane and two structures, the lips and cheeks, that are associated with the mouth, but are not a part of the digestive system per se.

MUCOUS MEMBRANE

All tubular structures and hollow organs of the body that open either directly or ultimately onto the surface of the body have a mucous membrane lining these structures and organs with a "wet" epithelial surface.

A *mucous membrane* consists of a non-keratonized, *epithelial layer* and an underlying, loosely woven, fibrous connective tissue

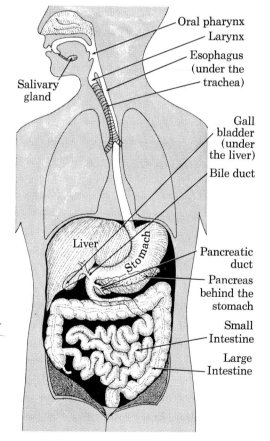

Oral pharynx
Larynx
Esophagus (under the trachea)
Salivary gland
Gall bladder (under the liver)
Bile duct
Liver
Stomach
Pancreatic duct
Pancreas behind the stomach
Small Intestine
Large Intestine

193

layer called the *lamina propria.* The epithelial layer ranges from a simple epithelium designed for absorption and/or secretion, to a thick epithelial layer (squamous cells) designed for protection. It takes the latter form near body orifices, where the mucous membrane merges with the stratified squamous epithelium of the skin covering the surface of the body. The fibrous connective tissue of the lamina propria consists of a fine meshwork of connective tissue fibers which in many areas contains scattered smooth muscle fibers. The connective tissue fibers are predominantly reticular with a fair scattering of collagenous and elastic fibers. In many areas the lamina propria contains large numbers of lymphocytes, diffusely scattered or in the form of lymph nodules. Through its entire extent, a mucous membrane contains numerous goblet cells in its epithelium, supplemented by mucous secreting glands, whose secretions lubricate and maintain the moisture of the "wet" surface membrane.

STRUCTURES ASSOCIATED WITH THE MOUTH

The Lips

The lips are two highly sensitive, mobile folds composed of skin, muscles, glands, and mucous membrane that surround the oral orifice and form the anterior boundary of the oral cavity. The upper lip extends to the nose above and to the nasolabial sulcus laterally. The lower lip is separated from the chin by a groove called the mentolabial sulcus (Fig. 246).

STRUCTURE. Externally the lips are covered by skin, which is continuous with the mucous membrane that covers the rounded free margin of the lips and continues into the oral cavity to line the mouth. The junction between the skin and the mucous membrane is clearly marked by the change in color, from the pale color of the skin to the red color of the mucous membrane. On the inner surface of each lip, in the midline, the mucous membrane is elevated to form a narrow fold called the *frenulum labii,* which serves to connect each lip to the corresponding gum or gingiva.

MUSCLE. The orbicularis oris is a sphincter muscle that guards the oral orifice. It lies between the skin and the subcutaneous tissue on the outside, and the mucosa and submucosa on the inside of the lip.

GLANDS. In the submucosa of the inner surface of the lips are numerous, small, mucous secreting, *labial* glands which completely encircle the mouth. Their secretion serves to keep the mucosus membrane moist.

BLOOD SUPPLY. The labial branches of the facial artery supply blood to the lips.

LYMPHATICS. The upper lip and lateral parts of the lower lip are drained by lymph vessels that empty into the submandibular lymph nodes. The medial portion of the lower lip is drained by lymph vessels that empty into the submental nodes.

NERVE SUPPLY. The upper lip is supplied by branches of the infraorbital nerve, and the lower lip by branches of the mental nerve.

The Cheeks

The cheeks are located at the sides of the face and form the lateral boundaries of the oral cavity. They are continuous with the lips in front and closely resemble them in structure. The mucous membrane lining the cheeks is reflected onto the gums or gingiva.

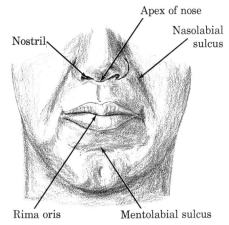

Fig. 246. The lips, the anterior boundary of the oral cavity.

MUSCLES.   The cheeks are formed by the buccinator muscles principally. Other muscles contributing to the formation of the cheeks are the platysma, risorius, and zygomaticus. These muscles are "sandwiched" in between the skin and subcutaneous tissue on the outside and the submucosa and mucosa forming the inner surface.

GLANDS.   Two sets of glands found in the cheeks are the *buccal* and the *molar*. The buccal glands are located in the submucosa of the inner surface of the cheeks and are similar in structure but smaller than the labial glands of the lips. There are about five molar glands, located between the buccinator and masseter muscles; their ducts open opposite the last molar teeth. These glands are similar in structure to the buccal glands, but larger.

The Parts of the Digestive or Alimentary System. (Fig. 247.)
 A. Digestive (alimentary) tract
  1. Mouth
       Accessory Organs
            Tongue
            Teeth
  2. Fauces
  3. Oral and laryngeal pharynx
  4. Esophagus
  5. Stomach
  6. Small intestine
       Duodenum
       Jejunum
       Ileum
  7. Large intestine
       Cecum
            Appendix
       Colon
       Rectum
       Anal canal
 B. Accessory organ—the gall bladder
 C. Accessory glands
     Salivary glands
          Parotid
          Submandibular (submaxillary)
          Sublingual
     Pancreas
     Liver

(Note: The first two segments of the digestive (alimentary) tract, the *mouth* and the *oral* and *laryngeal pharynx,* are not limited to serving the digestive system; they are also a part of the passageway conducting air into the lungs.

(The pharynx will be discussed with the organs of the respiratory system.)

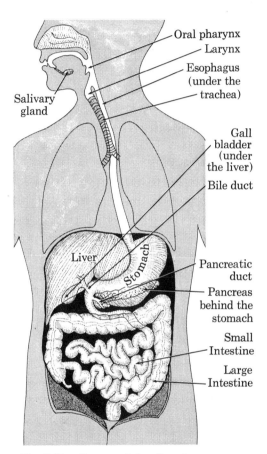

Fig. 247.   Organs of the digestive system.

DIGESTIVE OR ALIMENTARY TRACT

The digestive or alimentary tract is a long, musculo-membranous, tubular structure that extends from the lips to the anus and is lined throughout by a moist mucous membrane. For descriptive and practical purposes, it is subdivided into a number of segments that differ from one another in structural detail and specific function (Fig. 247).

THE MOUTH (ORAL CAVITY)

The first subdivision of the tubular alimentary tract is the mouth. Anteriorly it opens to the outside of the body; posteriorly it communicates with the oral pharynx.

BOUNDARIES.

Anterior—the lips guard and form the anterior wall of the mouth when it is closed.

Lateral—the sides of the mouth are formed by the cheeks.

Roof—the hard and soft palate form the roof.

Floor—the floor of the mouth is formed by the tongue, muscles, the alveolar arch of the mandible, and the reflection of the mucous membrane as it extends from the tongue to the inner surface of the cheeks, covering the muscles and the alveolar arch of the mandible.

Posterior—the palatine arches mark the line of junction between the mouth and the oral pharynx.

AREAS OF THE MOUTH. The mouth is divided into two areas or parts—the *vestibule* and the *mouth cavity proper.* The vestibule is a narrow, slit-like space bounded on the outside by the lips and cheeks and separated from the mouth cavity proper by the gingiva (gums) and the teeth. The reflection of the mucous membrane from the cheeks and lips to the gingiva forms the limits of the space above and below. When the jaws are closed, the vestibule communicates with the mouth proper by way of the spaces behind the last molar teeth and by the small intervals between adjacent teeth. The secretion of the parotid gland is emptied into the vestibule.

The mouth cavity proper is bounded in front and at the sides by the alveolar arches of the two jaws and their contained teeth; the roof is the hard and soft palate; the floor is formed by the tongue and the sublingual reflection of the mucous membrane from the tongue to the alveolar surfaces of the lower jaw. Posteriorly, the mouth proper communicates with the oral pharynx. The secretions of the submandibular (submaxillary) and sublingual glands are emptied into this cavity.

ORGANS AND STRUCTURES CONTAINED IN THE MOUTH. The mouth contains the tongue, gingiva, teeth, and the terminal ends of the ducts of the salivary glands.

THE TONGUE (Fig. 248). This is a mobile, tactile organ, composed primarily of striated muscles and covered by a mucous membrane continuous with the mucous membrane lining the mouth. It lies within the horseshoe-shaped curve of the body of the mandible and contributes to the formation of the floor of the mouth. As an accessory structure of the first part of the digestive tract (mouth), the tongue plays an important part in mastication of food and swallowing. The organs of taste, the *taste buds,* are contained within its mucosa and it is essential in the production of articulate speech. For descriptive purposes the tongue is divided into two parts—the *body* and the *root,* which are separated by a V-shaped groove on the dorsal (upper) surface called the *sulcus terminalis.*

Description. The body of the tongue makes up the horizontal, anterior two thirds of the organ. It presents two surfaces—the dorsal surface (the dorsum) and an inferior surface, which are continuous at the sides of the tongue. The dorsum (superior surface) is marked by a slight midline groove called the *median sulcus* marking the posi-

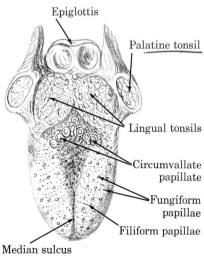

Fig. 248. Dorsum of the tongue.

Epiglottis

Palatine tonsil

Lingual tonsils

Circumvallate papillate

Fungiform papillae

Filiform papillae

Median sulcus

the pulp cavity through the apical foramen and the root canals of the tooth.

Except for the enamel, which is an ectodermal derivative, all of the tissues which form the tooth are of connective tissue (mesodermal) origin.

Enamel.   Enamel is the first dental tissue to form and is produced by cells of ectodermal origin, the *ameloblasts*. It is the most highly calcified and hardest tissue in the body, consisting of approximately 96 per cent inorganic (mineral) substance and only 4 per cent of organic material and water. It forms the outer layer of the crown of the tooth. The formation of the enamel organ is the first indication of tooth formation.

During the development of the tooth each ameloblast produces a hexagonal shaped, rod-like structure called an *enamel rod,* which is arranged nearly perpendicular to the surface of the underlying dentine. The enamel rods are bound together by a calcified inter-rod cement substance. When growth of the enamel rods is complete the ameloblasts degenerate, so that in the mature tooth the enamel is an acellular (containing no cells) substance, incapable of repair or regeneration.

Dentine. This substance makes up the greatest proportion of the hard shell of the tooth. In the area of the crown it is covered by a layer of enamel, and in the area of the root by a layer of cementum. Dentine is not as hard as enamel. It more nearly resembles bone, but differs in several ways. It has less organic material and less collagen in its intercellular substance than bone. Dentine is somewhat softer and more resilient than bone, and thus serves as a cushioning material for the hard, brittle enamel above it. The cells that produce dentine, the *odontoblasts,* are highly differentiated connective tissue cells. The first dentine to be formed is laid down almost simultaneously with the first enamel, and it is deposited on the inner or pulp side of the tooth. Continued formation of dentine occurs by appositional growth, similar to the growth of bone, but in dentine, growth takes place only along one surface, next to the pulp cavity. This explains the continued decrease in size of the pulp cavity during the development and growth of the tooth.

Cementum. This is the last of the three basic dental tissues to appear. The cementum forms a layer of non-vascular, calcified connective tissue that covers the dentine of the root of the tooth. Cementum resembles bone in a number of ways except that it contains no blood vessels. Transformed connective tissue cells, the *cementoblasts,* deposit cementum as *lamellae (layers)* in much the same way as osteoblasts deposit bone. The cementoblasts that become trapped by their own secretions are called *cementocytes* and they lie in spaces called *lacunae.* Fine *canaliculae* extend throughout the cementum, connecting adjacent lacunae and extending to neighboring tissues where nutrient materials are available.

Cementum may be formed at any time throughout the life of a tooth, in response to a shift in position of a tooth or a loosening of the tooth in its socket. By providing an anchorage for fibers from the periodontal membrane, it stabilizes the tooth in the alveolar socket.

Dental Pulp.   Dental pulp consists of a mesenchymal type of connective tissue composed of stellate-shaped cells and relatively few collagenous fibers in a soft gel-like matrix. It contains many thin-

Deciduous teeth.

walled blood vessels and sensory nerve fibers which terminate in relation to the odontoblasts that line the pulp cavity. The dental pulp serves primarily for the nutrition and maintenance of the dentine of the tooth. Destruction of the dental pulp results in degeneration of the adjacent dentine, and this in turn may have a marked effect on the character of the enamel as well.

General Description of the Teeth. The teeth are anchored in the alveolar sockets of the maxilla and the mandible, arranged in two (an upper and a lower) horseshoe-shaped rows, with the "toe" of the shoe directed anteriorly. The gums cover the alveolar surfaces of the maxilla and mandible, and extend slightly beyond the free margins of the alveolar processes in a thin fold (the gingiva). The gingiva surrounds and is attached to the exposed surface of each tooth, usually the crown.

Each tooth consists of three parts: the *root,* the *neck,* and the *crown.*

Root. The root of a tooth may be a single, conical structure, as in the incisors, or it may be divided into two or three separate conical projections as in the first upper premolars (two roots) and molars (three roots). The roots of the teeth fit into individual sockets (alveoli) of the jaw bones. A dense fibrous connective tissue membrane called the *periodontal membrane* (alveolar periosteum) extends between the root of the tooth and the wall of the socket to form a suspensory ligament that serves to anchor the tooth to the bone. The periodontal membrane also serves as the periosteum of the bone and as the covering of the root, having both osteogenic and cementogenic potential. At the margin of the tooth socket, the periodontal membrane merges with the periosteum of the jaw and in part with the dense fibrous tissue of the gums and gingiva.

Neck. This area joins the crown of the tooth to the root, and is marked by a slight depression or constriction on the surface of the tooth.

Crown. The extent of the crown varies somewhat depending on whether the anatomical or clinical crown is referred to. "Anatomical" crown is the portion of the tooth beyond the neck that is covered by enamel. "Clinical" crown is the exposed part of the tooth, beyond the point of attachment of the gingiva to the tooth. The area of the clinical crown varies with age. In a young person, the gingiva on a recently erupted tooth may attach rather high on the crown, so that the clinical crown is shorter than the anatomical crown. Later, as the tooth, through continued growth exposes more crown surface, the gingiva becomes attached to the neck of the tooth and the clinical and anatomical crowns are identical. In later life, with recession of the gingiva and the margins of the alveolar processes, the gingiva becomes attached to the cementum of the root of the tooth and the clinical crown is longer than the anatomical crown.

Positional Terms. If the teeth were arranged in a straight line rather than on a curved arch, the terms anterior, posterior, medial, and lateral would be adequate to describe comparable surfaces on any of the teeth. However, due to the curvature of the dental arches, these

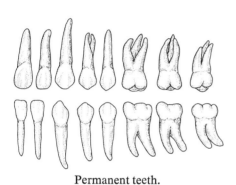

Permanent teeth.

terms do not apply, and a new set of terms has been introduced for descriptive purposes within the mouth, particularly for the teeth.

Labial and *buccal*—refers to a surface in contact with or directed toward the lips (labial) or the cheeks (buccal).

Lingual—applies to surfaces directed toward the tongue. This term should be restricted to structures of the lower jaw.

Palatal—a term for the upper jaw, comparable to lingual. This term is used to describe the "inner" surface or the surface directed toward the palate of the upper jaw.

Sides—referred to as the mesial or distal surfaces. *Mesial* is the anterior or medial surface depending on the position of the tooth in the dental arch. *Distal* is the posterior or lateral surface. These surfaces have "contact areas," where the sides of adjacent teeth touch each other.

Occlusal surface—the biting surface of a tooth; it is most extensive in the molars, which are designed for grinding food.

Form.   The deciduous (milk) teeth are quite similar in form to their counterparts in the permanent dentition. They are smaller in size, fewer in number, and not as highly differentiated (in the development of their roots, for instance) as the permanent teeth. The second molar of the deciduous teeth is the largest of the primary dentition. The deciduous molars are replaced by the permanent premolars, and the permanent molars are the "extra" teeth of the permanent dentition and have no exact counterparts in the deciduous dentition.

Because of the similarity of form between the teeth of the two dentitions, only the permanent teeth will be described.

Incisors—There are eight incisors, four in each jaw. They are centrally positioned, two on either side of the midline in each jaw. They are chisel-shaped teeth designed for biting or cutting and have a beveled, free (occlusal) cutting edge. Their roots are long, single, and cone-shaped.

Canines (Cuspids)—There are four cuspids, two in each jaw, one on either side, just beyond each lateral incisor. They are the longest of the teeth and are strongly constructed. They are designed to hold and/or to tear. The crowns of these teeth are conical in shape with a blunted tip. In man they project just slightly beyond the free occlusal surfaces of the other teeth. Their roots are single, larger, and longer than the roots of the neighboring incisors.

Premolars (Bicuspids)—There are eight premolars, four in each jaw, two on either side, positioned just beyond the cuspids. The occlusal surfaces of these teeth are modified for grinding. On the masticating surfaces of these teeth are two cusps, separated by a shallow groove. The roots of these teeth are usually single, except the first upper premolar which is normally double.

Molars—There are twelve of these teeth, six in each jaw, divided equally between the right and left sides; they are the last three teeth in each side of each dental arch. These teeth have large occlusal surfaces adapted for grinding food. The masticating surfaces are not flat but are marked by three to five cusps. The lower molars have two roots; the upper molars have three roots.

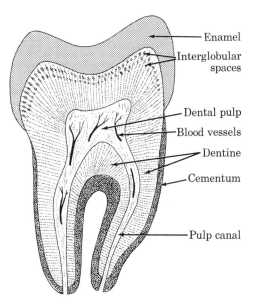

Vertical section through a molar tooth.

Blood Supply to the Teeth. The arteries to the teeth are distributed to the pulp cavity and to the surrounding alveolar periosteum as follows:

Teeth	Arteries
upper incisors and canines	anterior superior alveolar branches of the infraorbital artery
upper premolars and molars	posterior superior alveolar branches of the internal maxillary artery
lower incisors and canines	incisive branches of the inferior alveolar artery
lower premolars and molars	dental branches of the inferior alveolar artery

Veins returning blood from the teeth are closely associated with the arteries and have the same names as the arteries they accompany.

Lymphatics. The lymph vessels from the teeth usually drain into the three to six submandibular lymph nodes under the body of the mandible.

Nerve Supply. The teeth receive sensory nerve fibers from branches of the maxillary and mandibular divisions of the trigeminal nerve (5th cranial). Specifically, the innervation is as follows:

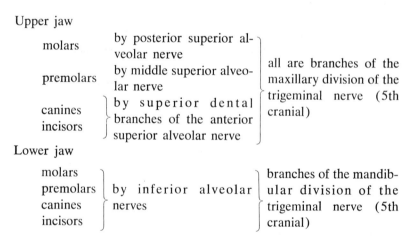

Upper jaw

molars	by posterior superior alveolar nerve	all are branches of the maxillary division of the trigeminal nerve (5th cranial)
premolars	by middle superior alveolar nerve	
canines incisors	by superior dental branches of the anterior superior alveolar nerve	

Lower jaw

molars premolars canines incisors	by inferior alveolar nerves	branches of the mandibular division of the trigeminal nerve (5th cranial)

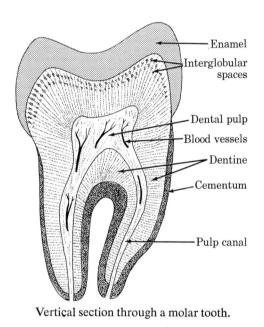

Vertical section through a molar tooth.

Enamel
Interglobular spaces
Dental pulp
Blood vessels
Dentine
Cementum
Pulp canal

THE FAUCES

This is a narrow area or passageway covered by mucous membrane that marks the junction between the mouth and the oral pharynx, bounded above by the soft palate; at the sides by the anterior and posterior pillars of the fauces; and below by the dorsum of the tongue. The sides of the fauces are marked by two vertically directed projections, the *anterior pillars* or the *glossopalatine arches,* formed by the underlying glossopalatinus muscles, and the larger *posterior pillars* or the *pharyngopalatine arches,* formed by the pharyngopalatinus muscles. These arches run downward and laterally, the anterior pillars deviating forward and the posterior pillars deviating backward, leaving a somewhat triangular space (tonsillar fossa) between them that contains the *palatine tonsils.*

Palatine Tonsils

These are two prominent, almond-shaped masses of lymphoid tissue located on either side of the fauces, between the anterior and posterior pillars. The exposed part of each tonsil is covered by stratified squamous epithelium that is continuous with the stratified squamous epithelium of the adjacent mucous membrane. The lower portion of each tonsil is embedded in the tissues of the wall of the fauces, from which it is separated by a heavy, collagenous tissue capsule. Each tonsil has from 15 to 20 crypts which are pitlike invaginations of the surface epithelium into the substance of the tonsil. Tonsillar tissue is more abundant in young children, in whom the palatine tonsils are much larger than in adults and in old people. The palatine tonsils are part of a group of lymphoid organs that encircle and guard the opening into the digestive and respiratory areas. This group of structures is known as *Waldeyer's tonsillar ring,* and is completed by the pharyngeal tonsils (adenoids) and the tubal tonsils above, and the lingual tonsils below. This ring of lymphoid tissue, which contains large numbers of phagocytic cells and lymphocytes, removes organisms and small, solid, foreign particles, which otherwise might gain entrance to the body by way of the lungs or the digestive tract.

BLOOD SUPPLY.   Blood is carried to the palatine tonsils by branches from the lingual, the external maxillary, the external carotid, and internal maxillary arteries, and sometimes a twig from a small meningeal artery. Veins conveying blood from the tonsils end in the tonsillar plexus of veins lateral to the tonsils.

LYMPHATICS.   From the palatine tonsils usually three to five lymphatic vessels drain into the superior deep cervical nodes.

NERVE SUPPLY.   The palatine tonsils are supplied by the tonsillar branches of the glossopharyngeal nerve (9th cranial) and by fibers from the sphenopalatine ganglion.

THE PHARYNX (ORAL AND LARYNGEAL DIVISIONS) (FIG. 252)

The oral cavity (mouth) communicates with the oral pharynx posteriorly through a somewhat constricted opening, the fauces. The oral part of the pharynx is the second division of the pharynx. It is continuous above with the nasal pharynx, and below with the third division or laryngeal pharynx. The oral pharynx extends from the soft palate to the level of the hyoid bone. Between the hyoid bone and the lower border of the cricoid cartilage, it becomes the laryngeal pharynx. At the level of the cricoid cartilage, the laryngopharynx is directly continuous with the esophagus below. Its anterior wall is deficient inferiorly, at the laryngeal aperture, where it opens into the larynx.

The description of the structure of the wall of the pharynx is given on page 230. Here it is sufficient to say that the entire pharynx is lined by a mucous membrane. The muscles of the pharynx are restricted to the oral and laryngeal portions and are arranged in two layers—an inner longitudinal and an outer circular layer. The muscles forming the inner longitudinal layer are the stylopharyngeus, salpingopharyngeus, and the pharyngopalatinus. On contraction these

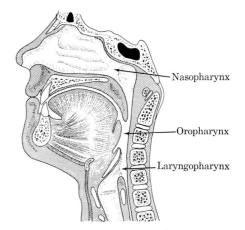

Fig. 252.   Sagittal section of the pharynx.

muscles elevate the pharynx (closing the opening into the larynx) and increase the diameter of the oral pharyngeal lumen. They also prepare the pharynx for the reception of material to be swallowed. The outer circular layer is formed by the superior, middle, and inferior constrictor muscles. The contraction of these muscles proceeds in a wave-like movement from above downward, producing a narrowing of the lumen of the pharynx. This plays an important part in the act of swallowing, forcing the bolus along the tube and into the esophagus.

THE DIGESTIVE TUBE PROPER

The digestive tube proper is that portion of the alimentary tract serving only the digestive system. It is a musculomembranous tube about 9 meters long that starts with the esophagus and terminates at the anal opening, the anus. For descriptive purposes, the digestive tube proper is subdivided into a number of sections based, in part at least, on their function.

Esophagus	Large intestine
Stomach	Cecum
Small intestine	Appendix
Duodenum	Colon
Jejunum	Rectum
Ileum	Anal canal

Through its entire extent, the wall of the digestive tube presents one basic structural pattern. Within each major subdivision variations of the basic structure occur which are associated with the particular function of the particular area.

The basic structure of the wall comprises five distinct layers.

1. Mucosa, consisting of an epithelium and the lamina propria, a layer of connective tissue.

2. Muscularis mucosa, a well-defined layer of smooth muscle fibers found only in the digestive tube.

3. Submucosa, consisting of a layer of coarse collagenous fiber bundles and elastic fibers. It gives support to blood vessels, lymphatics, nerve fibers, and glands.

4. Muscularis externa, two well-defined layers of muscle (usually smooth muscle) arranged to form an inner circular and an outer longitudinal layer. (Note: In the stomach, there are three layers of the muscularis externa—an inner oblique, middle circular, and outer longitudinal.)

5. Adventitia and/or serosa. An adventitia consists of a loose connective tissue layer. The serosa is loose connective tissue covered by a single layer of mesothelial cells. The serosa is actually the peritoneal lining of the abdominal cavity and serves as the "outer" layer of any organ covered by or enclosed within the peritoneal membrane.

The nerve supply of the digestive tube proper is derived from parasympathetic and sympathetic components of the autonomic system. These components form two extensive plexuses that extend throughout the entire length of the digestive tube. One, the myenteric or Auerbach's plexus, is located between the circular and longitudinal layers of the muscularis externa. The other, the submucosal or Meissner's plexus, is located in the submucosal layer. Stimulation of the parasympathetic components increases the peristaltic activity of the tract and muscle tone. Stimulation of the sympathetic components inhibits peristaltic activity and decreases the muscle tone.

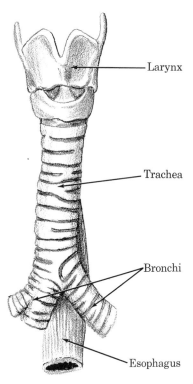

Fig. 253. Esophagus and trachea.

Larynx

Trachea

Bronchi

Esophagus

The Esophagus (Fig. 253)

This section is the first portion of the digestive tube proper. It starts at about the level of the cricoid cartilage as a distal continuation of the pharynx. Distally the esophagus enters the abdominal cavity through the esophageal opening of the diaphragm and is continuous with the stomach. The abdominal portion of the esophagus is short (about 2 centimeters). The esophagus is vertically positioned throughout its extent and lies posterior to the trachea. The esophagus is an anteroposteriorly flattened musculomembranous tube about 25 cm. long. The epithelium of the mucosal layer is a thick, stratified squamous cell layer designed primarily for protection, and it rests on a fairly loose layer of connective tissue, the lamina propria. The muscularis mucosa, a well-defined layer of smooth muscle bundles, separates the mucosa from the submucosa. Mucous secreting glands are found in both the mucosa and submucosa, and their secretions moisten the surface layer and furnish lubricating material to slide the bolus of food from the pharynx to the stomach. The muscularis externa consists of an inner circular and an outer longitudinal arrangement of muscle fibers. The muscle of both layers is striated in the upper third of the esophagus; it is mixed, striated and smooth muscle in the middle third and changes to smooth muscle in the lower third of the organ. The outer layer of that portion of the esophagus which is above the diaphragm is an adventitia.

BLOOD SUPPLY. Arteries supplying the esophagus are branches from the inferior thyroid (from the thyrocervical trunk), the descending thoracic aorta, the left gastric (of the celiac artery), and the left inferior phrenic (from the abdominal aorta). The veins draining the wall of the esophagus empty into the inferior thyroid, the azygos, hemiazygos, and the gastric (coronary) veins.

LYMPHATICS. The lymph vessels of the esophagus drain primarily to the inferior posterior mediastinal nodes.

NERVE SUPPLY. Branches are received from the parasympathetics (vagi), and from the sympathetic trunks which form two plexuses within the walls of the organ. One plexus (the myenteric) is located between the two layers of the muscularis externa and the other (the submucous) is in the submucosa.

The Stomach (Figs. 247, p. 195, and 254)

The stomach is the most expanded portion of the digestive tube. It extends from the distal end of the esophagus above to the first (upper) part of the small intestine below.

SHAPE. The shape of the stomach is extremely varied, but it is commonly described as being shaped like a capital letter "J." The lesser curvature does, in fact, conform more or less to the shape of a "J," but the greater curvature does not, due to the marked dilatation of the upper left fundic portion of the organ.

SIZE AND CAPACITY. The adult stomach is about 25 cm. long and 10 cm. wide and has an average capacity of about one liter.

POSITION. Most of the stomach lies to the left of the midline of the body in the upper left quadrant of the abdomen. It is most firmly anchored at the cardia, where it joins the esophagus. The remainder of the organ hangs more or less free and movable which accounts for

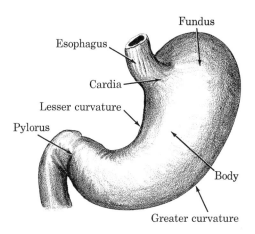

Fig. 254. Stomach. Anterior surface.

the variations in its position that occur under certain conditions. While several factors are responsible for shift in position of the organ, probably the most common cause of change in position is due to the amount of material (food or fluids) it contains at any one time. Another factor is body position. A pendant organ such as the stomach does not occupy the same position in a person who is standing as it does if he is reclining. Likewise, the shape and size of adjacent organs affect the position of the stomach.

GENERAL DESCRIPTION. The stomach presents two margins. The *minor ventricular curvature* (*lesser curvature*) forms the right margin, continuing the line of the right margin of the esophagus in a relatively short, J-shaped curve, concave to the right, extending to the pyloric orifice. *The major ventricular curvature* (*greater curvature*) forms the left and lower margin of the stomach, and is about four times longer than the lesser curvature. It starts at the cardiac incisure to the left of the esophagogastric junction and forms a long convex curvature, directed at first superiorly, then to the left, and finally inferiorly and obliquely toward the right, to the pyloric orifice.

The two surfaces of the stomach are the *anterosuperior* and the *posteroinferior surfaces.*

There are two orifices. The *cardiac orifice* at the upper end of the stomach, is the opening between the esophagus and the stomach. This orifice has no well-developed sphincter muscle such as is found at the distal (pyloric) end of the stomach. The *pyloric orifice* lies roughly about 2.5 cm. to the right of the midline of the body. This orifice is characterized by a strong sphincter muscle which controls the release of the gastric contents into the small intestine.

An angular depression on the lesser curvature, which marks the separation of the body and pyloric portions of the stomach, is called the *angular incisure* or *notch.*

The acute angle found at the point of junction between the left margin of the esophagus and the start of the greater curvature is the *cardiac incisure* or *notch.*

PARTS. The stomach is divided into four component parts.

1. The *cardia* is a small restricted area about 2.5 cm. in width, adjacent to the junction with the esophagus.

2. The *fundus* is the blind sac-like dilatation of the upper portion of the organ above and to the left of the gastroesophageal junction.

3. The *body* is the wide expanded portion of the organ between the fundus and the pylorus. The lower limit of the body is marked on the lesser curvature by the angular notch.

4. The *pylorus* is the portion of the organ that lies to the right of a nearly vertical plane that would bisect the organ at the level of the angular notch of the lesser curvature. It consists of the relatively wide *pyloric antrum* that lies just to the right of the angular notch and a short tapering segment beyond it called the *pyloric canal.* Its junction with the small intestine is marked by the constricted pyloric orifice, guarded and controlled by the *pyloric sphincter.*

STRUCTURE OF THE STOMACH WALL. The variations of the basic structure of the alimentary tract that occur in the stomach involve primarily the mucosa and muscularis externa. In the stomach the mucosa is a relatively thick layer (Figs. 255 and 256). The epithelium lining the stomach is a simple columnar epithelium that covers

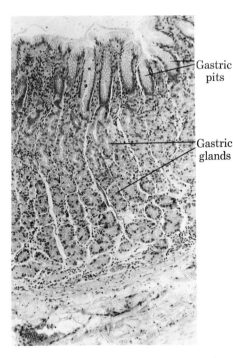

Gastric pits

Gastric glands

Fig. 255.   Mucosa of the fundus of the stomach.

the surface and extends into invaginations called *gastric pits*. In the base of the pits it is continuous with the epithelium of the numerous glands that extend throughout the width of the lamina propria below, and empty their secretions into the gastric pits. The glands of the mucosal layer secrete mucous, enzymes, and hydrochloric acid. Three specific cell types are found in the epithelium of the gastric glands—*mucous secreting cells, chief cells* that produce enzymes, and *parietal cells* that produce hydrochloric acid. If a stomach is cut open and the inner surface examined, one can see that the mucosa presents a number of folds (*rugae*), directed longitudinally. These folds are well marked along the line of the lesser curvature. The muscularis externa in the stomach consists of three layers of smooth muscle—an inner oblique, a middle circular, and an outer, somewhat erratically arranged longitudinal layer. The outermost layer of the stomach is the tunica serosa (peritoneum).

FUNCTION.   The stomach receives the softened mass of food, the *bolus,* that has been masticated and mixed with saliva in the mouth and delivered by way of the pharynx and esophagus. The action of the stomach on the bolus of food is both mechanical and chemical. The muscular wall of the stomach must complete the physical breakdown of large bits of food that the teeth failed to grind up. The glands of the stomach produce hydrochloric acid and enzymes which are thoroughly mixed with the food, converting the bolus in time into a semifluid mass called *chyme.* The chyme is then delivered to the small intestine, while solid particles are retained in the stomach until they too are converted to chyme. Practically no absorption of food takes place in the stomach.

Blood Supply.   Arteries carrying blood to the stomach are the left gastric, right gastric and right gastroepiploic (branches of the hepatic artery), and the left gastroepiploic and short gastric branches (from the splenic artery). The veins of the stomach accompany the arteries and ultimately drain into the portal vein.

LYMPHATICS.   The vessels that drain the surfaces of the stomach empty into the superior gastric nodes. The fundus and body of the stomach to the left of a vertical line dropped from the esophagus are drained by vessels that empty into the pancreaticolienal nodes. The remaining portion to the right of the vertical line, the right part of the greater curvature to the pyloric junction, is drained by vessels empty-ing into the inferior gastric nodes. The pylorus is drained by vessels that empty into the hepatic, subpyloric, and superior gastric glands.

NERVE SUPPLY.   The stomach is innervated by both parasym-pathetic and sympathetic fibers. The parasympathetic innervation is by way of the two vagus nerves—the posterior surface of the stomach is supplied by the right vagus and the anterior surface by the left vagus. The sympathetic innervation is by way of branches from the celiac plexus.

THE PERITONEUM AND THE STOMACH.   The peritoneum covers the stomach on both sides except for a small bare area behind the cardiac orifice. Along each curvature the layer covering the front and that covering the back of the stomach join to form a two-layered peritoneal membrane. From the lesser curvature this doubled-layered membrane, called the *lesser omentum,* extends to the liver and the beginning of the duodenum. The doubled layer of the peritoneum from the greater curvature spreads out and extends downward and

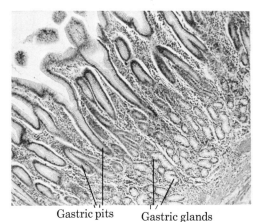

Gastric pits   Gastric glands

Fig. 256.   Mucosa of the pylorus of the stomach.

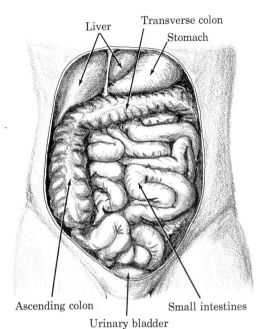

Fig. 257.   Abdominal viscera.

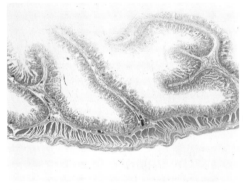

Fig. 258.   Photomicrograph of a section through the wall of the jejunum showing the plicae circulares.

forward superficial to the coils of the small intestine, to the level of the umbilicus where it forms a fold and doubles back on itself, to reach the lower border of the transverse colon. This apron-like arrangement of the serosa is called the *greater omentum*. On reaching the lower border of the transverse colon, the double posterior layer splits to enclose the transverse colon, then unites again along the superior border and extends to the posterior abdominal wall.

The Small Intestine

The small intestine is a long, tubular structure. It is continuous with the stomach at the pyloric orifice above, and empties into the large intestine below at the ileocecal orifice in the lower right quadrant of the abdomen (Figs. 247, p. 195, and 257). It is arbitrarily divided into three parts—the duodenum, the jejunum, and the ileum.

SIZE AND SHAPE.   The entire tube is approximately 7 meters long. It is largest above, at its junction with the stomach, and gradually diminishes in size toward its junction with the large intestine.

POSITION.   The small intestine occupies most of the central and lower part of the abdominal cavity. At the sides and above, the colon "frames" the small intestine. Anteriorly it is covered by the greater omentum and the anterior abdominal wall.

ATTACHMENT.   Roughly the first 25 cm. of the small intestine (the duodenum) is retroperitoneal and is anchored to the posterior abdominal wall. Throughout the remainder of its extent, the small intestine is relatively free and mobile. It is attached rather loosely to the posterior abdominal wall by a double layer of peritoneum called the *mesentery*.

The mesentery is a long, rather narrow, fan-shaped fold of peritoneum that encloses the entire length of the jejunum and ileum in its free marginal fold. Where the double layer of the mesentery is attached to the posterior abdominal wall it is "gathered" to fit into a restricted area for attachment. By this arrangement the intestine is maintained in a fairly regular series of loops, diminishing the danger of such a lengthy tube becoming knotted or tangled. Blood vessels, lymphatics, and nerves are conveyed to the intestine between the two layers of the mesentery.

STRUCTURE OF THE WALL OF THE SMALL INTESTINE.   The basic plan is modified in the small intestine primarily to facilitate the absorption of nutrient materials, most of which occurs throughout the small intestine. Two modifications characterize this area of the digestive tract, and both of them serve to increase the absorptive surface area of the small intestine without increasing its length. These modifications are the plicae circulares and the villi (Figs. 258 and 259).

The *plicae circulares* are permanent, shelf-like folds which project into the lumen of the tube and take a slightly spiral course throughout most of the small intestine. They are formed by the mucosa, muscularis mucosa, and the submucosal layers. The plicae are absent in the first part of the duodenum, reach their greatest height in the jejunum, and gradually diminish again throughout the extent of the ileum. The plicae serve to increase the surface area and therefore the area of absorption; they churn and mix the chyme and the digestive juices, at the same time slowing down the passage of the chyme so that more complete absorption can occur.

The *villi* are minute projections of the mucosal layer on and between the plicae. They vary in size and shape in the various segments, but are most numerous and largest in the duodenum and jejunum. The villi contain scattered smooth muscle fibers within their connective tissue cores, so that they can shorten and elongate slightly.

GLANDS. Short, simple tubular glands occur in the mucosa of the small and large intestine. These glands are called the *crypts of Lieberkühn* and in the small intestine they open in the intervillous spaces. The duodenum has an additional group of compound branched glands (*Brunner's glands*) located in the submucosa. The secretion of these glands is emptied into the lumen of this segment by way of ducts.

FUNCTION. Most of the digestion and absorption of food takes place in the small intestine. The glands produce secretions that contribute to the digestive juice. Some cells of the mucosa also produce a substance called *secretin* that enters the blood, is carried to the pancreas and the liver, where it serves to stimulate the cells of these organs to secrete. The plicae slow down the movement of the chyme through the tube thus allowing time for absorption of the nutrient material.

PARTS OF THE SMALL INTESTINE. DUODENUM. The duodenum is the shortest and widest segment of the small intestine (Fig. 260). It is roughly 30 cm. long. Starting at the pyloric orifice, it tapers slightly to its junction with the jejunum. Throughout its very curved course it is described as having four parts. The first part of the duodenum (superior portion) is directed backward and upward. The second part (descending portion) turns sharply downward and to the right. The third part (horizontal portion) is formed when the duodenum makes a second sharp bend, passing horizontally and slightly upward from the right to the left side of the vertebral column. The fourth part is short (about 2.5 cm. long) and directed upward, turning once more sharply forward to end in the jejunum. Because of its extremely curved course the terminal portion of the duodenum lies very close to its beginning, forming an incomplete circle with the convexity directed to the right. The concave curvature of the duodenum cradles the head of the pancreas. The duct of the pancreas separately, or joined with the common bile duct, enters the second part of the duodenum. The duodenum has no mesentery.

Jejuno-ileum. This part is comprised of the jejunum and the ileum which form the more mobile portion of the small intestine that is suspended from the posterior abdominal wall by a mesentery. There is no sharp line of demarcation between these two segments.

JEJUNUM. The jejunum starts at the duodenojejunal junction and accounts for the first two fifths (about 2.5 meters) of the total length of this mobile portion. Its junction with the ileum is arbitrary and not marked by any specific gross morphological characteristics. However, it is true that the jejunum is wider, its walls thicker and more vascular than the ileum.

ILEUM. The ileum makes up the remaining three fifths (about 3.7 meters) of this part of the small intestine. The distal portion of the ileum lies in the pelvis. Distally the ileum empties into the medial

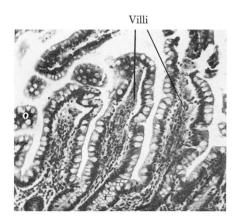

Fig. 259. Photomicrograph of a section through the wall of the small intestine showing the villi.

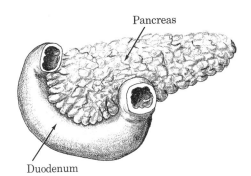

Fig. 260. Duodenum and pancreas.

side of the cecum of the large intestine (Fig. 247, p. 195). Its entrance into the cecum is guarded by the ileocecal valve which prevents regurgitation of material from the cecum into the ileum (Fig. 261).

In about two per cent of individuals there is found a small, pouch-like evagination of the wall of the ileum, usually about 1 meter above the ileocecal junction. This structure is called a *Meckel's diverticulum* and is the remnant of the vitelline duct of the fetus that extended from the primitive digestive tract to the yolk-sac.

BLOOD SUPPLY OF THE SMALL INTESTINE. Arteries carrying blood to the duodenum are the right gastric and superior pancreatico-duodenal branches of the hepatic and the inferior pancreaticoduo-denal branch of the superior mesenteric; to the jejunum and ileum, the branches of the superior mesenteric. Veins draining the wall of the duodenum are tributaries to the lienal and superior mesenteric veins; draining the walls of the jejunum and ileum are veins which have the same names as the arteries they accompany, and they empty into the superior mesenteric veins.

LYMPHATICS. The lymph vessels are arranged in two plexuses, one in the mucosa and submucosa and a second in the muscular coat of the organ. The vessels of the two plexuses communicate freely with each other. The lymph vessels that start as blind-end capillaries in the villi are called lacteals. The small vessels drain to larger vessels along the mesenteric border of the tube and these larger vessels empty into one of the many mesenteric nodes, and ultimately the lymph is carried to the cisterna chyli.

NERVE SUPPLY. Nerve fibers from the celiac (solar) plexus enter the intestinal wall and extend to two plexuses. One, *Auerbach's plexus,* located between the circular and longitudinal muscle layers consists of nerve fibers (chiefly sympathetic, with some vagus fibers), and ganglion cells. Fibers from this plexus supply the muscular coats of the intestine, and extend to a second plexus in the submucosa called *Meissner's plexus.* This plexus also contains ganglion cells. Fibers from Meissner's plexus supply the submucosa and the mucosa.

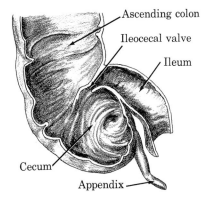

Fig. 261. Ileocecal valve and adjacent portions of intestine viewed from the front.

Ascending colon

Ileocecal valve

Ileum

Cecum

Appendix

The Large Intestine

This portion of the digestive tube extends from the ileocecal junction to the anus. Its arrangement is such that it forms a "frame" (deficient only on the lower right half) for the small intestine (Fig. 247, p. 195).

SIZE AND SHAPE. The entire large intestine measures roughly 1.5 meters in length. This portion of the digestive tube is widest at its beginning (the cecum) and gradually tapers toward its termination at the anus.

POSITION. The large intestine begins in the lower right side of the abdominal cavity as a dilated blind sac called the cecum. It then ascends (ascending colon) along the posterolateral wall of the abdomen to the inferior surface of the liver. Here it makes a sharp turn to the left and crosses the abdominal cavity (transverse colon). On reaching the left side it turns again sharply downward (descending colon) and extends along the posterolateral wall of the left side of the abdomen. It again turns to form an S-shaped double curve (sigmoid colon) and on reaching the midline of the pelvic area it turns sharply downward (rectum) through the pelvis and terminates at the anus.

GENERAL DESCRIPTION. The large intestine has several external features which distinguish it from the small intestine.

1. Throughout most of its extent it is wider.

2. It has *taeniae coli* (Fig. 262). These are three thickenings of the external longitudinal muscle layer. They are roughly about 2.5 cm. wide and equally spaced around the circumference of the cecum and the colon. In the rectum, the three taeniae give way to a single, very heavy thickening on the posterior surface of the tube and sometimes there may be a poorly developed anterior thickening.

3. Between the taeniae coli the walls of the cecum and colon bulge to form a series of sacculations called *haustra coli* (Fig. 262).

4. *Epiploic appendages* are numerous small polypoid structures formed of peritoneal "blebs" containing fat. They hang from the outer surface of the wall of the colon near the taeniae coli.

There are two microscopic structural modifications in the wall of the large intestine that involve the mucosa and the longitudinal layer of the muscularis externa. The mucosa of the large intestine presents a relatively smooth surface because no villi are present. There are numerous simple tubular glands (crypts of Lieberkühn) extending from the muscularis mucosa to the lumen. These glands produce mucous. The three taeniae coli can be readily identified in a cross section of the colon or the cecum.

FUNCTION.   An important function of the large intestine is the absorption of water from the material in its lumen. The unabsorbed food residue of the fluid chyme that has passed through the small intestine is emptied into the large intestine. In its passage through this segment of the digestive tube the contents are gradually dehydrated. By the time this waste material reaches the rectum it is a semisolid to solid mass called *feces*. The feces consist of undigested food, putrefactive bacteria, and cellular debris from the mucosal lining, mixed with mucous secreted by the goblet cells of the crypts of Lieberkühn. Relatively little absorption of nutritive material occurs in the large intestine. No enzymes are produced by the cells of the large intestine, and any digestion that might take place in this part of the tube would depend on the continued action of enzymes from the small intestine, or substances (vitamin K and some of the B complex) released into the lumen of the large intestine through the action of putrefactive bacteria.

THE PERITONEUM AND THE LARGE INTESTINE.   In the majority of individuals the ascending and descending segments of the colon are fixed to the posterior abdominal wall by loose connective tissue, and the peritoneum is reflected only over the sides and anterior surface of these two segments. However, it is not uncommon for them to be completely enclosed by peritoneum which forms a narrow mesocolon for attachment to the posterior abdominal wall. The transverse colon is connected by a wide mesocolon (transverse mesocolon) to the inferior border of the pancreas. The sigmoid colon is surrounded by peritoneum and is attached to the abdominal wall by the sigmoid mesocolon. Only the upper two thirds of the rectum is covered by the peritoneum. At first the peritoneum covers the sides and the front of the rectum, and then covers only the front of the rectum as the peritoneum is reflected forward onto the posterior surface of the pelvic organs (in the male, the seminal vesicles and bladder; in the female, the vagina and uterus).

PARTS.   The large intestine is arbitrarily divided into the cecum and attached appendix, the colon—ascending, transverse, descending, and sigmoid portions—the rectum, and the anal canal.

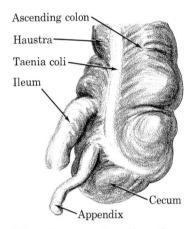

Ascending colon

Haustra

Taenia coli

Ileum

Cecum

Appendix

Fig. 262.   Cecum and portion of ascending colon showing taenia coli and haustra. Note the appendix attached to the cecum where the three taenia coli converge.

CECUM.   The cecum marks the beginning and is the first division of the large intestine. It is a relatively short but wide, blind sacculation that lies below the ileocecal junction. Above the ileocecal junction, the cecum is continuous with the ascending colon (Figs. 261 and 262).

Position.   It lies on the posterior wall in the lower right quadrant of the abdominal cavity, above the lateral half of the right inguinal ligament. In the standing position, the cecum may slip into the cavity of the pelvis.

The Peritoneum and the Cecum.   The cecum is usually entirely covered by peritoneum.

Openings.   Two structures open into the cecum. The ileum opens into the upper left side of the cecum. The opening is guarded on the cecal side by the *ileocecal valve.* The ileocecal valve is made up of two horizontally directed folds of mucous membrane and muscle (circular layer of muscle of the wall of the ileum) which form a slit-like opening that prevents contents of the large intestine from passing backwards into the ileum. The second opening is the orifice through which the vermiform appendix communicates with the cecum. It is at the tip of the cecal sacculation.

On the external surface of the cecum can be seen the taeniae coli, which converge toward the appendix.

APPENDIX (FIGS. 261 AND 262).   This is a worm-like, blind tubular structure that extends from the apex of the cecum. It is roughly 8 to 10 centimeters long and its position is extremely variable. Most commonly, however, it lies behind the cecum (retrocecal) or over the rim of the pelvis. It is entirely covered by peritoneum and is held in place by a small triangular fold of peritoneum, the *mesenteriolum.* The blood vessels to the appendix run near the free margin of the mesenteriolum. The lumen of the appendix extends through the entire length of the structure and communicates with the cecum. The layers of the wall of the appendix correspond in number and arrangement to those of the remainder of the digestive tube.

COLON.   The colon makes up the greater portion of the large intestine. It extends from the cecum in the lower right quadrant upward, across, and then downward to the rectum in the midline of the pelvic cavity (Fig. left).

Ascending Colon.   This is the segment of the colon between the ileocecal valve and the right colic flexure. It tapers from its cecal junction to its continuation with the transverse colon. It lies along the right side of the posterior abdominal wall. Its anterior surface and sides are covered by peritoneum, and it sometimes has a mesocolon attaching it to the posterior abdominal wall. At the right colic flexure it touches the right lobe of the liver.

Transverse Colon.   This portion is the longest segment of the colon, and extends from the right colic (hepatic) flexure to the left colic (splenic) flexure. The transverse colon is suspended by a mesocolon from the inferior border of the pancreas and it hangs in a loop with a downward convexity. The reflected posterior layer of the greater omentum is fixed to the inferior margin of the transverse colon, and splits to enclose the transverse colon. The two layers join again on the opposite side to form the transverse mesocolon. Above the transverse colon is the greater curvature of the stomach, the liver, the gall bladder, and the lower end of the spleen. Below, it is in contact with the coils of the small intestine. Immediately behind it lie the descending

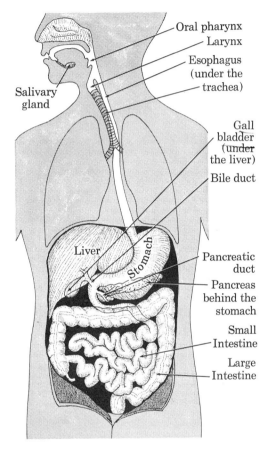

Oral pharynx
Larynx
Esophagus (under the trachea)
Salivary gland
Gall bladder (under the liver)
Bile duct
Liver
Stomach
Pancreatic duct
Pancreas behind the stomach
Small Intestine
Large Intestine

LOCATION.   The pancreas is located in the upper posterior part of the abdominal cavity. It lies more or less horizontally and extends from the duodenum to the spleen. It lies behind the stomach and in front of the first and second lumbar vertebrae.

DESCRIPTION.   The pancreas is a somewhat soft, lobulated, glandular organ, with an extremely thin capsule, and having a reddish or yellowish, greyed color. Its shape has been described as that of a lazy "J" (a "J" that is lying on its long axis). Its average weight is approximately 85 grams, and its length about 12 to 15 centimeters, and its width about 5 centimeters.

DIVISIONS OR PARTS.   It is divided into four parts—a *head,* which is the larger portion of the gland and is toward the right, lying within the duodenal loop to which it is firmly attached; a *neck,* slightly constricted and curved; a *body,* somewhat pyramidal in shape and lying transversely, and a *tail* which is directed to the left where it contacts the spleen.

MICROSCOPIC STRUCTURE.   While the pancreas does not have a distinct connective tissue capsule, it is covered by a layer of loose connective tissue which condenses on its surface and sends septa into the substance of the gland to divide it into a number of small, primary lobules and large, secondary lobules. The septa in man are often incomplete. The ducts, blood and lymphatic vessels, and nerves extend throughout the organ by way of the connective tissue septa.

The *exocrine portion* of this organ consists of tubulo-acinar secreting end pieces together with a rather complex system of branching ducts which are organized to form a compound tubulo-acinar gland. Each secreting acinar end piece drains into a tiny duct which joins with neighboring ducts to form larger and larger ducts within each lobule. The ducts from each lobule open into a main duct (*duct of Wirsung*) which empties into the second part of the duodenum. In the majority of cases, the duct of Wirsung joins with the common bile duct just prior to entering the lumen of the duodenum. An accessory pancreatic duct (*ductus Sartorini*) is usually present; it may open either directly into the duodenum or it may join the duct of Wirsung.

The *endocrine portion* of the pancreas is represented by clumps of cells known as the islands of Langerhans (Fig. 269). These clumps of cells are more or less spherical and are scattered among the acini. They vary greatly in size; an islet may be only a few cords of cells, or one of the largest islands may be visible without the aid of magnification. The islands of Langerhans are most abundant in the tail of the pancreas. There are quite a few of them in the body of the pancreas, but few or none in the head. As is typical of any endocrine gland, these clusters of cells are usually arranged in cord-like manner in contact with capillaries. The insulin they produce is secreted directly into the blood stream.

FUNCTION.   The pancreas produces both exocrine and endocrine secretions.

The *exocrine secretion* is produced by the acinar cells of the pancreas and is known as *pancreatic juice.* It is an alkaline secretion and contains the three enzymes trypsin, amylase, and lipase. Trypsin is a proteolytic enzyme that breaks down proteins to form amino acids; amylase converts starch into sugar; and lipase is the fat-splitting enzyme. The acinar cells are stimulated or activated to produce their secretion either by a hormone, secretin, which is produced

Islands of Langerhans

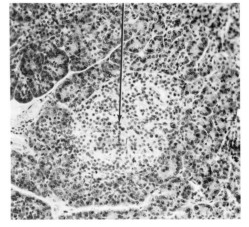

Fig. 269. Photomicrograph of a section of the pancreas showing an island of Langerhans surrounded by acinus tissue.

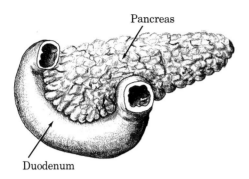

Pancreas

Duodenum

in the mucosa of the small intestine and reaches the cells by way of the blood stream, or by nerve impulses through stimulation of the vagus nerve.

The *endocrine secretion* produced by the islet cells of the pancreas is known as *insulin*. This substance is essential in the proper carbohydrate metabolism of the body. Lack of it produces a disease known as diabetes.

BLOOD SUPPLY. The pancreas receives arterial blood from branches derived from the lienal artery and the pancreaticoduodenal branches of both the hepatic and superior mesenteric arteries. Blood from the pancreas is carried by veins which drain into the lienal and superior mesenteric veins.

LYMPHATICS. The lymph vessels draining the pancreas empty into the pancreaticolienal nodes along the posterior surface and upper border of the pancreas, and ultimately into the celiac nodes.

NERVE SUPPLY. The pancreas receives its nerve supply by way of small filaments from the lienal plexus.

10

THE RESPIRATORY SYSTEM

All living things engage in some form of respiration. For members of the animal kingdom this consists of the absorption of oxygen and the discharge of carbon dioxide as a waste product of cellular metabolism.

In simple unicellular organisms, the exchange of gases is relatively simple. The organism takes the oxygen directly from its environment (air or water) and eliminates the carbon dioxide into the same medium. In the higher, multicellular forms of the animal kingdom, the exchange of gases is more involved. The process is the same as occurs in the unicellular animals, but in multicellular forms it is complicated by the distance the cells are from their source of air. This requires some vehicle for the transportation of oxygen to and carbon dioxide from all the cells of the organism. The blood meets this requirement and serves as the intermediary for transport. The oxygen and carbon dioxide are actually carried by means of a loose chemical combination with the hemoglobin of the red blood corpuscles.

A group of organs is required that will provide a series of tubular and cavernous spaces for directing air into and out of the body and a special organ where the exchange of the gases may occur. This exchange is known as respiration. Two kinds of respiration occur in the body—external and internal. *External respiration* is the exchange of oxygen and carbon dioxide between the alveolar air in the lungs and the blood. *Internal respiration* is the exchange of these gases between the blood and the cells of the body.

The respiratory system includes the respiratory tract, consisting of the *nose, pharynx, larynx, trachea, bronchi* (extrapulmonary), *bronchial tree* (intrapulmonary), and the essential organs of respiration, the *lungs* (paired); the lower part of the trachea, the bronchi, bronchial tree, and lungs are contained within the thoracic cavity (Fig. 270).

NOSE

This is the first division of the tubular structure of the respiratory system that conveys air from the outside of the body to the lungs. It will be described under the following subheadings: the external nose, the internal nose (nasal cavity), and the accessory structures—the paranasal air sinuses.

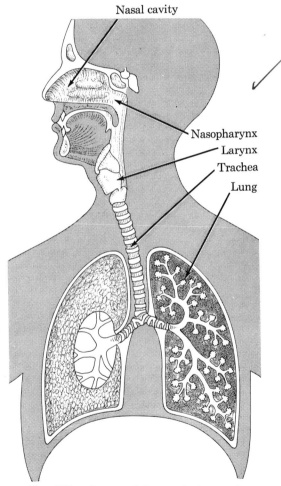

Fig. 270. Organs of the respiratory system.

225

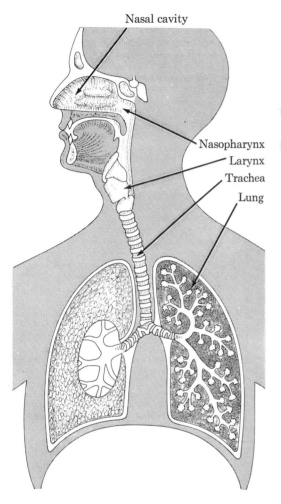

Nasal cavity

Nasopharynx
Larynx
Trachea
Lung

External Nose

The anterior extension of the bone and cartilage framework of the nasal fossae forms the external nose, which is covered externally by skin and lined by an extremely vascular mucous membrane.

LOCATION.   The external nose protrudes from the anterior surface of the middle of the face.

SHAPE AND SIZE.   Noses vary markedly in both shape and size. In general, the shape of the external nose is roughly that of a three-sided pyramid, with two lateral surfaces of similar shape and size, and a smaller inferior surface.

PARTS.   The following parts may be identified.

The *root* is located between the eyes, at the point of junction of the superior extension of the nose with the frontal bone.

The *dorsum* is the anterior border of the organ, extending from the root to the inferior tip (apex) of the nose. When examined in profile (from the side), the dorsum may appear straight, convex, concave, or wavy (irregular).

The *apex* is the tip of the nose. It is in line with the dorsum if the nose is straight in profile; if the dorsum is convex the apex is depressed; if the dorsum is concave, it is tilted upward.

The *bridge* is the superior portion of the dorsum, superficial to the nasal bones.

The *base* is the smaller, inferiorly directed surface of the pyramid.

The *alae* or *wings* are convex, flared portions of the inferior lateral surfaces of the external nose. Each ala is separated from the upper lateral surface by a groove or sulcus.

The *nasal septum* is a vertical partition of bone and cartilage, covered by mucous membrane, that divides the nasal cavity into the bilateral nasal fossae. Inferiorly the nasal septum is covered by the skin of the inferior surface and separates the nostrils.

The *vestibule* is the dilated portion of the passageway just inside the nostrils and bounded laterally by the flared alae of the external nose.

Internal Nose (Nasal Cavity)

BOUNDARIES.   It is bounded above, by the bones forming the floor of the cranium; below, by the hard and soft palate. Anteriorly, it opens onto the face at the nostrils; and posteriorly, it opens into the nasopharynx.

DIVISIONS.   A vertical median septum divides the nasal cavity into two roughly symmetrical halves, the *nasal fossae,* which open to the exterior through the *nostrils (anterior nares)*, and posteriorly, communicate with the nasopharynx through the *choanae (posterior nares)*. The nasal fossae also communicate through small openings with the paranasal air sinuses located within adjacent bones.

If the external nose were cut off using a vertical, coronal section, the two nasal fossae would appear as roughly triangular spaces. The shortest sides of the two triangles would form the floors. The lateral walls of the fossae, the hypotenuse of each triangle, would slant upward and medially from the lateral angles of the floors (base). The medial walls of each triangle would be formed by the vertical median septum of the nasal cavity. While the bases (floors) and the medial walls of the triangles appear relatively straight and smooth, the lateral walls are irregular due to three, thin, projecting, scroll-like shelves called the *superior, middle,* and *inferior conchae* (Fig. 271). The conchae extend anteriorly, medially, and downward, and consist of a thin bony core covered by a highly vascular mucous membrane. The drooping, shelf-like conchae produce three groove-like passageways called *meatuses* (superior, middle, and inferior). Each meatus lies below and lateral to the corresponding concha. The space above and posterior to the superior concha is called the *spheno-ethmoidal recess.*

FUNCTION. The extremely vascular mucous membrane lining the fossae is an important feature responsible for warming very cold air before it reaches the delicate alveolar tissue of the lungs. The mucous and the cilia of the epithelial layer serve to trap (filter) and remove dust and other fine bits of particulate matter in the inspired air, also serving to protect the lung tissue. Some moisture may be added by the mucosa to extremely dry air as it is drawn through the nasal fossae.

When peoples of the world were restricted to particular geographical regions and travel was limited, anthropologists studying "racial" groups correlated shape and size of nose, shape and size of nostrils and fossae to geographic locations and climatic conditions. Northern Europeans were characterized by having high, long, narrow noses. This necessitated small quantities of air being taken in with each inspiration and the air could be warmed through contact with the highly vascular mucous membrane lining the fossae. The people living in the tropics, on the other hand, had broad, short noses with large, wide nostrils. The tropical air, not needing to be warmed, could be taken into the lungs in great gulps without danger of damaging the alveolar tissue.

MICROSCOPIC STRUCTURE OF NASAL MUCOSA. The tissue lining the nasal fossae is both varied and interesting. The skin of the external nose extends into each nostril and lines each vestibule. Just inside the nostrils there are large, coarse hairs which serve to filter out coarse particles of materials that may enter the fossae with inspired air. Toward the back of the vestibules the skin changes from the keratinized, stratified squamous epithelium of the surface skin to a non-keratonized, stratified squamous epithelium typical of many mucosal surfaces. In the nasal fossae the mucous membrane appears typically as a thick, vascular type of mucosa attached directly to the periosteum of the bone or to the perichondrium of the cartilage that forms the frame of the nasal fossae. A histologic difference occuring in the epithelium lining the nasal fossae has led to a division of the fossae into respiratory and olfactory areas.

The *respiratory area* is quite extensive and covers the lower part of each nasal fossa and is associated with the respiratory system and the transport of air. A modification of the mucosa in the respiratory area, covering the middle and inferior conchae should be noted. Here the mucosa contains large venous-like spaces, that under certain conditions (erotic stimuli) become engorged with blood, in much the same way as erectile tissue of the genital organs responds during sexual excitement. This produces marked swelling of the mucous membrane which interferes with the passage of air and makes breathing through the nose difficult. This relationship between the tissue lining the nose and the erectile tissue of the genital organs is not understood.

The *olfactory area* is restricted to the uppermost part of the roof of each fossa and extends down the sides for a short distance. Laterally

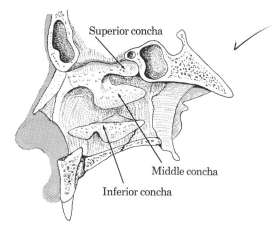

Fig. 271.   Lateral wall of the nasal cavity.

Superior concha

Middle concha

Inferior concha

it covers most of the superior conchae, and medially it extends down the wall of the septum for about 1.25 cm. The cells of the olfactory epithelium that respond to odor stimuli are considered to be bipolar neurons. Details of the olfactory region will be discussed under the organs of special sense, page 305.

Accessory Sinuses (Paranasal Air Sinuses).

These spaces are formed during the third to fourth month of fetal development by evagination of the mucous membrane lining the nasal fossae into adjacent areas of forming bone. In the adult, the paranasal sinuses are spaces containing air, found within the substance of some of the facial and cranial bones forming the boundaries of the nasal cavity. They vary in number, size, and shape, and are lined by a mucous membrane that is continuous through small connecting apertures with the mucous membrane lining the fossae with which they communicate. These air spaces are associated with specific bones and are named accordingly: maxillary, frontal, sphenoid, and ethmoid sinuses.

The *maxillary sinuses* are the largest of the paranasal sinuses and are located in the body of the maxilla. These sinuses are paired, reasonably symmetrical, and pyramidal in shape. They present four surfaces or walls that correspond to the anterior, nasal, orbital, and infratemporal surfaces of the maxillae, and an apex which extends laterally into the zygomatic processes of the maxillae. These sinuses vary in size even in the same individual. In the adult, the average capacity of the maxillary sinus is about 14.75 cc. This sinus is a small space in the newborn, and is not fully developed until after puberty and the eruption of the second dentition. The maxillary sinus communicates with the nasal fossa of the same side by an opening into the middle meatus.

The *frontal sinuses* are usually paired air spaces, but are seldom symmetrical. They are located between the inner and outer compact layers of the frontal bone, behind the supraciliary arches. The so-called typical frontal sinus is described as being pyramidal in shape, but actually the frontal sinuses vary markedly in shape, size, and even in number. At birth these sinuses have not yet developed; by the eighth year they are fairly well started, and they reach their maximum development after puberty. Each frontal sinus communicates with the nasal fossa of the same side by means of the nasofrontal duct, which opens into the corresponding middle meatus. One or both frontal sinuses may fail to develop.

The *sphenoid sinuses,* found within the body of the sphenoid bone, are often paired, but not symmetrical. They vary tremendously in shape and size, opening into the spheno-ethmoidal recess of the fossa on their respective sides. These sinuses may be present at birth as tiny air spaces, but their greatest growth occurs after puberty.

The *ethmoid sinuses* are more properly referred to as "ethmoidal air cells" because they consist of numerous small, thin-walled spaces in the ethmoid bone where they form an ethmoidal labyrinth or maze of adjoining and intercommunicating spaces or "cells." They are located above the nasal fossae and between the bony orbits. These thin-walled air cells are described as being arranged in three groups on either side of the ethmoid bone—an anterior and a middle group that communicate with the middle meatus of the corresponding side,

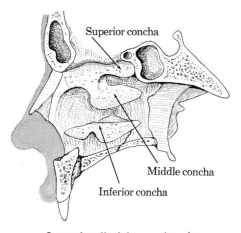

Superior concha

Middle concha

Inferior concha

Lateral wall of the nasal cavity.

and a posterior group that opens into the superior meatus of the same side.

OPENINGS OR APERTURES. Openings or apertures into the meatus mark channels of communication between the nasal fossae and the paranasal air sinuses, and between the nasal fossae and the nasolacrimal ducts that drain excess tears from the eyes. These openings and their locations are as follows.

Into the spheno-ethmoidal recess	sphenoid sinuses
Into the superior meatus	posterior ethmoidal sinuses
Into the middle meatus	nasofrontal duct from frontal sinus
	maxillary sinus
	anterior and middle ethmoidal air cells
Into the inferior meatus	nasolacrimal duct

FUNCTION. The paranasal air sinuses lighten the weight of the skull (solid bones would add considerably to the weight of the skull) and serve as resonance chambers. If these air spaces become infected, pus may accumulate within them, their openings into the nasal fossae may become swollen and closed, and pressure develops within the spaces causing pain. Drainage of fluid from these spaces is poor, since the points of communication are designed for the transmission of air, not fluid. Inflammation of the mucous membrane lining these air spaces is called sinusitis.

BLOOD SUPPLY OF THE EXTERNAL NOSE AND THE NASAL CAVITY. The external nose is supplied by the external maxillary artery, the ophthalmic artery, and the infraorbital artery. The nasal cavity is supplied by branches from the internal maxillary, the ophthalmic, and the external maxillary arteries. In the external nose, blood is drained by small veins that enter the facial and the ophthalmic veins. The veins of the nasal cavity form a venous plexus beneath the mucous membrane. From this plexus blood is drained by way of veins that open into the sphenopalatine vein, into the anterior facial, and into the ophthalmic veins. Finally, and this is important from a clinical point of view, particularly in the possible spread of infection, a few veins join with veins of the frontal lobe of the brain and a vein often empties directly into the superior sagittal sinus within the cranial cavity.

LYMPHATICS. In the external nose, the lymph vessels drain to the submaxillary and parotid nodes. These lymph vessels also anastomose with lymph vessels of the nasal cavity. In the nasal cavity, lymph vessels from the anterior parts of the cavity drain into the submaxillary nodes. From the posterior portion of the cavity and from the paranasal air sinuses, the lymph vessels drain to the retropharyngeal and the superior deep cervical nodes.

NERVE SUPPLY. In the external nose, the motor nerves are branches of the facial nerve. Sensory fibers are derived from the trigeminal nerve by way of branches of its ophthalmic and maxillary divisions. In the nasal cavity, the olfactory nerve, which is the nerve of the sense of smell, arises from the fibers of the specialized bipolar cells of the olfactory epithelium. These are sensory fibers. The nerves that convey the usual sensation from the respiratory areas of the nasal cavity are derived from branches of the ophthalmic and maxillary

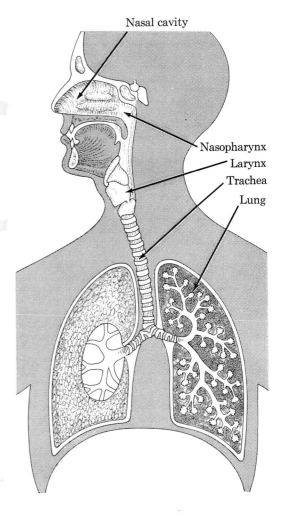

Nasal cavity

Nasopharynx
Larynx
Trachea
Lung

divisions of the trigeminal and from filaments directly from the sphenopalatine ganglion.

PHARYNX

This is a membranous tubular structure that serves both the respiratory and the digestive systems.

LOCATION. The pharynx is located behind the nasal cavity and the mouth and extends from the base of the skull downward to the level of the cricoid cartilage (Fig. left).

DESCRIPTION. The pharynx is broadest above, where it attaches to the base of the skull and gradually tapers to its termination at the junction with the esophagus inferiorly and the larynx anteriorly. It is attached by loose connective tissue to the bodies of the cervical vertebrae through its entire extent. Seven cavities and tubular structures openly communicate with it—the two nasal fossae, two Eustachian tubes (tympanic or auditory tubes), the mouth, and the esophagus and larynx below.

PARTS. For descriptive purposes, the pharynx is subdivided into three parts, which are from above downward: the nasopharynx, the oropharynx, and the laryngopharynx.

The *nasopharynx* extends from the base of the skull behind the nasal cavity to the soft palate. It serves only the respiratory system. Its tubular wall is incomplete anteriorly where it communicates with the nasal fossae by a broad opening. The posterior and lateral walls are fixed to bone and adjacent structures and thus, the tube always remains open. In the mucosa of the posterior wall of the nasopharynx is a mass of lymphoid tissue, the pharyngeal tonsil. When the pharyngeal tonsillar mass becomes infected and enlarged, as it often does in children, it forms an adenoid tumor referred to as adenoids. In the lateral walls of the nasopharynx are the openings of the Eustachian or auditory tubes. These tubes extend from the middle ear to the nasopharynx of the respective side and may serve as a pathway for the spread of infections from the respiratory area to the middle ear. Another restricted bit of lymphoid tissue called the tubal tonsil surrounds and guards the opening of the auditory (Eustachian) tube into the nasopharynx.

The *oropharynx* serves both the respiratory and the digestive systems. It extends from the soft palate to the level of the hyoid bone, where it becomes the laryngopharynx. Anteriorly, where its wall is incomplete, it communicates with the mouth through the somewhat narrowed fauces.

The *laryngopharynx* is the third and terminal part of the pharynx and serves both respiratory and digestive systems. It extends from the level of the hyoid bone to the lower border of the cricoid cartilage, where it is directly continuous with the esophagus. Its anterior wall is deficient inferiorly where it communciates with the larynx.

STRUCTURE OF THE WALL OF THE PHARYNX. The entire tubular structure is lined by a mucous membrane continuous with the membranes lining the cavities or tubes with which it communicates. The upper part of the wall of the pharynx is fibrous and serves to attach it to the base of the skull. The muscular layer is deficient in this area. The lower portion of the wall is thicker and presents an additional muscular layer composed of a poorly defined, thin inner longitudinal

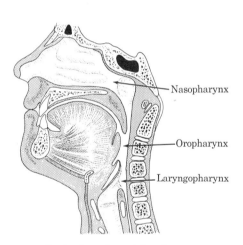

Sagittal section of the pharynx.

Nasopharynx

Oropharynx

Laryngopharynx

lage. The series (about 20 separate cartilages) of C-shaped cartilages present in the walls, keep its lumen constantly open, allowing free passage of air (Fig. 276). The open part of the C is directed posteriorly, and where the cartilage is deficient the gap is filled by the trachealis muscle and connective tissue. The cartilages are held together by dense connective tissue which also serves to space the rings a short but uniform distance apart. The mucosal surface consists of a pseudostratified, ciliated columnar epithelium containing a number of mucous secreting goblet cells. The beat of the cilia propels particulate matter caught in the mucous toward the outside of the body by way of the nose and mouth.

Bronchi (Extrapulmonary)

The bronchi are tubular structures that arise from the terminal division or bifurcation of the trachea. Above, the bronchi are continuous with the trachea, and below, they extend into the lungs, where they are continous with the intrapulmonary bronchi. The extrapulmonary bronchi and the trachea are practically identical in structure. The right bronchus is slightly wider and shorter, is directed more vertically than the left bronchus. These morphological differences between the two bronchi have great practical significance since they explain why, when children accidentally inhale solid objects such as buttons, safety pins, coins, and the like, these objects usually are lodged in the right lung (Fig. 277).

THORACIC CAVITY (CHEST CAVITY)

This cavity extends from the root of the neck down to the arched surface of the diaphragm. It is the space enclosed and bounded by the bones of the thorax (ribs, vertebrae, and sternum), together with ligaments, intercostal muscles, and fascial membranes. It is occupied by and furnishes protection for some of the vital organs of the body. The thoracic cavity is somewhat cone-shaped, broad below and narrow above. It is longer posteriorly than anteriorly, and it is flattened anteroposteriorly. The lateral portions of the cavity contain the lungs and their serous covering membranes, the pleura. The remainder of the thoracic organs are crowded into a relatively narrow, irregular central area that extends beyond the midplane of the body on both sides and forms a thick, median partition called the mediastinum. Organs contained within this mediastinal space are the thymus gland, the heart within its pericardial sac, the esophagus, the trachea, and the extrapulmonary bronchi, the great vessels, the thoracic duct, and nerves. The mediastinal organs are held together and enclosed by dense connective tissue.

Mediastinum

This is an elongated, fascial, walled space in the midline of the thoracic cavity.

BOUNDARIES.   Anterior—the sternum
      Posterior—anterior surface of the thoracic portion of the
          vertebral column
      Inferior—the diaphragm
      Superior—superior aperture of the thoracic cavity
      Lateral—the parietal pleura

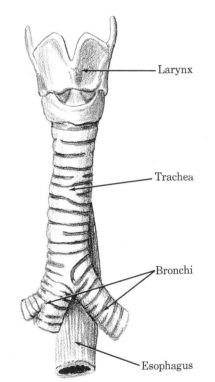

Fig. 277.   Trachea and esophagus.

Larynx

Trachea

Bronchi

Esophagus

CONTENTS.   The mediastinum contains all of the thoracic organs except the lungs.

DIVISIONS.   For descriptive purposes, the mediastinum is arbitrarily divided into a *superior portion* and an *inferior portion.* The inferior portion is subdivided into anterior, middle, and posterior segments.

SUPERIOR MEDIASTINUM.   This portion of the mediastinal space lies behind the manubrium sterni and is bounded posteriorly by the bodies of the first four thoracic vertebrae and their associated intervertebral discs. Laterally, the space is bounded by the parietal pleura. The inferior boundary is represented by an imaginary horizontal plane extending from the junction of the manubrium and body of the sternum in front to the intervertebral disc between the 4th and 5th thoracic vertebrae behind. Above, its limit is the aperture of the thorax. The superior mediastinum contains portions of muscles, vessels, nerves, and organs.

INFERIOR MEDIASTINUM.   The anterior division of the inferior portion of the mediastinal space is bounded in front by the body of the sternum; laterally, by the parietal pleura; behind, by the pericardium; and inferiorly by the diaphragm. It contains some loose areolar connective tissues and fat, vessels, and lymph nodes.

The middle division of the inferior mediastinum is the widest part of the mediastinal space. Its anterior and posterior boundaries are coextensive with the pericardium; laterally it is bounded by the parietal pleura. It contains the following vessels, nerves, and organs. The vessels include the ascending aorta and pulmonary artery dividing into right and left pulmonary arteries, the lower half of the superior vena cava, the azygos vein, and the right and left pulmonary veins. The nerves are the phrenic nerves. In the middle division of the inferior portion is found the heart within the pericardial sac, the trachea and right and left bronchi, and bronchial lymph nodes.

The posterior division of the inferior portion is bounded in front by the pericardium; behind, by the bodies of the lower eight thoracic vertebrae and their intervertebral discs; laterally, by the parietal pleura; and inferiorly, by the diaphragm. It contains vessels, nerves, and organs, and is surrounded and supported by connective tissue.

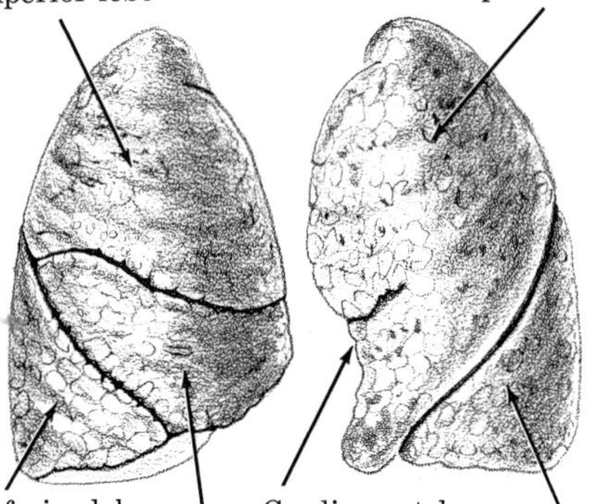

Pleura

The pleura is a very thin, continuous serous membrane that lines the lateral thoracic compartments and at the root of the lungs is reflected over the surfaces of the lungs contained in these compartments. The portion of the pleura that is adherent to the lungs is called the *visceral* (*pulmonary*) pleura; that which is attached to and lines the inner surface of the walls of the thoracic compartments is called the *parietal* pleura. The parietal pleura is subdivided into *mediastinal, costal,* and *diaphragmatic* pleuras for more precise descriptive purposes. While the two layers of the pleura are in contact, a potential space is present between the parietal and the visceral pleura which is called the *pleural cavity.* The mesothelial cells of the serous membrane bordering the pleural cavity secrete a serous fluid which lubricates the pleural surfaces and allows the lungs to move without friction during respiration.

Fig. 278.   Costal surface of the lungs viewed from the side-front.

Superior lobe

Superior lobe

Inferior lobe

Cardiac notch

Middle lobe

Inferior lobe

RIGHT LUNG   LEFT LUNG

LUNGS

The lungs are the organs of respiration where the exchange of oxygen and carbon dioxide takes place between the air and the blood of the pulmonary capillaries (external respiration).

LOCATION. There are two lungs, a right and a left, that lie in the corresponding lateral thoracic spaces. The lungs are separated from each other by the mediastinal space and its contained organs.

DESCRIPTION. The lungs are large, soft, pliable organs. Their outer surface is smooth and glistening. The lungs are light in weight, have a sponge-like texture, and will float in water because of the air trapped in the numerous alveoli. If the tissue of the lungs is compressed between the thumb and the finger, it will give a crackling sound (crepitation) due to the air in the alveoli.

COLOR. In the newborn the lungs are pinkish in color, but in the adult their color is a patchy dark gray to black, due to inhaled dust and smoke containing fine carbon particles which lodge in the lung tissue and color it. The lungs become blacker with age and the amount of carbon and dust particles inhaled.

SHAPE AND SIZE. Each lung is shaped like half a cone split longitudinally; its base is directed inferiorly and rests on the diaphragm, and its apex extends into the root of the neck, roughly 2.5 cm. above the clavicle of the corresponding side. The right lung is slightly larger and heavier than the left lung, and both lungs are heavier in the male than in the female.

SURFACES AND BORDERS. For descriptive purposes each lung may be said to have three surfaces: costal, mediastinal, and inferior or diaphragmatic (the base); and three borders: anterior, posterior, and inferior; and an apex.

The *costal surface* is the most extensive of the three surfaces. It is relatively smooth and convex and is in contact with and contoured to the walls of the thoracic cavity (Fig. 278).

The *mediastinal surface* is directed medially, and faces the lateral walls of the mediastinum (Fig. 279). It is concave, and marked by the pressure of the heart and the great vessels contained in the mediastinum. The impression made by the heart (cardiac fossa) is more marked on the left lung than on the right because the heart lies more to the left of the midline of the body. Above and behind the impression made by the heart, is the hilus of the lung where the bronchi, blood vessels, lymphatic vessels, and nerves enter and leave the substance of the lung. Together these structures form the root of the lung which is covered by pleura. Below the hilus the pulmonary and mediastinal pleurae merge to form the pulmonary ligament.

The *diaphragmatic* or *inferior surface* is directed inferiorly and is concave, being in contact with the convex, dome-shaped diaphragm. On the right, the diaphragm separates the right lung from the right lobe of the liver. On the left, it separates the left lung from the tip of the left lobe of the liver, the stomach, and the spleen.

The *anterior border* separates the costal and mediastinal surfaces. It is thin and sharp. The anterior border of the right lung is directed almost vertically and extends almost to the midline of the body. The anterior border on the left lung is directed vertically in its upper half and then is notched (cardiac notch) to accommodate the heart which pushes the lung tissue to the left. The anterior borders

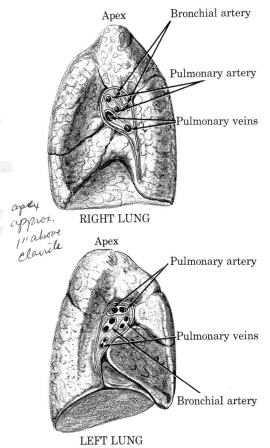

Fig. 279. Mediastinal surface of the lungs showing the roots of the lungs.

of the right and left lungs almost touch in the midline between the 2nd and 4th intercostal spaces.

The *posterior border* is broad and rounded. It separates the costal from the mediastinal area posteriorly.

The *inferior border* separates the inferior (diaphragmatic) surface from the costal surface, and is thin and sharp at this point; but medially, where it separates the inferior surface from the mediastinal surface, it is blunt and rounded.

The *apex* is blunt and rounded and extends up into the root of the neck for a distance of approximately 2.5 cm. above the level of the clavicle.

FISSURES AND LOBES OF THE LUNGS. The left lung is divided into two lobes, superior and inferior, by an obliquely directed interlobar fissure. The right lung has three lobes, a superior, middle, and inferior, formed by two interlobar fissures. One of the fissures of the right lung separates the inferior lobe from the superior and medial lobes, and its course is comparable to the fissure on the left lung, except that it is directed somewhat more vertically. The second interlobar fissure is horizontal and separates the superior from the middle lobe.

ROOT OF THE LUNG. The root consists of the structures that enter and leave the substance of the lung. It includes the bronchi, the pulmonary vessels, the bronchial vessels, the lymphatic vessels, nerves, and some areolar connective tissue, which are enclosed by the pleura reflected from the lungs onto the wall of the mediastinum. The relationships of structures within each root to the right and left lung can best be seen by studying Figure 279.

STRUCTURE. On entering the lung, the bronchi divide into a number of branches which enter the lobes. Here they continue to branch, each new division being smaller in diameter until they finally end in thin-walled air spaces (alveoli) where the exchange of oxygen and carbon dioxide takes place between the inspired air and the blood (Fig. 280). Because the numerous divisions and subdivisions of the primary bronchus so resemble the branching of a tree, the entire system of intrapulmonary tubules is often referred to as the *bronchial tree.* The succession of divisions of the bronchial tree in order are secondary bronchi, bronchioles, terminal bronchioles, respiratory bronchioles, alveolar ducts, alveolar sacs, and alveoli. The thickness and the microscopic structure of the walls of the various divisions of the bronchial tree undergo certain modifications throughout their course. Microscopic details of these changes will be found in a textbook of histology. Here it is sufficient to state that the pseudostratified epithelium lining the bronchi gradually changes to a squamous cell layer lining the alveoli.

The exchange of oxygen and carbon dioxide can take place only at the alveolar level, where the thickness of the wall is reduced to a minimum. However, since many alveoli open into the lumen of the respiratory bronchioles throughout their entire course, as well as into alveolar ducts and alveolar sacs, respiration can occur beginning with the respiratory bronchioles and continue throughout the remainder of the bronchial tree divisions. The alveoli are small cup-shaped structures. They are lined by very flattened squamous cells resting on a thin basement membrane around which is a fine network of reticular fibers and a supportive framework of scattered elastic fibers. Each alveolus is surrounded by a dense capillary network which is in close

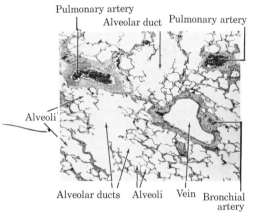

Fig. 280. Photomicrograph of a section of a lung.

contact with the alveolar wall, thus assuring a minimum distance for oxygen and carbon dioxide to traverse in the exchange between the inspired air in the alveoli and the blood within the adjacent capillary bed.

BLOOD SUPPLY.   Blood is conveyed to the lungs by way of two separate sets of blood vessels—the bronchial arteries of the systemic system and the pulmonary arteries of the pulmonary system. The bronchial arteries usually arise from the upper part of the thoracic aorta. They carry oxygenated blood and nutrient materials to the lung tissue and the bronchial lymph nodes. These vessels and their branches do not extend beyond the level of the distal portion of the terminal bronchioles. Here some of them end in capillary networks which anastomose with capillaries of the pulmonary vessels. Other branches that extend into the interlobular connective tissue end in capillaries which open into venules that drain ultimately into the bronchial veins. The pulmonary artery is large and elastic and arises from the right ventricle of the heart. Its branches convey "venous" blood to the lungs. Shortly after leaving the heart it divides into right and left pulmonary branches which enter the corresponding lung at the root. Within the lung, each pulmonary vessel gives off branches which follow the branchings of the bronchial tree to the walls of the alveoli. Around each alveolus the pulmonary capillaries form a dense network where the blood exchanges its carbon dioxide for oxygen.

The two pulmonary veins of each lung are formed by the union of numerous smaller tributary veins of the lung substance. These veins convey the freshly oxygenated blood from the lungs to the left atrium, where it is distributed through the entire body. A single bronchial vein is formed in the root of each lung by tributary (systemic) veins of the adjacent area. The right bronchial vein empties into the azygos vein and the left bronchial vein usually empties into the highest intercostal vein.

LYMPHATICS.   The walls of the alveoli have no lymphatic vessels. There are, however, two sets of lymphatic vessels, deep and superficial, associated with the lungs. Lymph capillaries form a superficial plexus under the pleura and give rise to superficial lymph vessels that empty into nodes in the hilus of the lung. A second, deep lymphatic capillary plexus is formed in the walls of the bronchioles and bronchi. From this deep plexus, lymphatic vessels arise which accompany the blood vessels and the bronchial tree back toward the hilus. These lymphatic vessels empty into the tracheobronchial nodes.

NERVE SUPPLY.   The lungs receive sympathetic and vagal innervation by way of fibers from the pulmonary plexuses. These fibers carry efferent impulses to the bronchial muscles and afferent impulses from the mucous membrane of the bronchial tree.

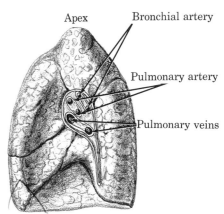

RIGHT LUNG

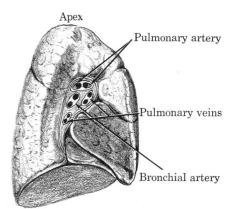

LEFT LUNG

11

THE URINARY SYSTEM

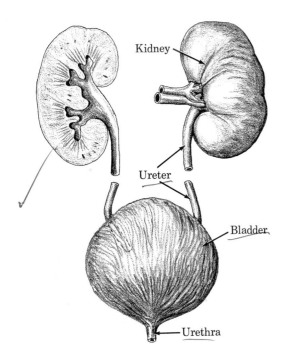

Kidney

Ureter

Bladder

Urethra

Fig. 281.   Organs of the urinary system.

The urinary system includes the organs that convert the soluble waste products of cellular metabolism into urine and elminate the urine from the body. These organs are two kidneys, two ureters, the urinary bladder, and the urethra (Fig. 281).

THE KIDNEYS

The kidneys are paired, compound, tubular glands, reddish brown in color and very vascular.

LOCATION.   The kidneys are located in the upper posterior part of the abdominal cavity, one on either side of the vertebral column (Fig. 282). They lie behind the peritoneal lining of the abdominal cavity and, therefore, are said to be retroperitoneal. The kidneys are surrounded by adipose tissue which helps to hold them in position, assisted by the pressure of adjacent abdominal organs. Because it is crowded by the liver, the right kidney is usually slightly lower than the left kidney. The upper end of the right kidney is on a line with the 12th rib, while that of the left kidney is about one rib higher, at the lower edge of the 11th rib. Their lower ends extend within about 5 cm. of the iliac crest posteriorly.

SHAPE AND SIZE.   The kidneys are shaped like lima beans. In the adult male each kidney is about 10 to 12 centimeters long, 5 to 6 centimeters wide, and about 3 to 4 centimeters thick.

AGE AND SEX DIFFERENCES.   In the newborn the kidneys are larger and heavier in proportion to body weight than in the adult. The adult ratio of kidney weight to body weight is reached usually by the eleventh year. In the male, the kidneys are usually slightly higher than in the female by about the width of half a vertebra. They are heavier in the male than in the female.

GROSS STRUCTURE.   Each kidney presents for gross examination two surfaces (anterior and posterior); two borders (lateral and medial); two extremities (superior and inferior); and a hilus that leads into a space called the renal sinus within the substance of the kidney. A cortex and medulla may be seen on the cut surface of a kidney that is sectioned longitudinally.

The two slightly convex surfaces are relatively smooth and covered by a connective tissue capsule. The *anterior surface* is directed anterolaterally, and the *posterior surface* is directed posteromedially.

The *lateral border* is strongly convex, and the *medial border* is convex above and below but presents a concave depression along its

240

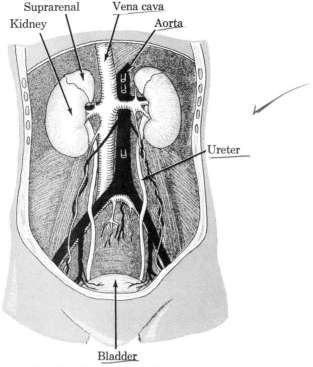

Fig. 282.   Position of the kidneys in the abdominal cavity. Drawing.

middle third. This concave portion contains a fissure or "doorway" called the *hilus,* through which pass structures entering and leaving the substance of the kidney.

The *superior extremity* is capped by the suprarenal gland and lies nearer the midline than the *inferior extremity.*

The *renal sinus* is the space within the substance of the kidney that opens onto the medial border through the hilus. Small conical prominences of renal tissue, the *renal papillae,* project into the sinus. The "space" of the sinus is obliterated by structures contained within it: the renal pelvis and its terminal calyces, the renal vessels, lymphatics and nerves. Adipose tissue fills in around these structures and eliminates all evidence of a "space." The shape and size of the renal sinus can be seen and studied only when the structures contained in it are removed.

If a kidney is split longitudinally by cutting through its borders, and one of the cut surfaces is examined, it will be seen to consist of two distinct areas (Fig. 283). These are an outer peripheral portion, called the *cortex,* that lies immediately beneath the capsule, and an inner zone of tissue between the cortex and the renal sinus, called the *medulla.*

The cortex forms the peripheral portion of the kidney and at intervals sends prolongations of its tissue downward through the entire inner medullary layer. These prolongations lie between the renal pyramids and are called the *renal columns.* The cortex is reddish brown in color, and scattered through it are numerous, small, round bodies, the *renal corpuscles (Malpighian corpuscles),* that are just

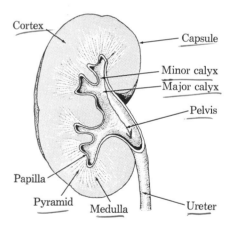

Fig. 283.   Vertical section through a kidney. Drawing.

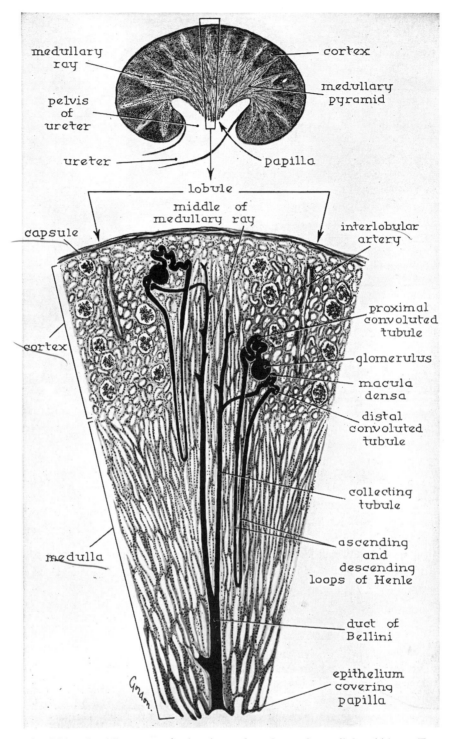

Fig. 284.   Semidiagrammatic drawings of sections of a unilobar kidney. Two complete nephrons (in black) have been inserted into the drawings so that their course in the kidney may be followed. Of course, complete nephrons cannot be seen in any single section. (From Ham and Leeson. *Histology*, 4th ed., J. B. Lippincott Co.)

visible to the eye. Besides the renal corpuscles, the cortex contains many tubular structures, some of which pursue a tortuous course throughout the area (Fig. 284).

The medulla consists of eight to fifteen pyramidal-shaped structures called the *renal* or *Malpighian pyramids,* which correspond to the number of lobes formed in the fetal kidney. Each pyramid has a *base* that is relatively broad and is directed toward the cortex, with which it is in contact. The *apex,* or *papilla,* is free and projects into the renal sinus. When the cut surface of a pyramid is examined, under low power magnification, it appears striated due to the arrangement of the large collecting ducts that extend through each pyramid and open by way of ten to twenty-five pores on the tip of the papilla.

MICROSCOPIC STRUCTURE.   Examined microscopically, the parenchyma of the kidney is seen to consist of renal corpuscles, tubules, and numerous blood vessels. The renal corpuscles are scattered throughout the cortex. The tubules are numerous and closely packed in both the cortex and medulla. Two types of tubules are present in the kidney—those that are part of the nephron and actively participate in the formation of urine and those tubules that serve only for the transportation of the urine toward the outside. The renal corpuscles together with the secretory portion of the kidney tubules form the *nephron.* Blood vessels are closely associated with both the renal corpuscles and the tubules.

THE NEPHRON.   This is the structural and functional unit of the kidney (Fig. 285).

Components.   It consists of a renal corpuscle and the attached, physiologically active uriniferous tubule that terminates at the collecting tubule, with which it is continuous.

Location.   Most nephrons lie in the cortex. Exceptions are the nephrons of the deeper portions of the cortex, whose tubular segments may extend into the medulla.

General Description.   Individually, nephrons vary considerably in length. They do not branch, but are extremely convoluted and follow a tortuous course from their origins to their terminations. It has been estimated that there are approximately 1,300,000 nephrons in each human kidney. The renal corpuscle of a nephron is a small ovoid structure having two poles—a vascular and a urinary pole. The *vascular pole* is a restricted area where the afferent and efferent vessels enter and leave the corpuscle. The *urinary pole* lies opposite the vascular pole, and is the point of attachment of the uriniferous tubule.

The corpuscle itself consists of a *glomerulus* (a tuft of capillaries arising from the afferent arteriole and emptying into the efferent arteriole), completely enclosed by a thin, two-layered, epithelial capsule called *Bowman's capsule.* This capsule is the upper, expanded, blind end of the urinary tubule which has been so completely invaginated by the glomerular component that grew into it during fetal development, that it ends up being a very thin, two-layered covering for the glomerulus. The outer or *parietal layer* of cells is continuous with the epithelial cells of the proximal convoluted tubule at the urinary pole. At the vascular pole the parietal layer reflects back on itself to form the *visceral layer* that is tightly adherent to the endothelial capillary walls of the glomerulus.

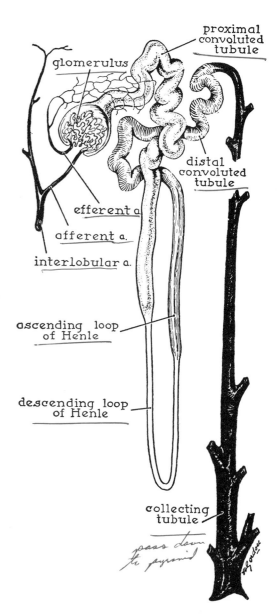

Fig. 285.   To make this diagram less complex, the ascending limb of the loop of Henle is not shown in its normal relation to the vascular pole of the glomerulus; actually it should return to the glomerulus and fit into its vascular pole to form a macula densa before continuing on as the distal convoluted tubule. (From Ham and Leeson. *Histology,* 4th ed., J. B. Lippincott Co.)

The uriniferous tubule is the tubular portion of the nephron (secretory portion) that extends from the renal corpuscle to the collecting tubules.

The tubular portion of the nephron is subdivided into segments. In order of location from the corpuscle outward these segments are the *proximal convoluted tubule,* the *loop of Henle* (descending limb, loop, and ascending limb) and the *distal convoluted tubule.*

Each of these segments is characterized by a specific type of epithelial cell lining and by the fact that it differs from each of the other segments by its length, diameter, and probably function.

The proximal convoluted tubules are lined by large pyramidal cells that rest on a well defined basement membrane. Their free surfaces have a *brush border* (numerous microvilli) that serves to increase the surface area for absorption. This segment of the tubule is twisted on itself at first, then it straightens and dips toward the medulla. It suddenly narrows and merges with the thin-walled descending limb of Henle's loop. The wall of the descending limb is lined by a layer of very flattened cells. This segment enters the medullary portion of the kidney and then makes a sharp hairpin turn (loop), ascends and re-enters the cortex. The epithelial cells lining Henle's loop suddenly change from the flattened cells of the descending limb to a cuboidal epithelium in the ascending limb. The point at which this change occurs is variable and abrupt. The ascending limb of each nephron returns to the glomerulus of its tubular origin, where it pushes between the afferent and efferent arterioles at the vascular pole. Where the tubule contacts the glomerulus, the epithelial cells of the wall of the tubule show an increased number of nuclei and this thickened cellular mass is called the *macula densa.* Certain changes also occur here in the cells of the media of the afferent arteriole immediately adjacent to the macula densa. These cells no longer resemble smooth muscle cells characteristic of the media, but are so modified as to more nearly resemble cuboidal epithelial cells with round nuclei, except that they have a granular cytoplasm. The modified cells are called *JG* (*juxtaglomerular*) cells, and are thought to secrete an enzyme, *renin.* Beyond the macula densa the tubular structure continues as the distal convoluted tubule. The cells lining this final, tortuous segment of the nephron are cuboidal at first and then become pyramidal. These cells resemble the cells lining the proximal convoluted tubule, but are not as tall and do not have a brush border.

The excretory tubular segments serve only to transport the urine. They are continuous with the tubular portion of the nephron, and begin with the arched tubule located in the cortical substance of the medullary ray. They empty into the smallest of the collecting tubules, the straight tubules. The smaller tubules unite to form larger collecting tubules, and ultimately merge to form larger ducts, the *papillary ducts,* that open at the apex of the papilla. A single papilla will contain from 10 to 20 terminal papillary ducts.

FUNCTION.   The kidneys perform the following functions.

Elimination of the soluble waste products of cellular metabolism.

Regulation of the fluid balance of the body.

Maintenance of proper electrolyte balance of the blood and tissue fluid by selective elimination of certain kinds and quantities of electrolytes in the urine.

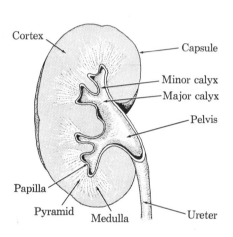

LOBE AND LOBULE. Before discussing the blood supply to the kidney, and to avoid confusion, it is advisable to define what is meant by the terms *kidney lobe* and *kidney lobule*. A kidney lobe is all of the kidney tissue of a medullary pyramid, including the cap of cortical tissue lying between the base of the pyramid and the capsule. The kidney lobule is not as easily defined or as clearly demarcated as the kidney lobe. The central portion or core of the kidney lobule is the medullary ray that is an extension of the medulla into the cortex. The medullary ray with the adjacent glomeruli and tubules that empty into the collecting tubules of the particular medullary ray constitute the kidney lobule. The lateral boundaries of the lobule are marked by the interlobular vessels.

BLOOD SUPPLY TO THE KIDNEYS (FIG. 286). Arteries—The renal artery, a branch of the abdominal aorta, enters the hilus of the kidney where it divides, usually into three branches (upper, middle, and lower). These branches divide again to form the interlobar arteries which ascend in the renal columns within the medulla. Small branches are given off as they ascend to supply the perirenal fat. Near the line of junction between the cortex and the medulla, the interlobar arteries divide to form the arcuate arteries, which arch over the bases of the pyramids. From the cortical side of the arcuate arteries branches are given off that extend perpendicularly toward the capsule. These are the interlobular arteries, and they end in capillaries just beneath the capsule. Some of these capillaries enter the capsule and anastomose with the capsular branches of the renal artery. From the interlobular arteries, lateral branches are given off that become the afferent arterioles, which enter the glomerulus and form the capillary tufts of the renal corpuscle. From the capillary tufts, the blood leaves the glomerulus by the efferent arterioles. The efferent arterioles from the glomeruli form capillary networks supplying the tubules of the cortex. In the outer part of the cortex they supply capillary networks around the convoluted tubules (proximal and distal). In the inner part of the cortex, some of the blood from the efferent arterioles supplies the capillary networks of this portion of the cortex, but some blood goes into long, straight vessels, the arteriolae rectae spuriae (false straight arterioles) that enter the pyramids of the medulla. From the glomeruli in the deepest part of the cortex, below the arcuate arteries, the efferent arterioles deliver most of their blood into the arteriolae rectae spuriae, which in turn end in capillary networks around the medullary tubules.

Veins—From the capillary beds of the kidney, the blood enters the venous vessels, which in general follow the same course and have the same names as the arteries (Fig. 286). The small veins from the capsule and the subcapsular part of the cortex converge, and because of the radiating arrangement of these small vessels they are called stellate veins. They empty into the interlobular veins, which receive many lateral veins; finally, the interlobular veins enter the arcuate veins which follow the course of the arcuate arteries. The arcuate veins also receive veins (venae rectae) which return blood from the medullary tubules of the pyramids. The arcuate veins empty into the interlobar veins, which merge to form the renal vein.

LYMPHATICS. Three lymphatic plexuses are formed in the kidney. The principal plexus is a network of capillaries around the tubules. A second, superficial capillary plexus is located in and

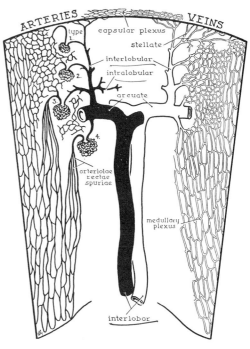

Fig. 286. Diagram to show how the capillary beds of the cortex and the medulla are supplied with blood. (Based on Morison. *Am. J. Anat.,* 37:93) (From Ham and Leeson. *Histology,* 4th ed., J. B. Lippincott Co.)

beneath the capsule, and a third plexus is in the perirenal fat. Several lymph vessels from the first and second plexuses leave the kidney at the hilus and drain to the upper lumbar lymph nodes. The vessels from the perirenal area go directly to the same upper lumbar nodes. From these nodes, the lymph goes to the cisterna chyli.

NERVE SUPPLY. Autonomic unmyelinated fibers from the celiac plexus and the renal plexus follow the blood vessels into the kidney to the renal corpuscles and to the convoluted tubules. Some of the fibers end on the basement membrane of the tubules; some penetrate the basement membrane and end in relation to the epithelial lining cells. Unmyelinated fibers also supply the wall of the blood vessels. Myelinated (probably sensory) fibers enter the wall of the renal pelvis, and some appear to end in the connective tissue of the capsule.

THE URETERS

The two ureters are mucous membrane lined muscular tubes about 25 to 30 centimeters long, that convey urine from the kidneys to the urinary bladder.

LOCATION. The ureters, like the kidneys are retroperitoneal. They lie on the posterior abdominal wall and extend along the medial side of the psoas major muscle to the pelvis. On reaching the pelvis they cross the pelvic floor to the lateral angle of the trigone of the urinary bladder and enter the bladder, piercing its wall obliquely.

GENERAL DESCRIPTION. For descriptive purposes the ureter consists of two portions—an upper expanded portion called the *renal pelvis* and a long, tubular portion, the *tubular ureter,* which extends distally to the bladder. Part of the renal pelvis is extrarenal and part of it lies within the renal sinus (Fig. 287). This intrarenal portion is subdivided into *major* and *minor calyces.* The minor calyces are small, funnel-shaped structures that fit over the apices of the renal papillae. Several minor calyces join to form the major calyces, which in turn unite to form the large expanded renal pelvis. On leaving the hilus of the kidney and becoming extrarenal, the renal pelvis tapers rapidly to form the tubular portion of the ureter, which extends downward and opens into the urinary bladder.

STRUCTURE. The wall of the ureters consists of a mucosa, a muscular coat, and an adventitia. The epithelium of the mucosal layer, lining the lumen of the ureter is a stratified epithelium, four to six cell layers thick, known as *transitional epithelium.* The surface cells of this epithelium are large, roughly cuboidal cells, with abundant cytoplasm (Fig. 288). The large amount of cytoplasm allows these cells to be "stretched," and thus the epithelial layer accommodates to dilatation of the bladder without tearing, as the bladder fills with urine. This type of epithelium is found only in organs of the urinary system.

FUNCTION. The ureter conveys urine formed in the kidney to the urinary bladder.

BLOOD SUPPLY. Blood is brought to the ureter by branches of the renal artery, the testicular (internal spermatic) or ovarian, internal iliac (the hypogastric), and the inferior vesical arteries. Venous blood is carried by way of small venous tributaries that drain into veins of the same names as the arteries which they accompany.

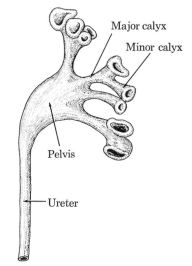

Fig. 287. Renal pelvis and calyces.

Major calyx

Minor calyx

Pelvis

Ureter

LYMPHATICS.   From the upper part of the ureter the lymph vessels drain into the lumbar nodes. From the lower part of the ureter the lymph vessels drain into the lower lumbar chain of nodes and the common iliac nodes.

NERVE SUPPLY.   The ureter is supplied by filaments from the inferior mesenteric, spermatic, and pelvic plexuses.

THE URINARY BLADDER

The urinary bladder is a large, hollow, muscular organ lined by mucous membrane.

LOCATION.   The empty bladder lies in the pelvis immediately behind the pubic symphysis. When distended, however, the bladder projects upward into the abdominal cavity.

FUNCTION.   The urinary bladder collects and stores the urine until it is expelled from the body.

GENERAL DESCRIPTION.

Shape—When empty this organ is shaped like a three-sided pyramid. When filled and distended, it becomes nearly spherical.

Size—The size of the bladder varies with the amount of urine it contains. The average capacity, without over-distension, is about 500 cc.

Surfaces—In the empty state, four surfaces can be identified: a *superior, two inferolateral,* and a *posterior.* These surfaces tend to merge when the bladder becomes distended. The superior surface is covered by peritoneum. This is a triangular-shaped surface which is concave in the empty bladder and convex in the filled bladder. The inferolateral surfaces meet anteriorly in the midline of the body in a rounded border. They rest on the floor of the pelvis, on the pelvic diaphragm. The flat posterior surface forms the fundus (base) of the organ.

Age Differences—In the newborn the bladder lies at a much higher level than in the adult and is actually an abdominal organ with the internal urethral orifice at the level of the upper margin of the symphysis pubis. The internal urethral opening and the bladder descend rapidly during the first three years of life, slowly from three to nine years of age. The bladder then maintains its position until after puberty when it slowly descends into the adult position.

Sex Differences—In the adult female the posterior and part of the superior surfaces are in relation posteriorly and superiorly with the upper part of the vagina and the body of the uterus. When the bladder is empty the uterus tilts forward and is in contact with the posterior part of the superior surface. The bladder of the female has relatively a somewhat greater capacity than the bladder of the male.

LIGAMENTS.   The bladder is "fixed" at two points. Inferiorly, it is attached near the urethral orifice and at the vertex (at the junction of the upper anterior border and the anterior angle of the superior surface). Inferiorly, in the male the ligaments are the medial and lateral puboprostatic ligaments that extend between the prostate gland and the pubic bone. In the female, the pubovesical ligaments extend between the bladder and the pubic bone. Posteriorly, the organ is anchored by the rectovesical ligaments (rectouterine folds in the female) which extend from the bladder to the sides of the rectum and sacrum. From the vertex of the bladder the middle umbilical

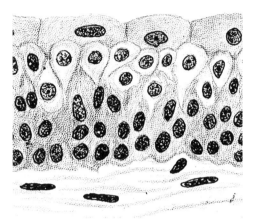

Fig. 288.   Transitional epithelium. Drawing.

ligament (the ligamentous remnant of the fetal urachus) extends from the bladder to the umbilicus. Besides these ligaments, there are folds formed by the reflection of the peritoneum from the abdominal walls to the bladder called the *false ligaments* of the bladder. These are anteriorly, the middle umbilical fold over the middle umbilical ligament, and the two lateral umbilical folds over the obliterated internal iliac (hypogastric) arteries; laterally, the lateral false ligaments; and posteriorly, the posterior false ligaments.

THE INTERIOR OF THE BLADDER.   The mucous membrane lining most of the bladder is loosely attached to the underlying muscular layer, so that when the bladder is empty and contracted the lining membrane is very wrinkled, but when the bladder is filled the inner surface appears smooth. One area on the posterior surface at the base of the bladder is always smooth. It is triangular in shape and called the *trigone* of the bladder. Here the mucous membrane is tightly fixed to the underlying muscle coat. The apex of the trigone is directed inferiorly and is marked by the internal urethral orifice. The base of the triangle is at the junction of the posterior and superior surfaces and it extends horizontally between the slit-like orifices of the ureters.

MICROSCOPIC STRUCTURE.   The wall of the bladder consists of four layers. An *inner mucous membrane* of transitional epithelium is continuous at the three orifices with the mucosa lining the ureters and the urethra; a *submucosa* of connective tissue; a *muscular layer* of smooth muscle fibers arranged in three poorly delineated layers as inner longitudinal, middle circular, and outer longitudinal; and the fourth layer is partly *adventitia* and partly *serosa* (the peritoneal reflection).

BLOOD SUPPLY.   Blood is brought to the urinary bladder by the superior, middle, and inferior vesical arteries which arise from branches of the anterior trunk of the internal iliac (hypogastric) artery. The middle hemorrhoidal artery also sends branches to the bladder. In the female small branches from the vaginal and uterine arteries also supply the bladder. Extensive venous plexuses along the inferior surface form veins which empty into the internal iliac (hypogastric) veins.

LYMPHATICS.   Lymphatic vessels follow the veins and drain to the internal iliac (hypogastric) nodes.

NERVE SUPPLY.   The urinary bladder is supplied by both sympathetic and parasympathetic innervation. The sympathetic fibers arise from the hypogastric plexus. Stimulation of these sympathetic fibers results in contraction of the internal sphincter muscle and relaxation of the musculature of the bladder wall, causing retention of urine in the bladder. The parasympathetic fibers from the 2nd and 3rd sacral nerves form the *nervi erigentes,* whose action is opposite that of the sympathetic fibers. If these parasympathetic nerves are stimulated, the musculature of the bladder wall constricts, the internal sphincter muscle relaxes, and the bladder expels its content of urine. The emptying of the bladder is called *micturition.*

THE URETHRA

This organ is a mucous membrane lined muscular tube that extends from the internal urethral orifice of the bladder to the exterior of the body. The urethra differs to such a degree in the two sexes that

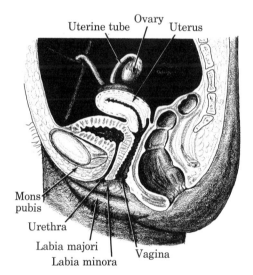

Uterine tube   Ovary   Uterus

Mons pubis

Urethra

Labia majori

Labia minora   Vagina

it is necessary to describe this tube separately for the female and the male.

The Female Urethra

This organ is a short, fairly straight tube that corresponds to the prostatic and membranous portions of the male urethra (Fig. 294, p. 259).

LOCATION. It lies behind the symphysis pubis in close association with the anterior wall of the vagina. From its origin at the internal urethral orifice of the bladder, the female urethra extends obliquely downward and forward. In its course it perforates the urogenital diaphragm closing the pelvic outlet, and opens onto the surface of the perineum directly anterior to the vagina and about 2.5 cm. behind the glans clitoris. As it passes through the urogenital diaphragm, the urethra is encircled by the sphincter urethrae muscle which is under voluntary control.

SIZE. The female urethra is a short, rather narrow tube about 3 to 4 cm. long with a diameter of about 0.6 to 0.7 cm.

FUNCTION. In the female, the urethra serves only the urinary system and carries the urine from the bladder to the exterior of the body.

STRUCTURE. The wall of the female urethra consists of three layers. There is an inner mucous membrane, consisting of an epithelium and a lamina propria whose deeper portion resembles a submucosa. This second submucosal-like layer contains plexuses of venous channels resembling erectile tissue. The third layer is a smooth muscle layer consisting of an inner longitudinal and an outer circular arrangement of fibers. Throughout most of its length the urethra is lined by a pseudostratified columnar epithelium which changes to transitional epithelium near the opening into the bladder. Near its external orifice the epithelium is a stratified squamous that is continuous with the stratified squamous of the surface structures.

The Male Urethra

This organ is a tubular structure lined by a mucous membrane.

LOCATION. As it extends from the urethral opening of the bladder to the external urethral orifice at the tip of the penis, it traverses, in order, the prostate gland, the urogenital diaphragm, and the corpus cavernosum urethrae of the penis. The course of the male urethra is not straight, its upper portion is vertical as it extends through the prostate gland and the floor of the urogenital diaphragm. It then turns forward and finally, if the penis is in a flaccid state, the cavernous portion of the urethra again is vertical.

SIZE. In the male the urethra is approximately 21 cm. long and is divided into three portions: the *prostatic,* the *membranous,* and the *cavernous* or *penile urethra* (Fig. right).

FUNCTION. In the male the urethra serves both the urinary system, conveying urine from the bladder to the exterior, and the reproductive system, serving as a transport route for the male germ cells, the sperm.

STRUCTURE. The prostatic portion extends from the internal urethral orifice of the bladder through the substance of the prostate gland to the upper border of the urogenital diaphragm. The prostatic urethra is about 2.5 cm. long and is the most dilated part of

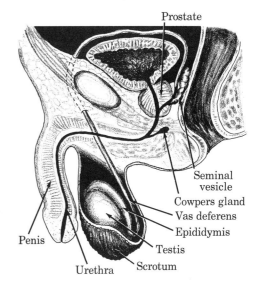

Prostate

Seminal vesicle
Cowpers gland
Vas deferens
Epididymis
Testis
Scrotum

Penis

Urethra

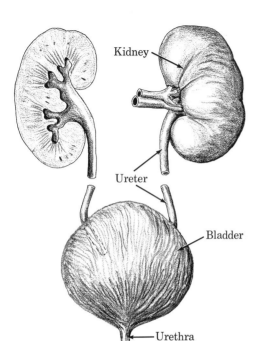

Kidney

Ureter

Bladder

Urethra

the canal. It is somewhat spindle-shaped and is narrowest where it joins the membranous urethra. Small ducts (the *ejaculatory ducts*) open into the prostatic urethra on its posterior aspect. Between these openings is a narrow, longitudinal ridge (the *urethral crest*). Contained within the urethral crest and above the ejaculatory ducts, is a tiny recess (the *prostatic urtricle*) which is homologous to the uterus of the female.

The membranous portion is the shortest and the narrowest part of the male urethra. It extends from the lower border of the prostate to the bulb of the urethra and is enclosed within the urogenital diaphragm. The membranous portion of the urethra is surrounded by the sphincter urethrae membranaceae muscle which is under voluntary control.

The cavernous portion is the longest portion of the male urethra. It is contained in the corpus cavernosum urethrae. This cavernous portion is approximately 16 cm. long and extends from the lower border of the urogenital diaphragm to the external urethral orifice on the tip of the glans penis. Several glands open into this portion of the urethra, the largest of which are the *bulbourethral glands* or *glands of Cowper*. The secretory portions of these glands are located in the membranous urogenital diaphragm, but their ducts open into the cavernous portion of the urethra.

BLOOD SUPPLY. Arteries are derived from vessels of the structures through which the male urethra passes. The male urethra receives branches of the prostatic vessels, branches from the artery of the bulb, and the urethral artery. The blood is returned by way of veins which follow the course and have the same names as the arteries which they accompany.

LYMPHATICS. The lymph vessels from the membranous and prostatic portions of the male urethra drain to the internal iliac (hypogastric) nodes. The lymph vessels from the cavernous portion drain to the deep subinguinal and external iliac nodes.

NERVE SUPPLY. The nerves supplying the male urethra are branches of the pudendal nerve and autonomic fibers from the cavernous plexuses.

12

THE REPRODUCTIVE SYSTEM

In Man the reproductive system of the body consists of those organs, in both sexes, which are concerned primarily with the propagation of the species, and the production of hormones that cause the development of the secondary sex characteristics of the male and female. In humans, the ability to reproduce occurs at puberty, when sexual maturity occurs. Since the reproductive systems of the male and female differ markedly, they will be treated separately.

THE MALE REPRODUCTIVE SYSTEM

THE SCROTUM. This is a pendant sac-like structure of skin and superficial fascia containing the two testes, epididymides, and the beginning of the spermatic cords with the ductus deferens (Fig. 289).

LOCATION. The scrotum hangs from the inferior surface of the perineum immediately behind the penis and a short distance anterior to the anus.

COMPONENTS. The wall of the scrotum consists of skin and the dartos tunic, which is a fascial connective tissue layer containing smooth muscle fibers. Lining the inner surface of the dartos layer is the parietal layer of the invaginated tunica vaginalis.

DESCRIPTION. In the adult, the skin of the scrotum is thin, has a brownish color, and is provided with thinly scattered, coarse hairs. The sebaceous glands are well developed and produce a secretion that has a peculiar and distinctive odor. Its surface usually shows a number of transverse folds or rugae (wrinkling of the skin) caused by the underlying smooth muscle of the dartos layer and the cremasteric muscle. The degree of wrinkling of the surface varies with the age of the individual and the temperature. In old men, and when warm, the scrotum is flaccid and its surface quite smooth, but under the influence of cold and in young, vigorous males, the scrotum is shortened and its surface very wrinkled.

The scrotum is divided into two lateral compartments by a septum derived from the dartos tunic. Each side contains a testis and associated structures. The two sides of the scrotum are not symmetrical. Due to the longer spermatic cord on the left, the left testis and the left half of the scrotum hang lower than the right side. Externally, the position of the median septum is marked by a slight ridge or raphe. This raphe is continuous anteriorly with a raphe of the urethral surface of the penis and posteriorly it disappears into the perineum.

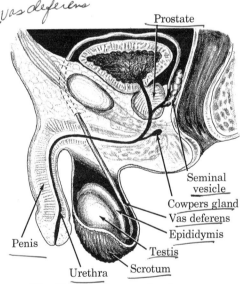

Fig. 289. Male reproductive organs.

251

ORGANS

The organs of the male reproductive system (Fig. 289) include

Testis (paired)
Tubular structures that convey the sperm from the testes to
      the exterior of the body. Starting at the testes, in
      order, these are:

        Epididymis (paired)
        Ductus (Vas) deferens (paired)
        Ejaculatory duct (paired)
        Male urethra
Accessory glands
        Seminal vesicle (paired)
        Prostate gland
        Bulbourethral (Cowper's) gland (paired)
Penis—the copulatory organ

Testes (Fig. 289)

These are paired, glandular organs that produce the male germ cells (sperm) and the male hormones.

LOCATION. They are suspended from the inferior surface of the body and are contained in the scrotum.

DESCRIPTION. Each testis is oval in shape, 4 to 5 centimeters long, 2.5 centimeters wide, and 3 centimeters in anteroposterior diameter, and weighs 10.5 to 14 grams. Each testis has a medial and lateral surface, an anterior and posterior border, and a superior and inferior extremity. All surfaces, borders, and extremities are convex and smooth, except the posterior border which is straight and affords attachment for the epididymis and the cord.

POSITION. Each testis is suspended obliquely in the scrotal sac, so that the lateral surface is directed backward and upward and the medial surface forward and downward.

STRUCTURE (FIG. 290). If a testis is cut longitudinally in a plane parallel to the two surfaces, it is seen to be enclosed in a tough fibrous capsule, the *tunica albuginea.* From the inner surface of the tunica albuginea connective tissue extends into the substance of the gland, dividing it into a number of small pie-shaped compartments called *lobules,* which converge toward the posterior border. Along the posterior border, the capsule is greatly thickened and projects into the substance of the organ forming the *mediastinum.* The connective tissue here presents a fenestrated arrangement which affords support for a network of epithelial-lined tubules conveying sperm from the testis to the epididymis.

Within the compartments formed in the testis are the long, coiled, *seminiferous tubules* that usually start at the periphery of the organ as blind-end tubules. These tubules are surrounded and supported by loose connective tissue containing groups of special cells, the *Leydig* or *interstitial cells,* which produce the male hormone. The tubules consist of an outer, well-defined, basement membrane and a thick inner layer of epithelial cells. Two types of cells are present in this layer, the *spermatogenic cells* and *Sertoli cells.*

The Sertoli or supporting cells are tall and tapering, extending from the basement membrane toward the lumen of the tubule.

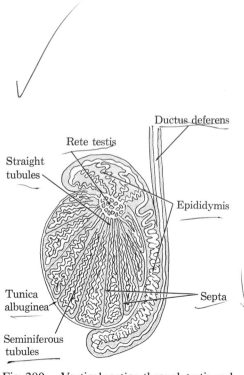

Fig. 290. Vertical section through testis and epididymis.

Labels: Ductus deferens, Rete testis, Straight tubules, Epididymis, Tunica albuginea, Septa, Seminiferous tubules

SHAPE AND SIZE.   It is usually described as being about the shape and size of a horse chestnut, with an average weight of about 20 to 25 grams.

DESCRIPTION.   The prostate gland is a firm textured organ consisting of both glandular and muscular tissue, enclosed in a dense fibrous connective tissue capsule. For descriptive purposes, it is said to have a base, an apex, and four surfaces—anterior, posterior, and two lateral.

The *base* is directed upward and contacts the inferior surface of the bladder. The urethra enters the organ slightly anterior to the center of this surface.

The *apex* is directed inferiorly and rests on the superior fascia of the urogenital diaphragm.

The *four surfaces* of the gland are slightly convex. The prostatic urethra leaves the *anterior surface* of the gland at the lower margin just above the apex of the organ. This surface is separated from the pubic symphysis by a small space (1.9 cm.) filled with fat and the pudendal plexus of veins. On the *posterior surface* the ejaculatory ducts enter the prostate gland near the upper border. A fold of peritoneum extends between the posterior surface of the prostate from the anterior surface of the rectum. The *lateral surfaces* are separated from the anterior portions of the levatores ani muscles by the prostatic plexus of veins.

FUNCTION.   The prostate gland secretes a thin, slightly alkaline, milky fluid which has a characteristic odor. This secretion is added to the seminal fluid and is said to exert an effect on the sperm, making them more motile. An important constituent of the prostatic secretion is an enzyme, acid phosphatase, whose presence in increased quantities in the blood stream is useful in diagnosing prostatic malignancy.

STRUCTURE.   The prostate gland is enclosed in a thin but dense capsule of fibrous connective tissue and smooth muscle fibers. From this capsule, septa extend into the gland to form the supporting stroma of the organ in which are embedded 15 to 30 branched tubuloalveolar glandular elements and their ducts. These ducts empty into the urethra near the prostatic utricle.

BLOOD SUPPLY.   The arteries that supply the prostate are branches of the internal pudendal, inferior vesical, and middle hemorrhoidal. Small veins of the prostate join to form a plexus (prostatic plexus) around the sides and base of the gland. These communicate posteriorly with the hemorrhoidal plexus and above with the vesical plexus and drain ultimately into the internal iliac (hypogastric) veins.

LYMPHATICS.   The prostate is richly supplied with lymphatics which drain to the internal iliac (hypogastric) nodes.

NERVE SUPPLY.   Nerve fibers are derived from the hypogastric plexus.

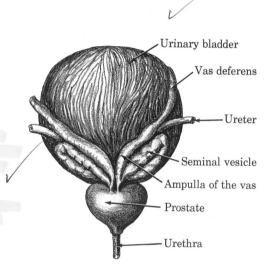

Urinary bladder

Vas deferens

Ureter

Seminal vesicle

Ampulla of the vas

Prostate

Urethra

Penis

This structure is the male copulatory organ.

LOCATION.   It is an elongated, pendant organ attached to the front and sides of the pubic arch. It is the more anteriorly positioned of the two external genital structures of the male, lying anterior to the scrotum.

DESCRIPTION. It consists of three cylindrically shaped, erectile tissue masses, the corpora cavernosa, bound together and encircled by fibrous connective tissue and covered by skin that is continuous with the skin covering the pubes anteriorly and above, the perineum laterally, and the scrotum posteriorly. Two of the cylindrically shaped masses, the paired *corpora cavernosa penis,* are arranged side by side on the dorsum of the organ. The third, the *corpus cavernosum urethra,* lies ventral to the other two and transmits the urethra through its entire length. The paired corpora cavernosa penis are attached by their diverging tapering posterior processes, the *crura,* to the rami of the ischium and pubic bones. As they pass forward their cylindrical masses merge and fuse. The median cylindrical mass, the corpus cavernosum urethra, is fixed to the inferior urogenital diaphragm posteriorly. This portion of the structure lies between the crura of the two lateral corpora and presents an expanded portion, the *bulb,* that surrounds the first portion of the penile urethra. Beyond the bulb the corpus cavernosum urethra is narrowed and lies in a groove between the fused corpora cavernosa penis. It extends somewhat beyond the free ends of the paired, fused corpora and forms an expanded, blunted, cone-shaped structure, the *glans penis,* which caps the corpora. On the tip of the glans is a slit-like orifice, the *external urethral orifice,* the opening of the urethra to the exterior.

ATTACHMENT OF THE PENIS. The cylindrical masses forming the penis are attached to bone (rami of the ischium and pubis) and to the fascia of the inferior surface of the urogenital diaphragm (Fig. 293). The urethra extending through the corpus cavernosum urethra, the muscles enclosing the crura, and the bulb also contribute to its attachment and support. The main ligament furnishing support for the organ is the *suspensory ligament* of the penis, a strong, triangular-shaped ligament extending from the symphysis pubis to merge with the deep fascia of the body of the organ.

The skin covering the penis is thin, dark, and contains no fat tissue. At the root of the organ, it is continuous above with the skin covering the pubes, and posteriorly with the skin of the scrotum and perineum. Anteriorly, just behind the glans a circular fold of skin, the *prepuce* or foreskin, extends forward over the glans. The prepuce is often surgically removed by an operation known as circumcision.

MECHANISM OF EJACULATION. In response to erotic stimulation, the penis becomes enlarged, hard, and is erected as a result of being engorged by blood. Two factors are responsible for this—an increased amount of arterial blood flowing into the organ and a slowing down of the venous drainage through constriction of the muscles and the peculiar construction of the walls of the veins that retards the return flow of blood. The forcing of semen from the organ, *ejaculation,* is caused by the rhythmic contraction of the smooth muscle of the wall of the ductus deferens and the striated fibers of the bulbocavernosus muscle. Each ejaculation expels a volume of semen of roughly two to four cubic centimeters.

COURSE OF THE SPERM AND FORMATION OF SEMEN. The male germ cells, the *spermatozoa,* are formed in the seminiferous tubules of the testis and make their way to the outside of the body by traversing a series of tubules: seminiferous tubules → straight tubules (tubula recti) → rete tubules → efferent ducts → duct of the epididymis → ductus deferens → ejaculatory duct → urethra (prostatic, membranous, and cavernous or penile segments) to the outside.

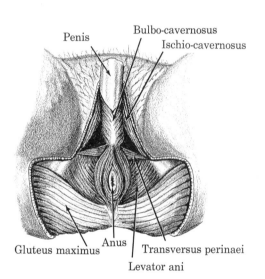

Penis   Bulbo-cavernosus
Ischio-cavernosus

Gluteus maximus   Anus
Transversus perinaei
Levator ani

Fig. 293.   Muscles of the male perineum.

As the sperm pass along this tubular passageway, fluid secretions are added, in turn, by the seminal vesicles, the prostate, and the bulbourethral glands to form the semen or ejaculate. Each ejaculate is estimated to contain approximately 300 million sperm.

FUNCTION. The penis serves both the reproductive and the urinary systems. Its primary function is the introduction of the sperm or male germ cells into the vagina of the female. Since it contains the terminal urethra, it also serves the urinary system.

STRUCTURE. The cavernous bodies of the penis are composed of *"erectile"* tissue which consists of narrow branching connective tissue trabeculae supporting numerous large, endothelial-lined, venous spaces called *lacunae* which become engorged with blood during sexual excitement, causing the penis to become hard and erect. When the penis is in a flaccid state, these spaces are practically free of blood.

MUSCLES (FIG. 293). The free medial surface of the crura is enclosed by the ischiocavernosus muscle. During sexual excitement these muscles prevent the return of venous blood, thus producing engorgement of the cavernous spaces and causing erection of the penis. The bulb of the corpus cavernosum urethra (corpus spongiosum) is enclosed by the bulbocavernosus muscle, which consists of right and left halves joined together on the superficial surface of the bulb by a median raphe. The contraction of the bulbocavernosus muscle expels urine or semen from this portion of the urethra.

BLOOD SUPPLY.

Arteries—Blood reaches the penis primarily by way of the penile branches of the internal pudendal arteries. Blood to the cavernous spaces of the organ is delivered by two branches of the penile artery—the *dorsal artery of the penis* (the superficial branch) and the *deep artery of the penis* (the arteria profunda). These vessels perforate the capsule along the upper surface, then divide into branches, some of which traverse the trabeculae and end in capillary networks that open into the cavernous spaces. Others form coiled dilated vessels (the *helicine arteries*) that open into the spaces and send some branches to supply the trabeculae.

Veins—Blood from the skin and periphery of the penis drains into the superficial dorsal vein along the dorsal midline of the organ. This vessel divides and ends in the external pudendal vein on its respective side. The deep venous vessels empty into the deep dorsal vein that ends in the pudendal plexus and sends a communicating vein to the internal pudendal vein.

LYMPHATICS. The organ has both a superficial and deep set of lymphatic vessels, both of which drain into the superficial inguinal nodes.

NERVE SUPPLY. The muscles of the penis are supplied by the deep branch of the perineal nerve. The substance of the organ is supplied by the dorsal nerve of the penis from the pudendal nerve. Sympathetic fibers are derived from the hypogastric and pelvic plexuses; parasympathetic filaments from the 3rd and 4th sacral nerves form the so-called nervi erigentes. Stimulation of these fibers produces erection of the penis.

THE FEMALE REPRODUCTIVE SYSTEM

In the female, the reproductive system consists of an external and internal (pelvic) group of organs (Fig. 294) and two accessory glands—the mammary glands.

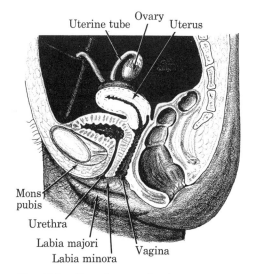

Fig. 294. Female reproductive organs.

EXTERNAL GROUP OF ORGANS (PUDENDUM OR VULVA)

The external group of organs include, the *mons pubis,* the *labia* (two *majora* and two *minora*), the *clitoris,* and *two vestibular structures* that warrant discussion here—the *bulb* and *Bartholin's glands.* Collectively these external organs are called the *pudendum* or *vulva* and are located in the perineal area (Fig. 295).

Mons Pubis

This is a prominent, skin-covered, fatty cushion that lies anterior to the pubic symphysis. After puberty, it becomes covered with coarse hair that is usually somewhat curly.

Labia Majora

These structures consist of two thick, rounded, folds of skin supported by loose areolar and adipose tissue. They meet anteriorly, forming the *anterior commissure,* and are continuous with the mons pubis. From the anterior commissure they extend posteriorly toward the anus decreasing in thickness as they extend posteriorly. About 2.5 cm. anterior to the anus they terminate in the skin of the *posterior commissure.* The lateral surface of each fold is somewhat pigmented and covered with coarse, rather scattered, curly hairs, similar to and continuous with that covering the mons pubis. Hairs are also present on the medial surface of each labia majora, but these hairs are finer and more scattered. The labia majora contain both sebaceous and sweat glands. They enclose and form the lateral boundaries of a space called the *pudendal cleft.* The labia majora are homologous to the scrotum of the male.

Labia Minora

These are two small, thin folds of skin that lie medial to the large folds of the labia majora and encloses an area, the *vestibule,* where the urethra, vagina, and the ducts of the greater vestibular glands open to the surface. Anteriorly the minor folds split to enclose the clitoris. Posteriorly the folds decrease in size and are connected by a slight transverse fold called the *frenulum pudendi (fourchette).* The skin of the labia minora is smooth, moist, without hairs, and is devoid of fat. Sebaceous glands are present.

Clitoris

This organ is homologous to the penis. It differs somewhat from it morphologically in that it does not contain the female urethra. The clitoris consists in the main of two, short, cylindrical masses of tissue, the paired *corpora cavernosa of the clitoris,* which corresponds to the corpora cavernosa penis of the male. These two corpora are fused and enclosed in a dense fibrous membrane which forms the body of the organ. Posteriorly, the corpora diverge to form two fairly well developed crura which are attached to the pubic rami. The free end of the clitoris presents a small, rounded, tubercle (the *glans*), which consists of erectile tissue and is well supplied with sensory nerve endings. The clitoris is a structure about 2.5 centimeters long and is supported by a *suspensory ligament* which extends from the pubic symphysis to the clitoris. Two small striated muscles, the *ischiocavernosi,* enclose the crura of the organ (Fig. 296).

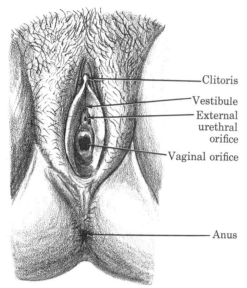

Fig. 295. External genital organs of the female.

Clitoris

Vestibule

External urethral orifice

Vaginal orifice

Anus

Vestibular Structures

Bulb

This consists of two relatively large masses of erectile tissue placed one on either side of the vaginal opening. Anteriorly, they unite to form a poorly developed and narrow median band of tissue termed the *pars intermedia*. Posteriorly, the bulbs are expanded and contact the greater vestibular glands.

Bartholin's Glands (The Greater Vestibular Glands)

These glands are homologous to the bulbourethral glands (Cowper's glands) in the male. They are two small, round, glandular structures situated in contact with the posterior ends of the bulbs of the vestibule. Each gland opens into the groove between the hymen and the labia minora by a duct approximately 1.9 centimeters long.

INTERNAL GROUP OF ORGANS

The internal group of organs of the female reproductive system consist of *ovaries* (2), *uterine* (*Fallopian*) *tubes* (2), *uterus,* and *vagina.* The organs that lie within the minor pelvis are closely associated with the transverse double fold of peritoneum called the *broad ligament* (Fig. 297). Before the internal reproductive organs are discussed, a brief description of the broad ligament will be given.

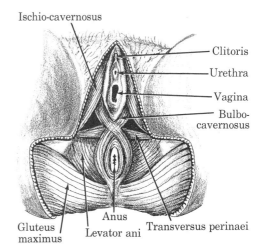

Fig. 296.   Muscles of the female perineum.

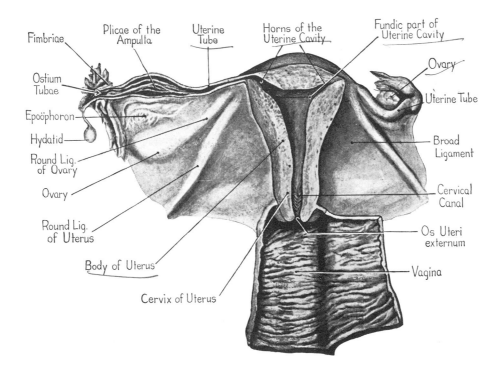

Fig. 297.   Internal reproductive organs of the female, spread out and viewed in ventral aspect. (Modified from Rauber-Kopsch: *Lehrb. u. Atlas der Anat. des Menschen.*) Vagina uterus and right uterine tube have been opened to show their internal configuration. (From Patten. *Human Embryology,* 2nd ed., Blakiston Div., McGraw-Hill Book Co.)

The peritoneum lining the abdominal cavity and the pelvis is reflected over the organs of the pelvic area in such a manner as to enclose the uterus and the uterine tubes within a transversely directed, double layered fold of peritoneum called the *broad ligament.* The broad ligament is attached laterally to the inner surface of the lateral walls of the pelvis. The posterior continuation of the peritoneum is reflected over the floor of the pelvis and onto the rectum and posterior wall of the pelvic and abdominal cavities. Between the uterus and the rectum the reflected peritoneum forms a pouch-like space called the rectouterine pouch, or *pouch of Douglas.* The superior folded margin of the broad ligament is free and contains the uterine tubes. In the most lateral portion of this free folded margin are the ovarian vessels, lymphatics, and nerves, held by loose connective tissue. These structures, together with the peritoneal covering, form the *suspensory ligament of the ovary.*

Ovaries

These are paired organs that produce the female germ cell, the *ovum,* and secrete some of the female sex hormones.

LOCATION. The ovaries are positioned vertically in relation to the lateral walls of the pelvis, one on either side of the uterus. They are attached to the posterior surface of the broad ligament near its lateral free border by short, double folds of peritoneum called the *mesovarium.*

DESCRIPTION. Each ovary is a somewhat flattened solid organ. The ovary is described as resembling an unshelled almond and weighs roughly four to eight grams. For descriptive purposes each ovary presents two surfaces—a medial and a lateral, two extremities —an upper and a lower, and two borders—an anterior and a posterior.

In the sexually mature female, the *two surfaces* of the ovary are irregular; they present prominences produced by underlying Graafian follicles, and have pitted, scarred areas marking the sites where mature follicles have ruptured.

The *upper (tubal) extremity* is rounded and affords attachment for the suspensory ligament. The *lower (uterine) extremity* is smaller and affords attachment for the ovarian ligament that connects the ovary to the uterus.

There is a convex *posterior border* and an *anterior border* that is relatively straight, which serves as the attachment of the mesovarium. The hilus of the ovary is on the anterior border where blood vessels, lymphatics, and nerves enter and leave the organ.

STRUCTURE (FIG. 298). The peritoneal layer with its covering of mesothelial cells that forms a mesovarium of the ovary terminates at the hilus. The surface of the ovary itself is covered by a single layer of cuboidal cells which form the *germinal epithelium* of the organ. These cells later migrate into the substance of the ovary to give rise to new follicles. The substance of the ovary is divided into an outer portion, the *cortex,* and inner portion, the *medulla.* There is no sharp line of demarcation between these two layers.

The cortex completely surrounds the medulla except at the hilus of the organ. It consists of connective tissue *stroma* and scattered *ovarian follicles.* The medulla consists of loose connective tissue containing many elastic fibers.

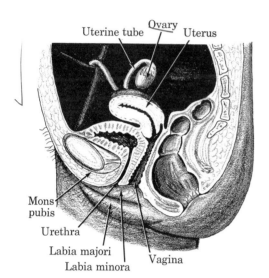

Uterine tube   Ovary   Uterus

Mons pubis

Urethra

Labia majori

Labia minora   Vagina

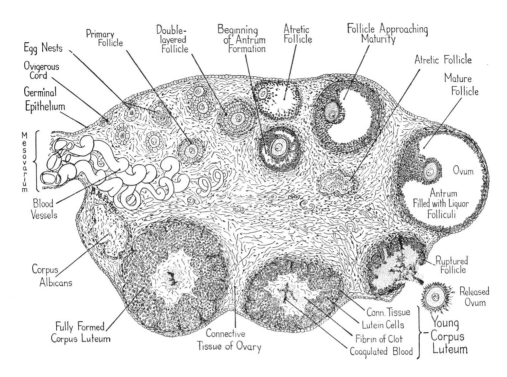

Fig. 298.   Schematic diagram of ovary showing sequence of events in origin, growth, and rupture of ovarian (Graafian) follicle, and formation and retrogression of corpus luteum. Follow clockwise around ovary, starting at mesovarium. (From Patten. *Human Embryology,* 2nd ed., Blakiston Div., McGraw-Hill Book Co.)

Two types of *ovarian follicles* are present in the ovary—*primary* and *Graafian (vesicular) follicles* (Fig. 298). The primary follicles consist of a large central cell, that will develop into the ovum, surrounded by a single layer of flattened follicular cells. The great majority of the numerous primary follicles that are present in the ovary of the newborn will undergo degeneration (atresia), and only a relatively small number will develop into mature Graafian (vesicular) follicles. The first indication of the primary follicle starting to develop is an increase in height and number of the follicular cells, and an increase in size of the enclosed *primary oocyte* (precursor of the ovum). Through the continued development of the follicular layer, clefts are formed between the cells which contain fluid, called *follicular fluid*. With continued growth of the follicle and the formation of more follicular fluid, the smaller pools of fluid merge until finally a single large central pool of follicular fluid is formed. The fully developed Graafian follicle becomes so large that it forms a prominence on the surface of the ovary itself. When the Graafian follicle is mature, it ruptures and expels the ovum. The rupture of the follicle and the discharge of the ovum is known as *ovulation*. After the discharge of the ovum, the space that was occupied by the ovum is filled in by large cells containing a yellow pigment which form a small glandular appearing structure known as the *corpus luteum* which secretes the hormone, *progesterone*.

In the sexually mature woman, a follicle develops and an ovum is released approximately every 28 days. It has been estimated that approximately 400 mature ova are produced during the reproductive period of a woman, which extends between the time of puberty and menopause.

BLOOD SUPPLY.   The ovaries are supplied by the ovarian arteries which are branches of the aorta. This vessel passes between the layers of the mesovarium to enter the ovary through the hilus. Veins leave the hilus in the form of a plexus of vessels called the pampiniform plexus which converge to form the ovarian vein.

LYMPHATICS.   The lymph vessels from the ovary drain into the lumbar chain of nodes.

NERVE SUPPLY.   The nerve supply to the ovary is by way of branches from the hypogastric plexus and from the ovarian plexus.

Uterine (Fallopian) Tubes

These are paired, mucous membrane-lined, muscular tubes for the transport of the ovum from the ovary to the uterus (Fig. left).

LOCATION.   Each tube lies in the free anterior border of the broad ligament, one on either side of the uterus. Each tube extends from the lateral walls of the pelvis, in close proximity to the respective ovary, to the superior lateral angle of the uterus.

DESCRIPTION.   For descriptive purposes each tube is divided into four portions.

Intramural portion—extends through the wall of the uterus.

Isthmus—a narrow, short segment between the intramural portion and the ampulla.

Ampulla—the longest and somewhat widened portion of the tube that lies between the isthmus and the infundibulum.

Infundibulum—the flared, funnel-shaped, terminal portion. The open end of the infundibulum is provided with a number of finger-like processes called *fimbriae,* one or more of which directly contact the ovary of the same side.

STRUCTURE.   The wall of the tube consists of three layers—an inner layer (the mucous membrane), a middle muscular layer, and an outer serosa and/or adventitial layer.

MECHANISM OF OVUM PICKUP AND TRANSPORT.   The question of how the ovum, which is actually expelled into the abdominal cavity, gets into the uterine tube is an intriguing and still unsolved problem. Each uterine tube contacts but does not completely enclose the ovary of its respective side. Many of the cells lining the tubes are ciliated cells whose rhythmic beating carries material toward the uterus. Experiments have been done in which the ovary on one side (i.e., right side) was removed and the tube of the opposite side (i.e., left side) was tied off, yet the animal later became pregnant and produced young. How did the ovum get across the pelvic cavity from the right side and enter the left uterine tube? We simply do not know. However, once the ovum enters the uterine tube it is moved into the uterus by the action of the cilia and the peristaltic contractions of the muscular layer of the tube.

FUNCTION.   The uterine tubes transport the ovum from the ovary to the uterus. Some of the epithelial lining cells produce a secretion that probably serves as a nutritive material for the ovum.

Uterine tube   Ovary   Uterus

Mons pubis

Urethra

Labia majori

Labia minora   Vagina

Fertilization of the ovum by the male sperm usually occurs in the upper free end of the uterine tube.

BLOOD SUPPLY. Blood is brought in to the uterine tubes by branches of the ovarian and uterine arteries. The veins draining the tubes empty into the ovarian and uterine veins.

LYMPHATICS. The uterine tubes are supplied by lymph vessels which drain into the lumbar nodes.

NERVE SUPPLY. The nerves supplying the ampulla and infundibulum are branches from the ovarian and hypogastric plexuses. Innervation to the isthmus is from the uterine branches.

Uterus (Womb)

This is a hollow, thick-walled, muscular organ of the female reproductive system. (See Figs. 294, p. 259; 297, p. 261; and 299.)

LOCATION. It lies in the pelvic cavity, behind the bladder and in front of the rectum.

FUNCTION. It is within the walls of this organ that the fertilized egg implants, and is protected and nourished while it undergoes growth and development during embryonic and fetal life.

DESCRIPTION. The following description of the uterus is based on the features of the organ as seen in an adult female who has never borne children.

The uterus is usually described as being a pear-shaped organ, somewhat flattened anteroposteriorly and with its broad end (fundus) directed upward.

It is about 7.5 centimeters long, 4.4 centimeters wide, and about 2.5 centimeters from front to back. It is usually somewhat larger in women who have borne children.

The organ is not a vertically positioned, midline structure as might be expected. The broad fundic end of the organ is directed forward and upward, and turned slightly to the right of the midline, while the cervical portion is directed downward and only slightly backwards. Most of the organ (the body) lies almost horizontally and rests on the superior surface of the urinary bladder. The body joins the cervix at a fairly wide angle and the cervix also forms a bit of an angle at its junction with the vagina (Fig. 294, p. 259).

PARTS. For descriptive purposes, the uterus is said to have a fundus, a body, and a cervix.

The *fundus* is the rounded upper end of the organ above the point of entrance of the uterine tubes.

The *body* extends from the fundus to the cervix and tapers as it extends downward. It presents two surfaces—anterior and posterior—and two broad rounded lateral margins.

The *anterior surface* is flattened and is in apposition to the bladder. It is covered by the peritoneum that covers the fundus of the organ and laterally forms the anterior layer of the double-layered broad ligaments. From the lower part of the organ the peritoneum is reflected onto the surface of the urinary bladder. The *posterior surface* is convex from side to side. It is also covered by peritoneum. Inferiorly this peritoneum continues onto the cervix of the organ and the upper part of the vagina and then is reflected onto the anterior surface of the rectum.

The *lateral margins* show some convexity. The uterine tubes pierce the wall of the uterus at the upper limits of the lateral margins,

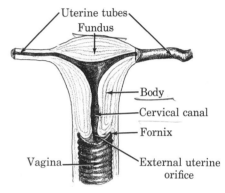

Fig. 299. Longitudinal section through the uterus. Drawing.

thus marking the junction between fundus and body of the organ. Just below and anterior to the tubes the round ligaments are attached to the uterus, and posterior to the tubes the ligaments of the ovaries are attached. All three structures, the tubes and the two ligaments, lie within the fold of the broad ligament.

The *cervix* is the inferior, smaller, constricted portion of the organ, about 2.5 cm. long. Its lower end extends into the upper portion of the vagina. Because of the slight angulation between the cervix and the vagina, the vagina attaches obliquely to the outer surface of the cervix. This attachment is lower on the cervix anteriorly and higher posteriorly. On the terminal, rounded, vaginal end of the cervix is a small, depressed opening, the *external cervical os,* by which the cavity of the uterus communicates with the vagina.

INTERIOR OF THE UTERUS (FIG. 297, p. 261).   Compared to the thickness of the walls, the cavity or lumen of the uterus is small. If the lumen were exposed by cutting the uterus longitudinally, the cavity within the area of the body would appear very narrow and slit-like from front to back. From side to side the space is roughly triangular, with the base of the triangle directed upward; at the lateral angles the uterine lumen is directly continuous with the lumen of the uterine tubes. Inferiorly the cavity is continuous with the fusiform-shaped canal of the cervix. The upper narrow constriction of the canal, at the junction of the body and cervix, is called the *internal cervical os.* The *external cervical os* is the constriction of the canal where it opens inferiorly into the vagina.

SUBPERITONEAL SPACE AND ENDOPELVIC FASCIA.   Before we consider the means of support for the uterus, we must consider the endopelvic fascia and the subperitoneal space which contains this fascia and certain pelvic organs with which this fascia is very closely associated.

The *subperitoneal space* is the area within the pelvis, between the pelvic diaphragm below and the reflection of the peritoneum above. It contains the urinary bladder, vagina, uterus, rectum, and the endopelvic fascia.

The *endopelvic fascia* fills the subperitoneal space and encloses the pelvic organs. It consists of a fibrous, loose areolar connective tissue and fat. Blood vessels from the pelvic wall traverse this fascial tissue to reach the pelvic organs, and at the base of the broad ligaments this tissue is continuous with the thin layer of areolar tissue that extends between the two peritoneal layers of the broad ligament. A condensation of the endopelvic fascia occurs between the pubis anteriorly and the sacrum posteriorly. As a result, the organs that lie in its path, enclosed by its reflections, produce a "segmentation" of this fascial condensation, and these segments (or so-called ligaments) are named according to the organs between which they lie. From front to back, they are the *pubovesical segments* between the pubis and the urinary bladder, the *vesicouterine segment* between the urinary bladder and the uterus, the *rectouterine segment* between the rectum and the uterus, and the *rectosacral segment* between the rectum and the sacrum. Only two of these "ligaments" are considered as uterine ligaments—the vesicouterine segment which forms the *anterior uterine ligament,* and the rectouterine segment which forms the *posterior uterine ligament.*

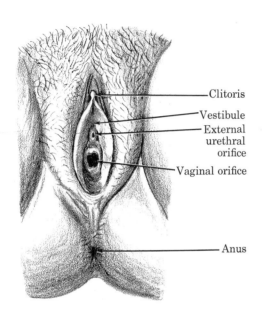

Clitoris

Vestibule

External urethral orifice

Vaginal orifice

Anus

LIGAMENTS.   The main ligaments of the uterus are as follows.

    Broad ligaments (paired)
    Round ligaments (paired)
    Uterosacral ligaments (paired)
    Cardinal ligaments (paired)

Besides these ligaments there are the two segments of the condensed endopelvic fascia which are referred to as ligaments and must be included. These are as follows.

    Anterior ligament (the vesicouterine segment of the endo-
      pelvic fascia)
    Posterior ligament (the rectouterine segment)

The two *broad ligaments* are transverse, wing-like, double folds of peritoneum extending from the lateral margins of the uterus to the lateral pelvic walls, one on either side of the uterus.

The two *round ligaments* are the fibromuscular cords extending between the folds of the broad ligament from the upper margin of the uterus on either side to the pelvic wall, through the inguinal canals to terminate in the substance of the labia majora of the corresponding side.

The two *uterosacral ligaments* are rather flattened fibrous bands containing muscle fibers that extend from each side of the upper part of the cervix of the uterus, on either side of the rectum to end at the sides of the sacrum. The peritoneum reflects over them to form the rectouterine folds.

At the sides of the cervix of the uterus and along the lateral sides of the vagina there is a marked condensation of fibrous tissue of the fascia that extends laterally to the wall of the pelvis. This fascial condensation forms the *cardinal ligaments* that serve as important ligaments for support of the uterus.

STRUCTURE.   The wall of the uterus consists of three layers—a relatively thick inner layer of mucous membrane, the endometrium; a thick middle layer of smooth muscle, the myometrium; and an outer thin, serous layer, the perimetrium.

The *endometrium* that lines the body and the fundus of the uterus consists of a simple columnar epithelium which covers the inner surface of the organ. It is continuous with the epithelium lining the long tubular glands that extend through the entire depth of the endometrial stroma. The stroma consists of delicate reticular connective tissue and numerous cells, many of which resemble embryonic mesenchymal cells. In the lower end of the cervix, the simple columnar epithelium changes to a stratified squamous, which becomes continuous with the epithelium lining the vagina. The glands of the cervix are branched and the stroma is denser and loses its embryonic character. From a functional standpoint, the endometrium lining the body and the fundus consists of two portions which are based, in part, on the arterial blood supply. The thick inner portion is known as the *functional layer* and is sloughed off during menstruation. The relatively thin portion next to the myometrium is called the *basiler portion.* This portion is retained and contributes to the regeneration of another functional layer following menstruation. (See p. 268.)

The *myometrium* (muscularis) is the thickest portion of the wall. It consists of long, smooth muscle fibers that are intermingled

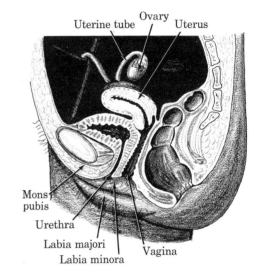

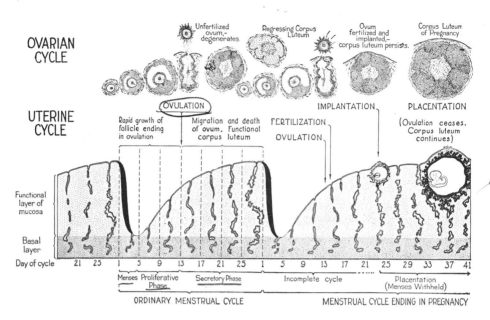

OVARIAN CYCLE

Unfertilized ovum,-degenerates.
Regressing Corpus Luteum
Ovum fertilized and implanted,-corpus luteum persists.
Corpus Luteum of Pregnancy

UTERINE CYCLE

OVULATION

IMPLANTATION

PLACENTATION

Rapid growth of follicle ending in ovulation

Migration and death of ovum. Functional corpus luteum

FERTILIZATION

OVULATION

(Ovulation ceases. Corpus luteum continues)

Functional layer of mucosa

Basal layer

Day of cycle   21   25   1   5   9   13   17   21   25   1   5   9   13   17   21   25   29   33   37   41

Menses   Proliferative Phase   Secretory Phase   Incomplete cycle   Placentation (Menses Withheld)

ORDINARY MENSTRUAL CYCLE   MENSTRUAL CYCLE ENDING IN PREGNANCY

Fig. 300. Graphic summary of changes in the endometrium during an ordinary menstrual cycle and a subsequent cycle in which pregnancy occurs. (Modified from Schroder.) The correlated changes in the ovary are suggested above in their proper relation to the same time scale. (From Patten. *Human Embryology,* 2nd ed., Blakiston Div., McGraw-Hill Book Co.)

to the extent that they appear as poorly defined layers described as an inner longitudinal, middle circular, and outer longitudinal. During pregnancy these fibers increase in both size and number.

The *perimetrium* (serosa) consists of a layer of mesothelial cells on a loose areolar connective tissue.

THE MENSTRUAL CYCLE. When the female becomes sexually mature at puberty, the uterus becomes functional under the influence of hormones from the pituitary gland and the ovary. This maturation is evidenced by the appearance of external bleeding known as *menstruation.* After its first appearance, menstrual bleeding recurs, following a cyclical pattern of 25-33 days (average about 28 days), and is correlated with changes taking place in the ovary. These changes occur throughout the reproductive period from puberty to the menopause, which usually occurs between the ages of 45 to 50 years.

The series of changes which occur in the endometrium of the uterus is the preparation of this organ to receive a fertilized ovum. If an ovum is released and is not fertilized, it is expelled to the outside and the endometrium breaks down, bleeding (menstruation) occurring. As soon as the bleeding stops, usually in about four days, the endometrial layer repairs and grows to again become a thick nutrient layer ready for the next ovulation and possible fertilized ovum (Fig. 300).

On the basis of the changes which have been observed microscopically during the menstrual cycling, four phases of endometrial activity are recognized.

1. The menstrual phase (days 1-4) occurs if no fertilized ovum becomes implanted. It consists of the death and sloughing of the functional portion of the endometrium, and bleeding.

2. During the proliferative phase (days 4-16) the basal layer repairs and its surface is re-epithelialized by cells from the basal ends of the uterine glands. This takes about two days and is followed by a period of rapid growth of a new functional layer. This phase is controlled by estrogen, a hormone secreted by the ovary as a Graafian follicle is maturing. Estrogen is produced until after ovulation. The proliferative phase actually extends about two days after ovulation takes place.

3. The secretory phase (days 16-30) follows the rupture of the mature follicle and ovulation, when a corpus luteum forms within the ruptured follicle and begins to secrete a second hormone, progesterone. About two days elapse before enough progesterone is available to affect the endometrium, and this is why the proliferative phase extends two days beyond ovulation. Ovulation is usually considered to occur on the 14th day following menstruation. It may occur as early as the 8th day, or as late as the 20th day, resulting in short or long cycles for the individual. The formation of a thick, succulent, nutrient filled endometrial tissue for a fertilized ovum is the effect of the hormone, progesterone, *after* estrogen has caused the proliferation of a new functional layer. Specifically, progesterone causes a further thickening of the endometrium due to an increase of cell population, an increase in tissue fluid (edema) in the endometrial stroma, and activation of the glands with accumulation of their secretions (glycogen). If no fertilized ovum implants, the functional layer breaks down and menstruation again occurs. The blood supply to the functional layer is by way of the *coiled arteries,* while the basal layer is supplied by *straight arteries.*

BLOOD SUPPLY. Blood is brought to the uterus by the uterine arteries, which are branches of the internal iliac (hypogastric) arteries, and by the ovarian arteries which arise from the abdominal aorta. Both pairs of vessels enter the uterus along its lateral borders. Comparable veins return blood from the organ and empty into the internal iliac vein.

LYMPHATICS. Lymphatic vessels from the uterus assume a "regional" arrangement of drainage as follows. Vessels from the body and fundus of the uterus extend laterally through the broad ligament and drain to the lumbar and preaortic nodes. Some of the vessels from the body drain to the external iliac nodes. A few of the vessels from the fundus and upper part of the body drain to the superficial inguinal nodes. Vessels from the cervix drain to the common iliac, external iliac, and internal iliac (hypogastric) nodes.

NERVE SUPPLY. The uterus receives sympathetic, parasympathetic, and afferent fibers from the uterovaginal plexus. For the most part, the autonomic fibers are vasomotor. The afferent fibers reach the spinal cord through the 10th, 11th, and 12th thoracic and 1st lumbar nerves.

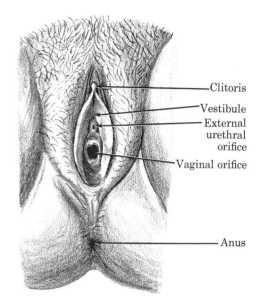

Vagina

This organ is a short, relatively thin-walled, muscular tube lined by a mucous membrane that extends from the lower margin of the uterus to the surface of the body. (See Fig. 297, p. 261.)

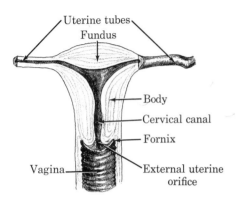

Uterine tubes
Fundus
Body
Cervical canal
Fornix
Vagina
External uterine orifice

LOCATION. The vagina is located in the lower part of the pelvic cavity, behind the bladder and in front of the rectum. Above it is attached to the outer surface of the cervix of the uterus. This attachment is lower in front and highest posteriorly and forms a recess or cul-de-sac, called the *fornix* (plural, fornices). The anterior fornix is the shallowest and the posterior fornix the deepest, while the lateral are intermediate. The vagina extends downward and forward, piercing the urogenital diaphragm, to open into the vestibule, between the labia.

DESCRIPTION. The vagina is flattened anteroposteriorly and its mucosal lining presents numerous transverse folds (rugae). Distally, the orifice of the vagina is partly blocked by a membranous partition in the young child and the virgin. This membrane, the *hymen,* is usually ruptured during the first sexual intercourse.

STRUCTURE. The walls of the vagina are composed of three layers—a mucosal layer, a muscular layer, and an adventitial and/or serosal layer.

FUNCTION. The vagina serves to enclose the penis during sexual intercourse. It conveys unfertilized ova from the uterus to the exterior, and it serves as a membranous portion of the birth canal at parturition.

BLOOD SUPPLY. Blood is carried to the upper part of the vagina by the vaginal branch of the uterine artery; to the middle part, by the vaginal branch of the inferior vesical artery; and to the lower part, by branches of the middle hemorrhoidal and internal pudendal arteries. Small vessels which form a plexus around the vagina drain into the internal iliac (hypogastric) veins.

LYMPHATICS. The vagina has numerous lymphatic vessels which drain into the internal iliac (hypogastric) and lateral sacral nodes and from the lower portion lymphatic vessels go to the inguinal nodes.

NERVE SUPPLY. The nerve supply to the vagina is by fibers from the hypogastric plexus and fibers derived from the 4th sacral and pudendal nerves.

ACCESSORY GLANDS (MAMMARY GLANDS)

The mammary glands are accessory glands of the female reproductive system. Developmentally and structurally these glands are closely related to the skin. They are specialized sweat glands with secreting glandular elements in the subcutaneous tissue of the pectoral area. Functionally, however, these glands are related to and controlled by the organs of the female reproductive system.

LOCATION. The paired mammary glands are located in the anterior thoracic region, one on each side of the midline.

SHAPE, SIZE, AND POSITION. Each mammary gland forms a hemispheric or conical prominence on the anterior thoracic wall. Viewed from the side the profile of the gland consists of a contour line above that forms a long, gentle convexity; below, the contour line is short and strongly convex. These two contour lines meet at the nipple slightly below the center of the organ.

The mammary gland has a greater vertical diameter than transverse diameter and it projects anteriorly 2.5 to 5 cm. from the wall of the thorax. The left breast is usually slightly larger than the right. In the young, sexually mature female who has never borne a child (nullipara), the glands are positioned at a higher level (between the 2nd to 6th rib) than in older women and in those who have borne children.

The shape, size, and position of the mammary glands vary markedly not only from one individual to another, but according to age, race, the nutritional state of the individual, and the functional state of the glands.

DESCRIPTION (FIG. 301). The skin over the mammary glands is thin and smooth. A little below the center of the gland is the pigmented, raised, conical *nipple* and a circular pigmented area surrounding it called the *areola*. Small openings on the summit of the nipple mark the orifices of the ducts of the underlying glandular elements. The skin covering the nipple is wrinkled. The areolar area has many small elevations due to the large sebaceous glands under the surface of the skin. In the nullipara female the color of this skin is pinkish; in the event of pregnancy, the color darkens to a permanently brownish shade.

STRUCTURE. Structurally, this gland is composed of about 20 distinct compound tubular glands (lobes), embedded in loose connective tissue and fat. Each gland is in a separate compartment or lobule formed by dense connective tissue septa extending between the separate glandular units. Each gland drains ultimately into a single duct called the *lactiferous duct* of the nipple. In each lactiferous

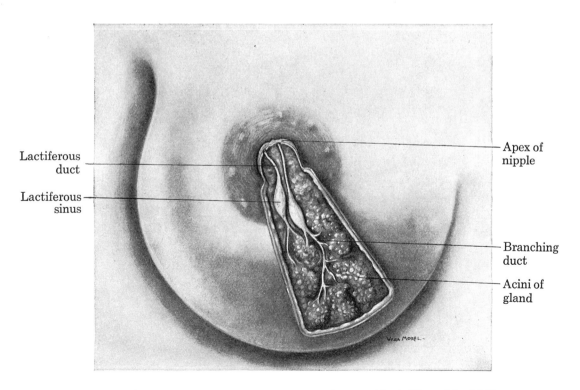

Fig. 301. The female mamma during lactation. (After Luschka.) (From Morris' *Human Anatomy,* 11th ed., Schaeffer, Ed., Blakiston Div., McGraw-Hill Book Co.)

duct, just before its termination, there is a fusiform dilatation in the duct called the *lactiferous sinus.*

FUNCTION.   The mammary gland, under control of the female hormones produced during pregnancy and at the birth of the child, produces milk for the nourishment of the newborn infant.

BLOOD SUPPLY.   The arteries carrying blood to the breast are branches of the internal mammary artery, branches from the axillary artery, and branches from adjacent intercostals. Veins returning blood from the breast empty into the axillary and internal mammary veins.

LYMPHATICS.   The breast is abundantly supplied with lymph capillaries which form dense plexuses within the gland. From these plexuses lymph vessels arise which drain into the pectoral, lateral, central, and apical groups of axillary nodes and into the internal mammary nodes.

NERVE SUPPLY.   Innervation is by way of the anterior and lateral branches of the 4th, 5th, and 6th thoracic nerves.

13

THE INTEGUMENTARY SYSTEM

The integument includes the skin and its derivatives: nails, hair, sebaceous and sweat glands.

THE SKIN

The skin is one of the most widespread and important organs of the body, and certainly the most available for study. For anyone versed in knowledge of the skin, the examination of this organ is extremely revealing. To the anthropologist, skin color is helpful in determining racial groupings of peoples. The black skin of the Negro, the yellow skin of the Oriental, the "red-skin" of the American Indian, and the white skin of the Caucasian are familiar criteria for classification of racial groups.

Careful examination of the skin by a competent physician gives him invaluable information about the individual. In the white person, the color of the skin may be helpful in the diagnosis of a number of abnormal conditions. The bright orange-yellow color of the jaundiced person indicates interference with the usual flow of bile that results in bile pigments entering the blood; there is a bluish gray cast to the skin of people poisoned by silver salts; the skin is bronzed in Addison's disease (hypofunction of the adrenal cortex); the skin is extremely white in the anemic person; and a bluish color is imparted to the skin of the cyanotic person.

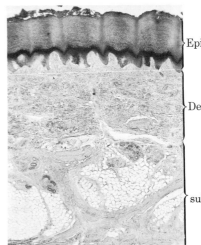

Epidermis

Dermis

Tela subcutanea

Certain generalized infections such as smallpox, chickenpox, measles, scarlet fever, syphilis, and others, produce specific types of pustules or rashes on the skin that serve as diagnostic criteria.

The advent of sexual maturity is indicated by the appearance of axillary and pubic hair in specific areas of the skin in both sexes, along with the appearance of the beard hair in the male. With puberty there is also an increase in pigmentation of the skin of the scrotum of the male, in the labia majora of the female, and in the skin around the anus, the nipple of the mammary gland, and the areolar area surrounding the nipple in both sexes. The pigment of the areolar area is increased still more, changing from a pinkish brown to a darker yellowish brown, in women who have borne a child.

Increase in the amount of skin pigment on areas of the body exposed to sunlight or ultra violet light is well known. Most people have been made painfully aware of this phenomenon more times than once.

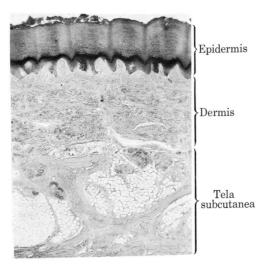

Fig. 302.   Vertical section of skin.

In certain areas of the body the skin is normally covered by varying quantities of coarse hair. The distribution of this hair is correlated with race, age, and sex, and will be discussed in the section on hair (p. 276).

DEFINITION.   Skin is the outer covering of the body.

LOCATION.   It extends over the entire surface of the body and is continuous with the internal mucous membranes at the various orifices of the body—mouth, nose, eyes, vagina, and urethral and anal openings.

STRUCTURE.   The skin consists of two distinct layers—the *epidermis,* which is a superficial layer of stratified squamous epithelium, and the *derma,* which is composed of a closely interwoven layer of dense areolar connective tissue. These two layers rest on a layer of loose areolar connective tissue, the *tela subcutanea* (Fig. 302), which tissue contains a relatively large number of elastic fibers that allow for varying amounts of fat to accumulate.

THE EPIDERMIS.   This layer varies in thickness over the body. Thick skin consists of four rather distinct strata or layers of cells, with each layer having certain specific characteristics. These layers, beginning on the deep, attached surface and moving toward the outer surface are:

1. The stratum germinativum
2. The stratum granulosum
3. The stratum lucidum
4. The stratum corneum

The first two layers are living, viable cells; the last two layers contain only dying or dead cells. This is the only place in the entire body where living and dead cells exist in such close proximity in normal tissue. In thin skin only two layers of cells are present, the germinativum and the corneum.

The *stratum germinativum* is several cell layers thick, and as might be assumed from the name, "germinativum," this is the layer where cells divide and increase in number, to push up and replace and maintain the peripheral epithelial layers. The lower edge of this layer is irregular due to moundlike elevations of the underlying derma (corium) which project into the epithelial layer and form the *dermal papillae.* The cells of the stratum germinativum vary in shape from low columnar cells in the basal row to polyhedral cells in the middle rows of cells, to flattened fusiform cells (long axis parallel to the base line) in the outer row.

The *stratum granulosum* consists of one to three rows of fusiform cells whose cytoplasm contains granules of a substance called *keratohyalin.*

The *stratum lucidum* appears as a homogeneous structureless layer due to the refractive properties of a material called *eleidin,* which fills the cytoplasm of the cells.

The *stratum corneum* is a layer of varying thickness, consisting of dead, cornified (kernatinized), scale-like cells. The surface layers of these cells are removed by desquamation.

The epidermis, like all epithelial tissues is avascular; the nearest capillaries are in the underlying dermal layer of the skin.

THE DERMA (CORIUM). This layer is formed of dense areolar connective tissue that is predominantly collagenous fiber bundles with relatively few elastic fibers. Its margin, adjacent to the epidermis, is usually papillated.

(The tela subcutanea underlies the skin. In different parts of the body it varies in thickness and the amount of fat it contains.)

COLOR OF THE SKIN. The color of the skin is due in part to pigment granules in the cells of the epidermis and to a lesser degree to cells in the dermal layer. The amount of pigment varies in the different parts of the body. It is greater in the skin over and around the nipples of the mammary glands, the axillae, around the anus, and over parts of the external genitalia.

FUNCTIONS OF THE SKIN. The functions of the skin are important and varied.

1. It acts as a guard or barrier between the deeper structures of the body and the external environment.

2. Its keratinized, waterproof, outer layers of cells prevent excessive loss of fluid, making it possible to live in air on dry land without dehydration of the tissues. It also protects the body when it is immersed in water.

3. The pigment of the skin protects the body from the damaging effects of sunlight (ultraviolet light).

4. It aids in the regulation of body temperature through the activity of the sweat glands and the capillary bed of the derma.

5. It serves as an excretory organ by effectively eliminating water and other waste products.

6. It is an important sense organ with receptor endings for pain, touch, and temperature.

7. Skin exposed to ultraviolet light produces vitamin D, the antirachitic vitamin.

BLOOD SUPPLY. The blood supply of the skin is a complicated network of vessels forming a vast plexus in the subcutaneous tissue, from which branches supply the hair follicles, and the sweat and sebaceous glands. Still other branches form a plexus in the derma, which sends capillary vessels into the papillae that project into the epidermis. Veins returning the blood follow a course comparable to that of the arteries, only in the reverse direction.

LYMPHATICS. Lymphatic vessels are arranged in a superficial and deep network and are continuous with lymph vessels of the tela subcutanea.

NERVE SUPPLY. Skin is supplied by cutaneous branches of peripheral nerves.

DERIVATIVES OF THE SKIN

The derivatives of the skin are the nails, hair, and two kinds of glands—sweat and sebaceous glands.

Nails

Nails are flattened, plate-like structures located on the dorsal surface of the terminal phalanx of each digit (fingers and toes). Each nail consists of an exposed portion, the *body*, made up of dead cells of the modified corneal layer of the skin, and a portion embedded in the skin, the *root*. Distally the nail ends in a free margin which overlies the tip of the digit. The folds of skin along lateral edges of the nail are called the *nail wall;* the fold over the root is the *nail fold*.

The nail rests on the *nail bed,* composed of an epithelial layer that is continuous with the stratum germinativum of the skin, and a corium which forms the deepest portion of the nail bed (Figs. 303

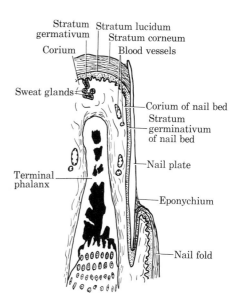

Fig. 303. Nail, longitudinal section. Drawing.

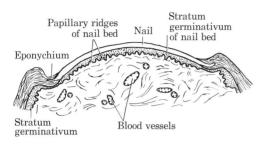

Fig. 304.   Nail, cross section. Drawing.

and 304). The epithelial layer increases in thickness beneath the root of the nail to form the *matrix,* the position of which corresponds roughly to the opaque white, crescentic area, the *lunula* at the base of the nail. The cells of the epithelial layer of the nail bed distal to the lunula (matrix) do not contribute to the formation or growth of the nail plate. Growth of the nail occurs by the addition of cells at the root, resulting in the body of the nail being pushed distally over the nail bed without losing its attachment to the underlying stratum germinativum.

Nails grow at a faster rate in summer than in winter, and the rate is faster for the fingernails than for the toenails. General health of the individual affects the growth rate of the nails.

Nails protect the distal ends of the digits and serve as tools for picking up small objects, for scratching, and as "defensive weapons."

Hair

Hair is a derivative of the skin and is distributed over nearly the entire surface of the body. It is not present on the soles of the feet or the palms of the hands. Most of the hair covering the body is short, fine, and hardly noticeable. In certain areas, however, such as the scalp, above the orbits, the axillae, and the pubic region, the hairs are coarse, thickly set, and vary in length according to the area. The amount of hairiness and the patterns of distribution are correlated with race, age, sex, and endocrine gland secretion. In general, the male Caucasian has the greatest amount of body hair. It occurs over the thorax, arms, dorsal surface of the forearms, back and shoulder areas, thighs, and calves of the legs.

Head hair and eyebrows are common to all normal peoples and are present in the child. The axillary and pubic hair in both sexes and the beard hair of the male appear at puberty and are signs of sexual maturity.

With aging, hair becomes finer, and its rate of growth is diminished or growth may cease altogether.

Each hair consists of a *shaft,* most of which extends above the surface of the skin, and a *root* located in a tubular *follicle* below the skin surface. The lower end of the root is enlarged to form the *bulb,* the lower part of which is invaginated by a cone-shaped projection of connective tissue, the papilla. The follicle is actually an invagination of the epidermis and corium of the skin. It is obliquely placed in the skin so that the contained hair emerges from the follicle at an angle (Fig. 305).

The root of the hair which caps the papilla, forms a matrix of growing and dividing cells (Fig. 306). As these new cells are formed, the older cells are pushed upward and become differentiated into the cellular elements of the shaft of the hair (cuticle, cortex, and medulla) and the hair "grows." The hair shaft in the upper part of the follicle and the exposed part of the shaft above the skin consists of dead, cornified cells. Cutting the exposed part of the shaft has no effect on the growth of the hair.

The arrectores pilorum muscles are small, obliquely-directed bundles of smooth muscle, that arise in the upper part of the corium; each inserts into the lower side of a follicle, below the attachment of the sebaceous glands (Fig. 305). When these muscles contract,

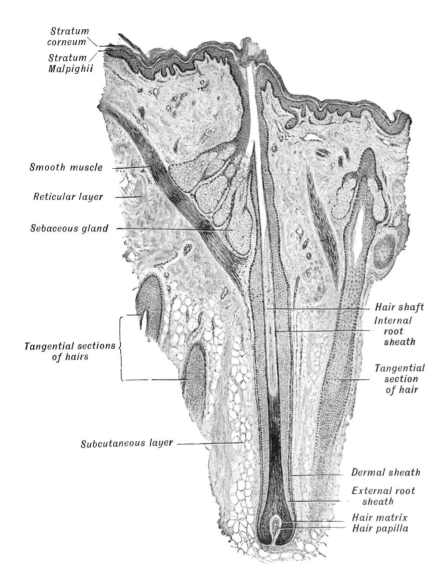

Stratum
corneum
Stratum
Malpighii
Smooth muscle
Reticular layer
Sebaceous gland
Tangential sections
of hairs
Subcutaneous layer
Hair shaft
Internal
root
sheath
Tangential
section
of hair
Dermal sheath
External root
sheath
Hair matrix
Hair papilla

Fig. 305.   Scalp of a man. Root of a hair in longitudinal section. 32 X. (After Schaffer.) (From Bloom and Fawcett. *A Textbook of Histology,* 8th ed., W. B. Saunders Company, 1962.)

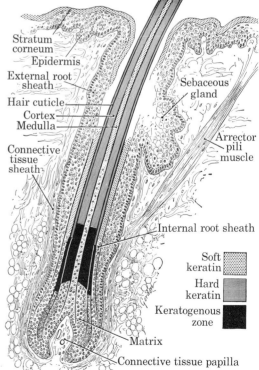

Stratum
corneum
Epidermis
External root
sheath
Hair cuticle
Cortex
Medulla
Connective
tissue
sheath
Sebaceous
gland
Arrector
pili
muscle
Internal root sheath
Soft
keratin
Hard
keratin
Keratogenous
zone
Matrix
Connective tissue papilla

Fig. 306. Diagram of a hair follicle, showing the distribution of soft and hard keratin and keratogenous zone. (From Ham and Leeson. *Histology,* 4th ed., J. B. Lippincott Co.)

the follicle and its contained hair are erected or become more vertically positioned. On contraction, these muscles compress the sebaceous gland, thus aiding in forcing its secretion into the hair follicle.

Hairs do not grow continuously and uniformly throughout the life of an individual. Each type of hair (beard hair, axillary hair, head hair) has its own life cycle and rate of growth. When the growth of a hair is completed the hair is shed, and after a period of rest, the root of the hair produces a new hair. In the human not all hair of the head, for example, is shed at one time. The cycles of growth are staggered and some hairs are constantly being shed. In lower animals, the shedding is more obviously seasonal, as anyone who has ever curried a horse in the spring is well aware.

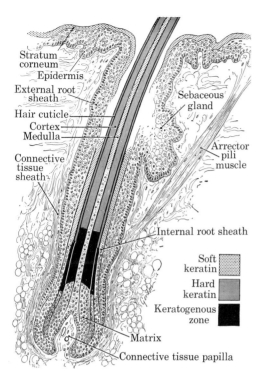

Stratum
corneum
Epidermis
External root
sheath
Hair cuticle
Cortex
Medulla
Connective
tissue
sheath

Sebaceous
gland

Arrector
pili
muscle

Internal root sheath

Soft
keratin
Hard
keratin
Keratogenous
zone

Matrix

Connective tissue papilla

(From Ham and Leeson. *Histology,* 4th ed.,
J. B. Lippincott Co.)

The blood supply to the hair follicle is by way of small branches of cutaneous vessels, that enter the papilla as capillary networks, and some capillaries are distributed to the outer surface of the bulb. Blood is returned by small veins from the papilla and around the bulb which join larger veins in the subcutaneous tissue and the corium.

Sensory nerve fibers supply the papilla and follicle. Unmyelinated nerves supply the walls of the blood vessels and the sebaceous glands.

Sebaceous Glands

Associated with the hair follicles are the sebaceous glands, also derived from the skin. They are large, saccular glands that open into the follicle from its under surface. (See Fig. 305, p. 277.) The secretion of the gland, called *sebum,* is an oily substance which lubricates the shaft of the hair.

Sweat Glands

Sweat glands (sudoriferous glands) are found in the skin in nearly all parts of the body. They are simple, coiled, tubular glands whose coiled terminal portions lie just beneath the corium in the subcutaneous tissue beneath the skin. Sweat glands are not present in the external auditory meatus (medial portion) or the prepuce and glans of the penis. They produce a thin, watery secretion called *sweat.*

14

THE ENDOCRINE SYSTEM

The endocrine system consists of a number of ductless glandular structures and organs that are widely scattered throughout the body (Fig. 307). These organs and their general location are:

Hypophysis (Pituitary)	in the cranial cavity
Thyroid Parathyroid	} in the neck
Suprarenals (Adrenals) Islands of Langerhans of the pancreas Cells of the duodenal mucosa Ovaries (in the female)	} in the abdominal cavity
Leydig cells of the testes (in the male)	in the scrotum below the perineal region

One other organ, the pineal, whose function is unknown, will be discussed in this chapter even though it is not listed or yet proven to be an endocrine gland.

The endocrine glands have several characteristics which are common to all of them. They are all derived from some type of embryonic epithelium. They have no ducts to carry away the secretions of their glandular cells. This necessitates that each secreting cell must abut on a capillary. It follows, then, that endocrine glands are extremely vascular. While several of the so-called endocrine glands listed above are discrete structural entities or organs, some of them occur as small clusters of endocrine secreting cells embedded in another gland (exocrine), i.e., the islands of Langerhans of the pancreas, or the Leydig cells (interstitial cells) of the testes.

In spite of their differences in location and in the chemical nature of their specific secretions, there seems to be a marked and definite physiological interdependence and interrelation among the various endocrine organs which justifies grouping them together as a "system."

The *secretions* produced by the endocrine glands are called *endocrine secretions* and their active principles are called *hormones.* The hormones are extremely potent chemical substances that are effective in very minute quantities. They are excreted into the blood stream and transported throughout the body. Hormones are quite specific as to the cells or organs they exert an effect on, and these "target" organs may be quite distant from the cells producing the hormone. Hormones may also modify the organs that produce them.

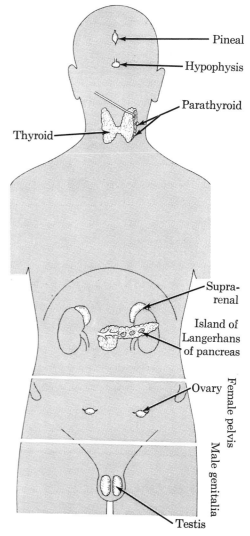

Fig. 307.   Endocrine glands.

279

The action of a hormone is probably to activate or inhibit the speed (rate) of intracellular reactions governed by particular enzyme systems.

THE HYPOPHYSIS

The hypophysis, or pituitary gland, is a small organ attached to the floor of the brain by a short stalk called the *infundibulum*.

DERIVATION. The hypophysis is derived from two separate ectodermal sources—the *hypophyseal diverticulum (Rathke's pouch)* from the roof of the oral cavity of the embryo, and the *infundibular diverticulum* from the floor of the third ventricle of the brain. The hypophyseal diverticulum gives rise to the *pars distalis (anterior lobe)*, *pars intermedia,* and *pars tuberalis.* The infundibular diverticulum develops into the *pars nervosa (posterior lobe)* (Fig. 308).

LOCATION. The hypophysis lies in a bony cavity, the hypophyseal fossa of the *sella turcica* of the sphenoid bone. It is retained in its position by a fold of the dura mater that forms a roof called the *diaphragma sellae.* The dura also sends an extension into the bony sella turcica, encloses the hypophysis, and forms a capsule for the organ. The stalk of the hypophysis passes through a small opening in the diaphragm.

SHAPE AND SIZE. It is a flattened, ovoid structure, roughly 12.5 millimeters wide, 8 millimeters long (anteroposterior measurement), and 6 millimeters high.

DESCRIPTION. The hypophysis has two lobes—an anterior lobe and a posterior lobe (Fig. 309). The anterior lobe is the larger of the two and consists of the pars distalis, pars intermedia, and the pars tuberalis. The anterior lobe is referred to as the *adenohypophy-*

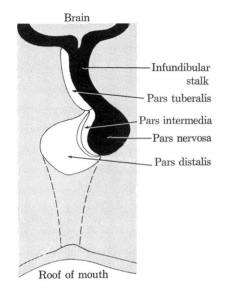

Fig. 308. Schematic drawing of a sagittal section through the hypophysis, showing the portions of the gland derived originally from the brain (in black) and the portions derived from the ectoderm of the roof of the oral fossa (left white).

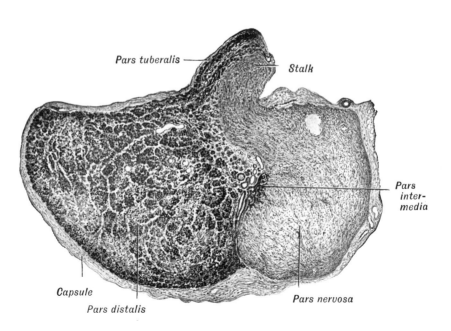

Fig. 309. Median section through hypophysis of a 45-year-old man. 16 X. (After Schaffer.) (From Bloom and Fawcett. *A Textbook of Histology,* 8th ed., W. B. Saunders Company.)

sis, and its structure is typical for endocrine secreting organs. The posterior lobe resembles nerve tissue in appearance. It is often referred to as the *neurohypophysis.*

FUNCTION.   The hypophysis produces several hormones and is considered to be the "master" gland of the endocrine system because it regulates the action of other endocrine glands. Hormones have been extracted from both major lobes of the hypophysis. The precise number of specific and distinct hormones produced by this organ is questionable. There are at least six that have been accepted as secretions of the anterior lobe on the basis of chemical and biological evidence. The hormones extracted from the posterior lobe, however, are not produced there. Instead, these hormones are produced by neurosecretory cells of the brain, in the supraoptical and paraventricular cell masses called nuclei. The neurohypophysis (posterior lobe) serves as a storage and release center for these hormones, and therefore it is not a true endocrine gland. The hormones extracted from the posterior lobe affect blood pressure (pressor action), contraction of smooth muscle (oxytocic action), and inhibit loss of fluid through the kidneys (antidiuretic action).

The hormones produced by the hypophysis are as follows:
Anterior lobe (Fig. 310)

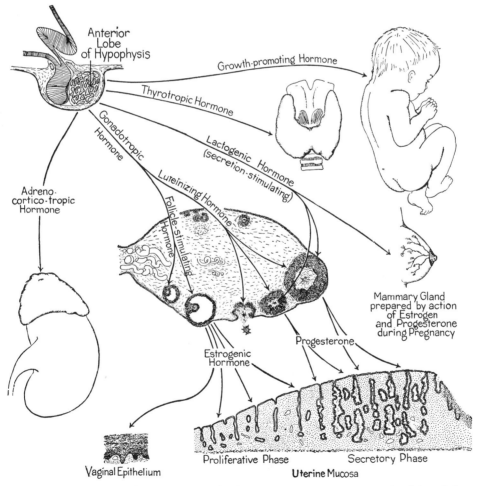

Fig. 310.   Diagram indicating some of the hormones arising in the anterior lobe of the hypophysis with special emphasis on those involved in regulating cyclic activities of the female reproductive organs. (From Patten. *Human Embryology,* 2nd ed., Blakiston Div., McGraw-Hill Book Co.)

1. Growth or somatotropic hormone (STH) that stimulates growth, specifically of bones, muscles, and viscera.

2. Lactogenic hormone (prolactin) that stimulates the secretion of milk by the mammary gland after it is "conditioned" by other female hormones.

3. Gonadotropic hormones that stimulate the gonads. Follicle stimulating hormone (FSH) in the female causes growth of ovarian follicles and transforms ruptured follicles into corpora lutea. Interstitial cell stimulating hormone (ICSH) in the male stimulates spermatogenesis in the testes and promotes production of male sex hormone by the Leydig cells.

4. Thyrotropic hormone (TSH) that stimulates the thyroid gland.

5. Adrenocorticotropic hormone (ACTH) that stimulates the adrenal cortex.

6. Lutenizing hormone (LH) that effects rupture of the follicle and release of the ovum, thus stimulating the formation of a functional corpus luteum.

Posterior lobe

1. Oxytocin that acts specifically on the smooth muscle of the uterus, causing it to contract.

2. Pitressin that contains two active principles—vasopressor principle that causes contraction of the smooth muscle of the walls of blood vessels, and antidiuretic principle that inhibits excretion of urine by the kidney.

The specific cell type responsible for synthesizing each of the six hormones produced by the anterior lobe of the hypophysis is not certain. Only two kinds of actively secreting cells are present, the "basophils" and the "acidophils." Each of these cells is subdivided into types of cells whose functions are more specific. Within the scope of this text, it is sufficient to indicate the source of hormones as follows:

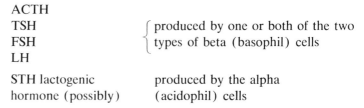

ACTH	
TSH	produced by one or both of the two
FSH	types of beta (basophil) cells
LH	
STH lactogenic hormone (possibly)	produced by the alpha (acidophil) cells

BLOOD SUPPLY. The anterior lobe receives its blood supply from the superior hypophyseal branches from the circle of Willis and the internal carotid arteries. The posterior lobe receives blood from the posterior hypophyseal branches of the internal carotid arteries. There are both systemic and so-called "portal" veins in the hypophysis. The latter involve circulation of blood through a second capillary bed in the anterior lobe, before it is returned to the systemic

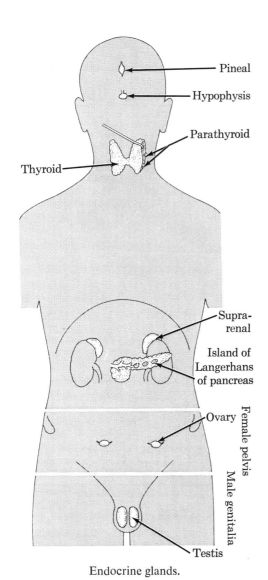

Endocrine glands.

circulation. The portal veins are short vessels that arise from capillaries of the hypophyseal stalk and empty into the sinusoids of the anterior lobe. The systemic veins are the veins of the infundibular process and the lateral hypophyseal veins, which return the blood from the hypophysis and empty it into the cavernous sinus.

LYMPHATICS.   Relatively little is known about the lymphatics of the hypophysis.

NERVE SUPPLY.   The gland receives fibers from the hypothalamus that extend through the infundibular stalk where most of them terminate in the posterior lobe. However, some fibers probably continue into the anterior lobe. The anterior lobe also receives unmyelinated fibers from the carotid plexus.

THE THYROID GLAND

This gland is the largest of the endocrine system. It lies under the skin and fascia in the neck.

DERIVATION.   Embryologically, the thyroid develops from a median ventral diverticulum of the pharynx. This hollow, tubular structure grows downward and develops a slight terminal swelling which ultimately develops into the thyroid gland. The duct that joined the developing thyroid to the pharynx, the *thyroglossal duct,* disintegrates. In the adult the only remnant of this duct is the *foramen cecum* of the tongue above and the *pyramidal lobe* of the thyroid below. Occasionally, however, the duct may persist as a patent duct called the *ductus lingualis.*

LOCATION.   The thyroid gland lies in the anterior part of the neck, near the junction of the larynx with the trachea (Fig. 311).

SHAPE AND SIZE.   It is a U-shaped organ, consisting of two pyramidal-shaped *lateral lobes,* connected inferiorly by a narrow strip of thyroid tissue called the *isthmus.* Each lateral lobe is roughly 5 centimeters long, 3 centimeters wide, and 2 centimeters thick. However, the size of the gland is extremely variable; it deviates with age, reproductive cycle in the female, geographical area, and diet.

DESCRIPTION.   The *lobes* of the thyroid are vertically positioned, with the apices directed upward and slightly laterally, and the base directed downward. Each lobe has two surfaces—*lateral* and *medial,* and two borders—*anterior* and *posterior.* The lateral surface is convex. It is covered by skin, fascia, and portions of four neck muscles—the sternocleidomastoid, omohyoid (superior belly), sternohyoideus, and sternothyroideus. The medial surface is irregular and molded by adjacent organs and structures. The anterior border is thin and is directed obliquely upward and laterally. The posterior border is thick and rounded. The *isthmus* is a narrow strip of thyroid tissue that joins the two lateral lobes in their lower third. It lies in front of the trachea covering the second and third rings of cartilage.

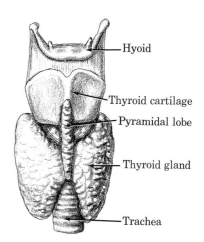

Fig. 311.   Thyroid gland.

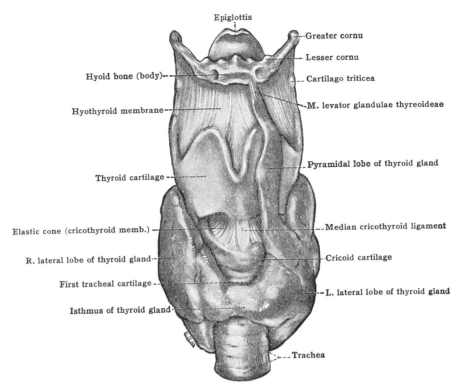

Epiglottis

Greater cornu

Lesser cornu

Hyoid bone (body)

Cartilago triticea

M. levator glandulae thyreoideae

Hyothyroid membrane

Pyramidal lobe of thyroid gland

Thyroid cartilage

Elastic cone (cricothyroid memb.)

Median cricothyroid ligament

R. lateral lobe of thyroid gland

Cricoid cartilage

First tracheal cartilage

L. lateral lobe of thyroid gland

Isthmus of thyroid gland

Trachea

Fig. 312. A thyroid gland with a pyramidal lobe attached to the hyoid bone. (From Morris' *Human Anatomy,* 11th ed., Schaeffer, Ed., Blakiston Div., McGraw-Hill Book Co.)

From the upper margin of the isthmus a third or *pyramidal lobe* sometimes arises and extends upward in the midline of the neck to the level of the hyoid cartilage (Fig. 312).

STRUCTURE.   The thyroid is enclosed by two layers of connective tissue. The outer layer or *sheath* is formed by the deep fascia of the neck, which splits to enclose the gland. The inner layer, the *true capsule* of the gland, is a thin, fibrous connective tissue layer that adheres closely to the organ and sends delicate septa into its substance, dividing it into *lobules.* Each lobule consists of a number of structural units called the *follicles.*

The follicles are irregularly-shaped, epithelial-lined vesicles that usually contain a homogeneous, acidophilic staining substance called colloid. The epithelium lining the follicles is a single layer of cuboidal or columnar cells forming a secretory epithelium. The height of these cells varies, depending on the secretory activity of the cells. Between the follicles, in the interfollicular spaces, there is a loose connective tissue containing lymphocytes, histiocytes, and occasionally small "nests" of epithelial cells. The significance of the epithelial cells is obscure.

The *colloid* is the stored secretion of the follicular epithelial cells. It consists primarily of a glycoprotein called *thyroglobulin,* which contains iodine and is the source of the thyroid hormones.

FUNCTION.   The thyroid gland functions primarily in the regulation of body metabolism. It stimulates growth and differentiation of tissues and organs, and has a profound effect on the functioning of the nervous system. The hormones of the thyroid gland are *thyroxin* and *triodothyronine.* They are the iodine-containing compounds derived from thyroglobuline when it is hydrolyzed by a proteolytic enzyme.

BLOOD SUPPLY.   The thyroid gland is supplied by branches of the superior and inferior thyroid arteries. The venous plexuses of the thyroid gland give rise to the superior and middle thyroid veins that empty into the internal jugular veins, and the inferior thyroid veins that empty into the brachiocephalic (innominate) vein.

LYMPHATICS.   Lymph capillaries around the follicles form lymph vessels which drain into the deep cervical lymph nodes, the pretracheal and paratracheal nodes, and the supraclavicular nodes.

NERVE SUPPLY.   Unmylelinated nerve fibers from the middle and inferior cervical ganglia of the sympathetic chain accompany the arteries to the gland.

THE PARATHYROIDS

In Man there are usually four parathyroid glands, arranged in pairs—two superior and two inferior parathyroids (Fig. 313).

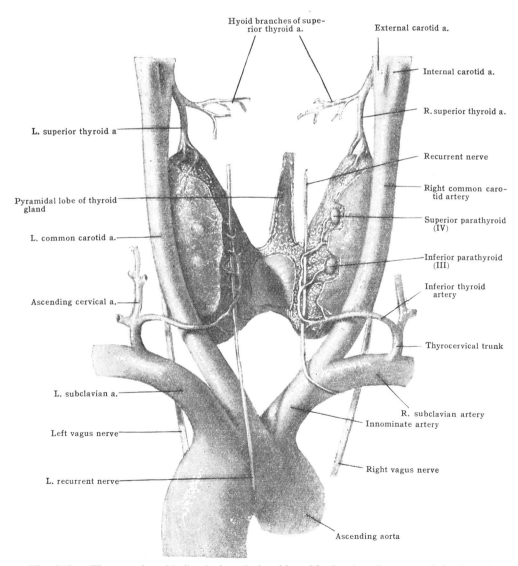

Fig. 313.   The parathyroid glands in relationship with the dorsal aspect of the lateral lobes of the thyroid gland. (From Morris' *Human Anatomy,* 11th ed., Schaeffer, Ed., Blakiston Div., McGraw-Hill Book Co.)

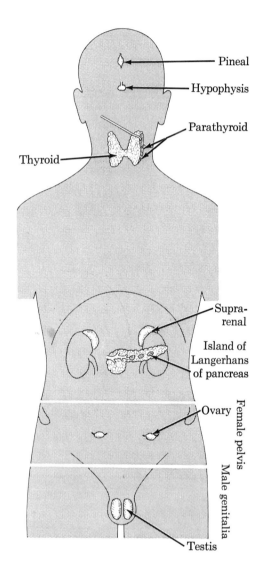

Pineal

Hypophysis

Parathyroid

Thyroid

Supra-renal

Island of Langerhans of pancreas

Ovary

Testis

Female pelvis

Male genitalia

DERIVATION. They are developed as outgrowths of the 3rd and 4th pharyngeal pouches of the embryo. The pair derived from the 4th pouch form the superior parathyroids; the 3rd pharyngeal pouch gives rise to the inferior parathyroids.

LOCATION. The parathyroid glands lie near the posterior border of the thyroid gland. The superior pair are on a level with the lower border of the cricoid cartilage, and the inferior pair are near the lower limit of the lateral lobes.

SHAPE AND SIZE. They are small, flattened, oval structures, reddish in color. They are about the size of a pea, with an average length of 6 millimeters and a breadth of 3 millimeters.

DESCRIPTION. The parathyroids are enclosed in a thin, fibrous connective tissue that sends delicate septa into the substance of the gland incompletely dividing it into lobules. The parenchymal cells are arranged in anastomosing cords of cells that border on capillary sinusoids. Two types of cells form the parenchyma—*chief cells* and *oxyphil cells.* The chief cells are the most numerous, and during the first ten to twelve years of life are the only cells present. The oxyphil cells appear about the eleventh year and are large cells with a relatively large amount of acidophilic staining cytoplasm. These cells may occur singly or form small or large, round or oval, clusters.

Follicle-like structures containing colloid may be found in the parathyroids. While they closely resemble the follicles of the thyroids, the colloid does not contain iodine.

FUNCTION. The parathyroid glands are essential for life. They exert a profound effect upon the calcium and phosphorus metabolism of the body. The exact mechanism involved is unkown. The parathyroids are apparently not under the control of the hypophysis.

These glands produce a single hormone, *parathormone,* a protein which is probably secreted by the chief cells.

BLOOD SUPPLY. The arterial supply of the parathyroid glands is by way of branches from the inferior thyroid artery. These branches communicate directly with the sinusoidal capillaries of the gland. The venous drainage is by way of the thyroid plexus of veins.

LYMPHATICS. The lymphatic vessels drain into the cervical lymph nodes.

NERVE SUPPLY. The glands are well supplied with vasomotor fibers from the thyroid branches of the cervical sympathetic ganglia.

THE SUPRARENAL GLANDS (ADRENAL GLANDS)

These are paired endocrine glands of the abdominal cavity that consist, both structurally and functionally, of two distinct tissues.

DERIVATION. The outer portion of the gland, the *cortex,* arises from splanchnic mesodermal cells at the base of the dorsal mesentery. The inner *medullary portion* is of ectodermal origin, from cells of the neural crest (along with the sympathetic ganglia).

LOCATION. These glands lie in the back of the abdominal cavity, behind the peritoneum. Each gland is embedded in the retroperitoneal fat close to the superior pole of a corresponding kidney.

SHAPE AND SIZE. In the human, the right suprarenal is pyramidal in shape, the left is crescent-shaped (Fig. 314). The left suprarenal gland is usually somewhat larger than the right and it lies at a slightly higher level (the left kidney is placed higher than the right kidney). The glands are usually about 4 to 6 centimeters long, 1 to 2 centimeters wide, and 4 to 6 millimeters thick.

DESCRIPTION.   The right suprarenal gland is roughly pyramidal in shape with the apex directed upward and the concave base resting against the upper part of the kidney. It presents three surfaces for examination—*anterior, posterior,* and *basal (renal),* and two borders—*superior* and *medial.* On the anterior surface is a short, grooved depression, the *hilus,* marking the point of emergence of the suprarenal vein. The left suprarenal gland is crescentic in shape and also differs from the right suprarenal in having a third border called the *left border.* Each gland is enclosed in a fibrous connective tissue *capsule* from which numerous fine septa extend into the gland between the rows and groups of cells.

Each adrenal has two parts—an outer yellowish *cortex,* and an inner reddish-brown *medulla.* The cortical area is much wider than the medullary area. Each represents a distinct gland that differs from the other in origin, structure, and function.

FUNCTION.   Both the cortex and the medulla of the suprarenal gland produce hormones. The cortex is essential for life, the medulla is not. The cortical hormones include a number of steroid compounds that can be classified as follows.

1. Glucocorticoids, which regulate intermediary metabolism of proteins and carbohydrates.
2. Mineralocorticoids, which regulate salt and fluid balance.
3. Sex hormones, which have actions similar to androgen, estrogen, and progesterone.

The medullary hormones are

1. Epinephrine (or adrenaline) which produces an effect similar to that observed after stimulation of the sympathetic nerves. It increases heart rate and vascular tone, mobilizes blood sugar, and reduces gastrointestinal tract activity. It prepares the body for "fight or flight."
2. Norepinephrine, which is similar but not identical to epinephrine. Its effects are generally weaker than those produced by epinephine.

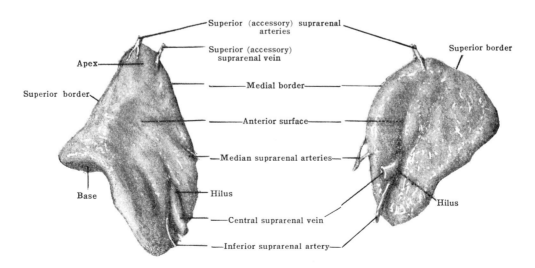

Fig. 314.   The suprarenal glands, ventral view. (From Morris' *Human Anatomy,* 11th ed., Schaeffer, Ed., Blakiston Div., McGraw-Hill Book Co.)

Blood Supply. The suprarenal glands are extremely vascular, and are supplied by the superior suprarenal arteries from the inferior phrenics, the middle suprarenal arteries from the aorta, and the inferior suprarenal arteries from the renal arteries. These vessels branch and anastomose before entering the gland and then send numerous small vessels into the gland. One group of vessels supplies the capsule, a second group opens into sinusoids of the cortical area, and a third group opens into the sinusoids of the medulla. Small veins of the gland unite to form larger vessels which ultimately empty into the central vein of the medulla and leave the hilus of the gland as the suprarenal vein. The suprarenal veins are tributaries of the inferior vena cava.

Lymphatics. Lymph vessels from the suprarenal gland ultimately empty into the lumbar nodes.

Nerve Supply. The suprarenal cortex is supplied chiefly by sympathetic fibers from the celiac and renal plexuses. Some of these fibers form a plexus in the capsule, from which fibers accompany the arterial vessels between the cords of cells. These fibers supply the vessel walls and end in relation to the cortical secretory cells, particularly the cells of the inner cortical zone. Most of the innervation of the medulla is by way of preganglionic fibers (of the sympathetic) that extend through the cortex and end in relation to the cells of the medulla. Ganglion cells and postganglionic fibers are present in the medulla. Parasympathetic fibers also extend to the gland, but their function is not known.

THE ISLANDS OF LANGERHANS

These are spherical clusters of cells that are the endocrine structures of the pancreas (Fig. 315).

LOCATION. They are scattered throughout the exocrine secreting lobules of the entire pancreas, but are most numerous in the tail, and fewest in the head of the gland.

SHAPE AND SIZE. The islets are more or less spherical in shape. They vary markedly in size, the smallest ones consisting of only a few cords of cells, while the largest are grossly visible.

DESCRIPTION. The cells forming the islets are arranged in cords or irregular clusters with each cell bordering a sinusoidal capillary.

FUNCTION. The cells of the islands of Langerhans produce *insulin,* which is essential in the metabolism of carbohydrates of the body.

Blood supply, lymphatics, and nerve supply of the pancreas are discussed on page 224.

Islands of Langerhans

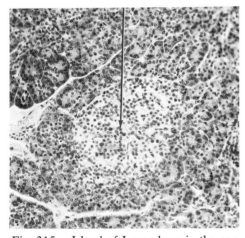

Fig. 315. Island of Langerhans in the pancreas. Photomicrograph.

THE CELLS OF THE DUODENAL MUCOSA

Certain cells of the duodenal mucous membrane are thought to secrete a hormone called *secretin.* This hormone, on reaching the pancreas, stimulates it to secretory activity.

THE OVARY

The structures of the ovary associated with the endocrine function are the *Graafian follicles* and the *corpus luteum.* For the general description of the structure of the ovary and its component structures, see page 262.

FUNCTION.   The ovarian follicle produces the hormone, *estrogen*. Naturally occurring estrogens are *estradiol, estrone,* and *estriol.* The estrogens are essential for the development of the secondary sex characteristics of the female. They cause growth of ducts of the mammary gland, are responsible for the development of the female body configuration, and trigger the phenomena terminating in menstruation.

The corpus luteum produces the hormone, *progesterone*. Progesterone, acting on uterine endometrium that has been stimulated by estrogen, causes the endometrium to enter its secretory phase in preparation for the reception and implantation of a fertilized ovum or egg. It also stimulates the development and growth of the glandular alveolae of the female breasts.

THE LEYDIG CELLS (INTERSTITIAL CELLS) OF THE TESTIS

The general discussion of the testis is given on page 252.

FUNCTION.   The Leydig cells produce the hormone, *testosterone,* the most potent of the male hormones (androgens). Testosterone is essential for the normal development of the reproductive organs of the male and for the development of the male secondary sex characteristics.

THE PINEAL GLAND (PINEAL BODY)

The pineal gland is usually listed with the endocrine glands even though not yet definitely proven to produce any hormones.

DERIVATION.   The pineal develops as an outgrowth from the third ventricle of the brain.

LOCATION.   It is attached to the posterior part of the roof of the third ventricle of the brain.

SHAPE AND SIZE.   It is cone-shaped and small in size—only about 8 mm. in length.

AGE DIFFERENCES.   The glandular elements in the pineal reach their maximum development at about the seventh year of life. After puberty, the glandular tissue is gradually replaced by connective tissue. The appearance of laminated calcified bodies called *brain sand* in the pineal substance is associated with advancing age of the individual and the degeneration of the glandular elements.

DESCRIPTION.   The pineal is enclosed in a capsule that is continuous with the pia mater of the brain. From the capsule, connective tissue septa extend into the organ, forming incomplete partitions that divide the parenchymal portion into lobules incompletely separated from one another. Two kinds of cells are present in the pineal— neuroglia cells and epithelioid cells.

FUNCTION.   The pineal produces no known hormones and its function is unknown.

BLOOD SUPPLY.   The arterial supply is by the posterior cerebral artery. From a venous plexus over the pineal, larger veins form, that empty into the vena cerebri magna (vein of Galen).

LYMPHATICS.   None.

NERVE SUPPLY.   The gland is supplied by sympathetic fibers carried in on the walls of blood vessels.

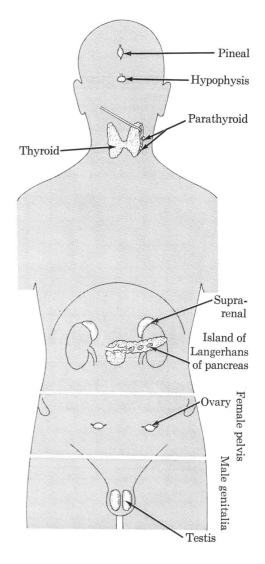

Pineal

Hypophysis

Parathyroid

Thyroid

Suprarenal

Island of Langerhans of pancreas

Ovary

Testis

Female pelvis

Male genitalia

15

THE ORGANS OF SPECIAL SENSE

The organs of special sense include the ear, the eye, the taste buds of the tongue, and the area of olfactory epithelium of the nasal cavity.

THE EAR

Nearly everyone is aware that the ear is the organ of hearing, but few people know that it also receives impulses controlling equilibrium. To most people "the ears" are the two appendages attached to the lateral sides of the head. To the anatomists and those professional people who study the ear and are interested in problems of hearing, it is a complicated and interesting organ made up of a series of bony and membranous cavities, tubular structures, and specialized epithelial areas that, for the most part, are hidden within the petrous portion of the temporal bone of the skull.

For descriptive purposes the anatomist divides the ear into three areas: the external ear, the middle ear (tympanic cavity), and the inner ear which consists of a bony and membranous labyrinth (Fig. 316).

THE EXTERNAL EAR

The external ear includes the *auricle* and the *external acoustic meatus*.

The Auricle

This is the portion of the external ear most people refer to as "the ear."

LOCATION. The paired auricles are located on the lateral aspects of the head. They surround and partially guard the opening of the external auditory canal.

SHAPE. Each auricle is an ovoid, dish-shaped structure, the larger end of which is directed upward.

STRUCTURE. The auricle is made up of a thin layer of skin stretched over a framework consisting of a thin, irregular plate of elastic cartilage which gives shape to the auricle. There is no cartilage in the lowest portion called the *lobe*. Both intrinsic and extrinsic muscles find attachment on the auricle.

DESCRIPTION. The lateral surface of the auricle is concave and very irregular and is usually directed laterally and only slightly for-

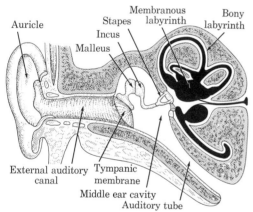

Fig. 316. Schematic representation of the right ear showing external, middle, and inner portions.

Auricle
Membranous labyrinth
Bony labyrinth
Stapes
Incus
Malleus
External auditory canal
Tympanic membrane
Middle ear cavity
Auditory tube

ward. It is attached to the head by means of soft tissues. This area of attachment is restricted to a relatively short area along its anterior margin; the remainder of the periphery of the auricle is free. The configuration of the auricle and its named topographical features are shown in Figure 317.

AGE AND SEX DIFFERENCES. In the male the auricles are usually larger than in the female, but the lobe is usually larger in the female. Aging produces a change in the length-breadth ratio of the auricle. In the newborn it is nearly as broad as it is long. With aging, it appears to become longer and relatively narrower, due in part to the loss of elasticity of the skin covering the auricle.

FUNCTION. The functional importance of the auricle in Man is debatable. In the higher pronograde animals (animals that walk on four legs) the "ears" serve a definite and important function. In the horse, for example, the "ears" are fairly large and the tips are free, elongated, pointed, and erect. As the horse feeds, the "ears" move almost constantly, turning forward and backward, trying to catch sound waves that warn of approaching danger. But Man, who stands erect, does not need to move his "ears," he can easily turn his head in the direction of the sound to catch the sound waves. Notwithstanding the fact that man's auricle is relatively small and no longer turns freely, it is still a structure that receives sound waves and directs them into the external auditory canal.

BLOOD SUPPLY. Arteries to the auricles are branches of the external carotid, the superficial temporal and the occipital arteries.

NERVE SUPPLY. Muscular branches from the facial nerve supply the intrinsic and extrinsic muscles of the auricle, while sensory nerves to the area are derived from the cervical plexus, the vagus, and the mandibular nerves.

External Acoustic Meatus

This is a tubular structure approximately 2.5 centimeters long.

LOCATION. It extends from the auricle to the middle ear. The inner (medial) end of the meatus is closed by the obliquely directed *tympanic membrane (ear-drum)* (Fig. 316).

SHAPE. The meatus is an oval-shaped, tubular canal that forms a slightly S-shaped curve as it extends from the auricle inward.

STRUCTURE. The external acoustic meatus is lined by skin over a framework of cartilage and fibrous connective tissue in its lateral one-third and bone in its medial two-thirds. The skin lining the meatus is continuous laterally with the skin covering the auricle, medially where it is reflected over the lateral side of the ear-drum the skin is modified, the epithelium being thinner and no papillae being present over most of the area of the drum (short papillae are present along the drum margin). Beneath the skin, in the subcutaneous tissues of the outer third (above the cartilaginous portion of the canal) there are tubular glands considered to be modified sweat glands, whose ducts open either directly onto the surface of the skin or into the hair follicles of the outer third of the canal along with the sebaceous glands. These glands are called *ceruminous glands* and produce the cerumen (ear-wax).

FUNCTION. The external auditory meatus serves to direct sound waves to the tympanic membrane, which is thereby set to vibrating.

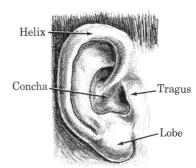

Fig. 317. Right auricle.

BLOOD SUPPLY.   Arteries supplying the area are branches of the posterior auricular, internal maxillary, and the temporal arteries.

NERVE SUPPLY.   Innervation is by branches of the mandibular and vagus nerves.

THE MIDDLE EAR

The middle ear consists of an air-filled space within the temporal bone, called the *tympanic cavity* (Fig. 316, p. 290).

LOCATION.   It lies between the external acoustic meatus and the inner ear and communicates with each of them. Laterally the tympanic cavity is separated from the external acoustic meatus by the tympanic membrane (ear-drum) (Fig. 318). It communicates with structures of the inner ear through two openings, the oval and round windows.

SIZE AND SHAPE.   While the shape of the middle ear is irregular, for descriptive purposes it is considered as a roughly rectangular space, flattened somewhat from side to side (lateromedially) and measuring about 15 millimeters high, 15 millimeters from front to back, and having a transverse measurement of about 6 millimeters above and narrowing to 4 millimeters below.

DESCRIPTION.   For descriptive purposes the tympanic cavity has six surfaces that form the walls of the cavity.

1.   The *roof* (*tegmental wall*) is formed by a thin layer of bone called the *tympanic tegmen,* which separates the middle ear cavity from the brain. With only this thin layer of bone serving as a barrier, it is easy to understand that a middle ear infection can be serious because of the possibility of the infection eroding or rupturing the tegman and invading the coverings of the brain (the meninges), with a resultant meningitis.

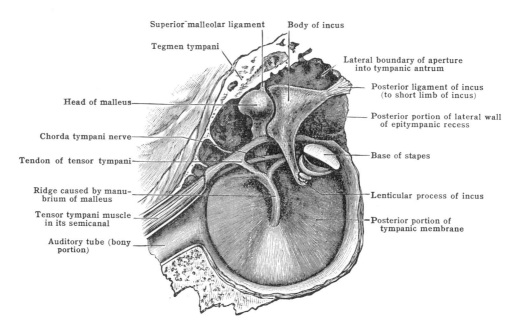

Fig. 318.   The lateral wall of the right tympanic cavity, with the auditory ossicles in position. X 4. (From Morris' *Human Anatomy,* 11th ed., Schaeffer, Ed., Blakiston Div., McGraw-Hill Book Co.)

2. The *floor* (*jugular wall*) consists of a thin layer of bone separating the tympanic cavity from the jugular fossa.

3. The *lateral wall* (*membranous wall*) is formed almost entirely by the tympanic membrane (ear-drum). Around the ear-drum, and affording attachment for it, is a narrow rim of bone which completes the lateral wall.

4. The *medial wall* (*labyrinthine wall*) is an incomplete and irregular wall of bone. Its two openings, the *oval window* (*fenestra vestibule*) and the *round window* (*fenestra cochlea*) are located in the medial wall. They connect the tympanic cavity with the vestibule and the cochlea respectively. The oval window is a kidney-bean shaped opening between the tympanic cavity and the bony vestibule of the inner ear. It is closed by the footplate of the stapes (one of the three auditory ossicles), which is held in place by the annular ligament. The round window is a small opening into the scala tympani of the cochlea of the inner ear. It lies a little behind and below the oval window, and is closed by a thin membrane called the secondary tympanic membrane.

5. The *posterior wall* (*mastoid wall*) is roughly triangular in shape. It presents an irregular opening affording communication with the mastoid air spaces.

6. The *anterior wall* (*carotid*) also is roughly triangular. On this wall is the opening of the auditory canal (Eustachian tube).

The entire tympanic cavity is lined by a thin layer of epithelium.

CONTENTS. The tympanic cavity contains the ossicles or ear bones, the auditory tube (Eustachian tube) which extends from the tympanic cavity to the pharynx, and tendons of the tensor tympani and stapedius muscles. The chorda tympani nerve traverses the tympanic cavity.

Auditory ossicles are a chain of three tiny bones extending across the tympanic cavity: the *malleus* (*hammer*), the *incus* (*anvil*), and the *stapes* (*stirrup*) (Figs. 319 and 320). The first and most lateral,

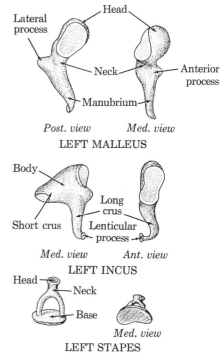

LEFT MALLEUS

LEFT INCUS

LEFT STAPES

Fig. 319.   Auditory ossicles.

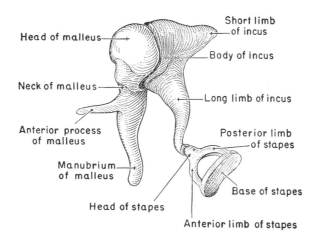

Fig. 320.   The auditory ossicles of the left middle ear, viewed from the anteromedial aspect. X 4. (Modified after Henle.) (From Morris' *Human Anatomy,* 11th ed., Schaeffer, Ed., Blakiston Div., McGraw-Hill Book Co.)

the malleus, is attached to the medial surface of the ear-drum. Medially the malleus articulates with the incus, the second and middle bone in the chain. The incus articulates medially with the head of the stapes which is the third and last bone in the chain. The stapes is shaped like a stirrup, and the footplate of the stirrup fits into and closes the oval window.

The *auditory tube* (*Eustachian tube*) (see Fig. 316, p. 290) extends from the tympanic cavity to the pharynx. It is a tubular structure whose framework consists in part of cartilage and fibrous connective tissue, and in part of bone; it is entirely lined by an epithelium continuous medially with the epithelium lining the pharynx. During the acts of yawning and/or swallowing, the pharyngeal end of the tube is opened and air is transmitted through the tube to the tympanic cavity, equalizing the air pressures on the two sides of the ear-drum.

The *tendons* of two small muscles, the tensor tympani and the stapedius, may be seen within the tympanic cavity. The tendon of the tensor tympani muscle, after making a right-angle turn, extends across the cavity to its insertion on the manubrium of the malleus. The belly of this small muscle is contained in the bony space (semi-canal) above the auditory tube. The action of this small muscle is to increase the tension on the ear-drum. It is innervated by a branch of the mandibular nerve by way of the otic ganglion. The tendon of the stapedius muscle extends from the medial wall and inserts on the neck of the stapes. The belly of this minute muscle arises from the inner walls of the pyramidal eminence, and the tiny tendon emerges from a small opening at the apex of the pyramid. This small muscle rotates the footplate of the stapes, and serves to decrease or dampen its vibrations. Innervation of the stapedius muscle is by way of a branch of the facial nerve.

The *chorda tympani nerve* is a branch of the facial nerve. As it traverses the tympanic cavity it is covered by the mucous membrane lining the cavity. It leaves the cavity by way of a tiny canal near the anterior border of the medial wall.

FUNCTION.   The auditory ossicles of the middle ear (tympanic) cavity transmit the vibrations produced by sound waves striking the ear-drum, across the middle ear cavity to the perilymph of the inner ear.

BLOOD SUPPLY.   There are six arteries that supply the middle ear. The two larger vessels are the anterior tympanic branch of the internal maxillary that supplies the tympanic membrane, and the stylomastoid branch of the posterior auricular artery that supplies the tympanic antrum and the mastoid cells.

NERVE SUPPLY.   The main nerve supply to the tympanic membrane is through branches of the mandibular nerve. On the medial wall of the middle ear is a plexus of nerves called the tympanic plexus from which fibers extend to supply the structures of the middle ear cavity.

THE INNER EAR

The inner ear is the essential part of the organ of hearing, located in the petrous portion of the temporal bone. (See Fig. 316, p. 290.) Because of its complex shape, the inner ear is referred to as the labyrinth, and it consists of a bony labyrinth and a membranous labyrinth.

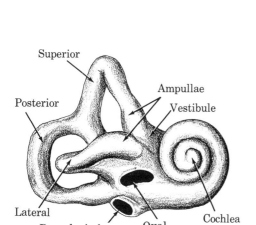

Fig. 321.   Diagram of the right bony labyrinth.

The Bony Labyrinth

The bony labyrinth is a series of intercommunicating canals and cavities in the petrous portion of the temporal bone (Fig. 321; see Fig. 316, p. 290). The entire labyrinth is lined by periosteum covered by mesenchymal epithelial cells, and contains a fluid—*perilymph*—and the component parts of the membranous labyrinth. The perilymph is formed by the mesenchymal epithelial cells.

DIVISIONS. The bony labyrinth consists of the vestibule, the bony semicircular canals, and the cochlea.

The *vestibule*—serves as the central cavity of the bony labyrinth. (See Figs. 316 and 321.) It lies medial to the tympanic cavity, anterior to the semicircular canals, and posterior to the cochlea. The vestibule is an ovoid chamber, slightly compressed from side to side. On its lateral wall is the oval window. Near the back of the medial wall is the opening leading into the vestibular aqueduct containing the membranous endolymphatic duct. Posteriorly are five orifices leading into the semicircular canals; anteriorly, a small opening leads into the cochlea. Throughout the vestibule are tiny perforations for the filaments of nerves that supply the membranous labyrinth.

Three *bony semicircular canals* (*superior, posterior,* and *lateral*) —extend above and behind the vestibule. Each canal forms roughly two thirds of a circle and lies at right angles to the other two. The canals have a diameter about 0.8 mm. across, and each expands into a widened ampulla just before entering the vestibule. Posteriorly the superior and posterior canals merge to form a common ampulla, so that actually there are only five openings into the vestibule.

The *cochlea*—looks like a snail shell. It is conical in shape and lies on its side forming the anterior extension of the bony labyrinth. Its base forms the bottom of the internal acoustic meatus, and its apex is directed forward and laterally. It has a tapered central bony axis, the *modiolus,* around which the *bony spiral canal* is wound. From the modiolus a thin shelf of bone (osseous spiral lamina) extends part way into the canal, paralleling its course, and partially dividing it into two portions. The conical modiolus forming the core of the cochlea contains small openings in its base for the transmission of nerves that extend up the center of the modiolus, giving off filaments which extend into the spiral lamina to innervate the membranous labyrinth. The bony spiral canal of the cochlea makes two and three quarters turns around the modiolus, and its diameter diminishes as it approaches the apex. There are three openings into the cochlea. One, the round window, is the orifice of communication between the scala tympani and the tympanic cavity, closed by the secondary tympanic membrane. A second orifice opens into the vestibule, and a third is the opening of the cochlear aqueduct.

The Membranous Labyrinth

The membranous labyrinth is a series of intercommunicating membranous canals and chambers contained within the bony labyrinth. They are much smaller than the corresponding bony structures, but except for the membranous vestibule, are generally similar in shape. Thus, the cochlear and semicircular ducts closely resemble the forms of the comparable parts of the bony labyrinth. However, in the vestibule, the membranous structures—the utricle and the saccule—are very different in configuration from the bony vestibule in which they lie (Fig. 322). The membranous labyrinth contains a fluid called *endolymph.*

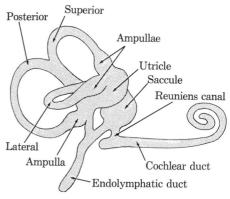

Fig. 322. Diagram of the right membranous labyrinth.

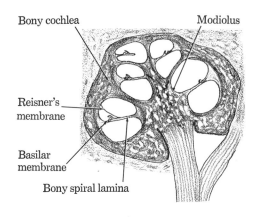

Fig. 323.   Cochlea and cochlear duct.

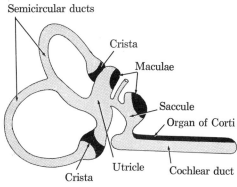

Fig. 324.   Schematic drawing of the right membranous labyrinth showing the location of the neuroepithelial elements.

DIVISIONS.   The component parts of the membranous labyrinth are the utricle and the saccule (two small saccular structures located within the bony vestibule), the membranous semicircular ducts, the cochlear duct, and the endolymphatic duct (Fig. 322).

The *utricle* (Fig. 322) is the larger of the two membranous structures within the bony vestibule. It is an elongated chamber that communicates posteriorly with the five ampullae of the membranous semicircular ducts. Anteriorly a small duct is given off, which joins the small duct from the saccule to form the *endolymphatic duct.* The tissue of the floor and anterior wall of the utricle is modified and thickened to form the *macula utriculi,* a neuroepithelial structure that receives stimuli and transmits impulses concerning equilibrium via branches of the acoustic nerve.

The *saccule* (Fig. 322) is the smaller membranous sac in the vestibule. It is rounder than the utricle, and from its posterior wall a small duct is given off that joins a similar duct of the utricle, forming the endolymphatic duct. The endolymphatic duct ends in a blind pouch called the *endolymphatic sac.* From the floor of the saccule a small, short canal, the *ductus reuniens,* connects the saccule with the cochlear duct. A modification of the cells lining a small part of the anterior portion of the saccule forms the *macula sacculi,* the neuroepithelial structure in the saccule that is concerned with equilibrium.

The *semicircular ducts* are comparable to the bony semicircular canals in form and number. They are small, about a quarter of the diameter of the bony canals. They have five ampullary expansions that open into the utricle (Fig. 322). The walls of the ampullae are modified so that externally they present a groove, the *ampullary sulcus,* and internally a ridge, the *cristae ampullari.* The cristae ampullari are the neuroepithelial receptor structures of the semicircular canals; they are concerned with the general sense of equilibrium.

The *cochlear duct* is the portion of the membranous labyrinth that is enclosed in the bony cochlea (Figs. 323 and 327, p. 298). It begins in the base of the cochlea as a blind pouch (the vestibular cecum), and like the spiral bony cochlea, makes two and a half turns from the base to the apex of the cochlea where it ends blindly as the cupular cecum. It appears roughly triangular in cross section. The floor of the cochlear duct is formed by the *basilar membrane,* which extends from the bony spiral lamina to the outer wall of the bony cochlear canal. The roof is formed by the thin vestibular membrane called *Reisner's membrane* which extends diagonally upward and outward from the bony spiral lamina. The outer wall of the duct is formed by the wall of the bony canal.

The cochlear duct occupies the middle segment of the cochlea; it is separated from the *scala vestibuli* above by Reisner's membrane, and from the *scala tympani* below by the basilar membrane (Fig. 327, p. 298). The two scalae communicate with one another only at the apex of the cochlea through a small opening called the *helicotrema.* Both scalae contain perilymph; the cochlear duct is filled with endolymph. Within the cochlear duct, attached to the basilar membrane is a neuroepithelial structure, the *spiral organ (organ of Corti),* for the reception of stimuli and transmission of impulses of sound.

NEUROEPITHELIAL STRUCTURES (FIG. 324).   The macula of the utricle, the macula of the saccule, the cristae of the ampullae of the semicircular canals, and the spiral organ (organ of Corti) of the cochlear duct make up the neuroepithelial structures of the membranous inner ear.

The *maculae* are named according to their location as the macula utriculi and the macula sacculi. They are modified areas of the membranous canal in which a small area is thickened by an increase in the fibrous tissue of the periosteum and a modification of the epithelial cells (Fig. 325). The modified epithelium of the area consists of two types of cells, the *supporting* or *sustentacular cells* which are tall, somewhat pyramidal-shaped cells, and *hair cells* that lie between the sustentacular cells. From the free surface of each hair cell there extends a single hair-like process made up of many fine non-motile cilia embedded in a thick, gelatinous structure, the *statoconial membrane* (*otolithic membrane*). In the statoconic (*otolithic*) membrane are tiny bits of calcium carbonate called *statoconia* (otoliths or *otoconia*). The statoconic membrane lies above the macular epithelium, and is separated from it by a narrow space filled with endolymph. A fine network of fibers of the vestibular nerve surrounds the bodies of the hair cells. The maculae receive stimuli related to equilibrium, particularly with regard to position of the head in space.

The *cristae* are contained in the ampullae, one crista ampullaris in each ampulla. Each is a tall mound-like ridge formed by the thickening and elevation of the subepithelial connective tissue (Fig. 326). The epithelium of the crista consists of sustentacular cells and hair cells. Capping the modified epithelial cells is a tall viscous, gelatinous structure, the *cupula cristae ampularis*. The "processes" of the hair cells extend across a narrow space filled with endolymph and penetrate the gelatinous material of the cupula. The cristae are receptor organs concerned with the general sense of equilibrium. Nerve fibers of the vestibular branch of the auditory nerve supply the cristae. The fibers penetrate the subepithelial connective tissue, the basement membrane, and branch into networks of fibrils around each of the hair cells.

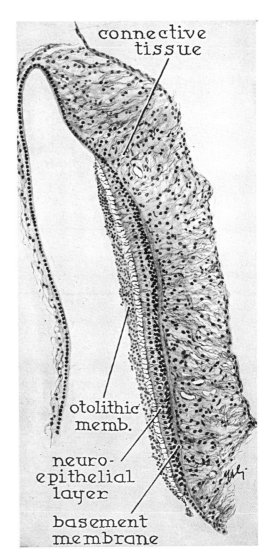

Fig. 325. Drawing of a longitudinal section (low power) cut through the macula sacculi of a child. (From Ham and Leeson. *Histology*, 4th ed., J. B. Lippincott Co.)

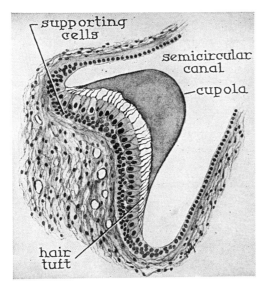

Fig. 326. Drawing of a cross section (low power) cut through the ampulla (slightly collapsed) of the lateral semicircular canal of the right ear of a child. It shows the crista ampullaris in cross section and the relation of the cupula to the hair cells of the sense organ. (From Ham and Leeson. *Histology*, 4th ed., J. B. Lippincott Co.)

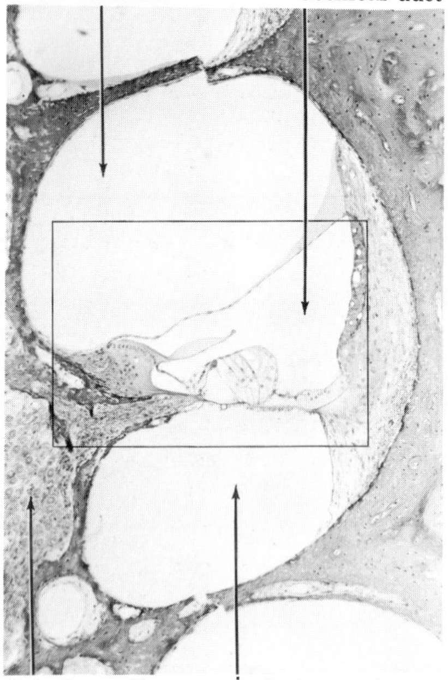

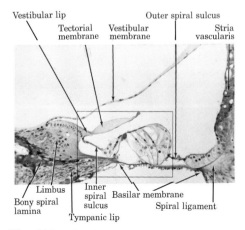

Scala vestibuli · Cochlear duct

Spiral ganglion   Scala tympani

Fig. 327.   Axial section of human cochlea. (From the collection of Dr. Dean M. Lierle.) Photomicrograph.

Vestibular lip   Outer spiral sulcus
    Tectorial   Vestibular   Stria
    membrane   membrane   vascularis

Limbus   Inner
            spiral   Basilar membrane
Bony spiral sulcus
lamina   Spiral ligament
       Tympanic lip

Fig. 328.   Section of the human cochlea. (From the collection of Dr. Dean M. Lierle.) Photomicrograph.

The *spiral organ* (*organ of Corti*) is a complicated neuro-epithelial structure that rests on the basilar membrane through the entire length of the cochlear duct (Fig. 327). Like the other neuro-epithelial structures, it consists of supportive or sustentacular and hair cells (Figs. 328 and 329). Fibers of the cochlear division of the auditory nerve enter the base of the modiolus and extend up the central canal to the apex. Within the central canal the nerve gives off bundles of fibers which go to the base of the bony spiral lamina where they synapse with the bipolar cells of the spiral ganglion. Networks of fibers from the ganglion cells are distributed around the hair cells of the spiral organ (organ of Corti).

THE MECHANISM OF HEARING

Sound waves directed into the external auditory meatus strike the ear-drum and set it to vibrating. The auditory ossicles transmit the vibrations across the middle ear cavity to the oval window, the entry to the inner ear. At the oval window the vibrations are converted to pressure waves in the perilymph. These waves are transmitted through the perilymph in the scala vestibuli and they set the thin Reisner's membrane, which forms the roof of the cochlear duct, to vibrating. This in turn sets up waves in the endolymph and starts the tectorial membrane and the basilar membrane vibrating, thus stimulating the hair cells of the spiral organ (organ of Corti). The stimulation of the hair cells sets up impulses that are conveyed by the fibers of the auditory nerves to the brain where they are interpreted as sound. If the original sound waves are of great magnitude such as would be produced by a very loud noise, the pressure waves produced in the perilymph would also be large. In this case they would spread from the perilymph of the scala vestibuli through the length of the cochlea, through the helicotrema to the perilymph of the scala tympani, and from there to the round window. Both the helicotrema and the membrane of the round window serve to "damp off" the waves and prevent injury to the spiral organ (organ of Corti).

Detailed discussion of the mechanisms involved in hearing can be found in any good textbook of physiology, and students having a particular interest in this area are urged to refer to such a text.

THE EYE

The organ and structures associated with the sense of vision are: the eyeball—the organ of vision—and accessory strutcures: eyelids, lacrimal apparatus, fascia, conjunctiva (the mucous membrane covering the eye), and ocular muscles.

THE EYEBALL (ORGAN OF VISION)

The eyeball is the highly specialized end organ for the reception of visual stimuli (Fig. 330).

There are special terms used in reference to the eyeball.

1. Anterior pole—the central point of the anterior corneal curvature.

2. Posterior pole—the central point of the posterior curvature of the posterior segment of the eyeball.

3. Axis of the eye (ocular axis) (Fig. 330)—an imaginary line extending between the anterior and posterior poles.

4. Visual axis (Fig. 330)—an imaginary line between an object being observed and the fovea centralis, the retinal area of most acute vision.

5. The equator—an imaginary line around the eyeball, midway between the two poles.

6. Meridians—circles drawn around the outer surface of the eyeball and passing through both poles.

LOCATION OF THE EYEBALLS. They are located in the fat-filled bony orbital cavities in the upper part of the face, one on each side of the root of the nose. A thin, fibrous membrane, the ocular fascia (capsule of Tenon) separates the eyeball from the orbital fat.

SHAPE. The eyeball appears quite round, but if it is cut in a mid-sagittal plane, it is seen to be formed by portions of two spheres of different sizes. The larger sphere forms the posterior four fifths of the eyeball, referred to as the *posterior segment,* and the smaller sphere forms the anterior one fifth, referred to as the *anterior segment.* The structures of the walls of the two segments, however, are continuous.

DIVISIONS. As stated above, the eyeball is first divided into segments corresponding to portions of the two spheres which form it. The next subdivision involves only the anterior segment, which is subdivided into two communicating *chambers* by the iris. The area in front of the iris and lens and behind the cornea is called the *anterior chamber;* the area bordered in front by the back of the iris, at the sides and back by the ciliary body, ciliary processes, suspensory ligament, and lens, is called the *posterior chamber.*

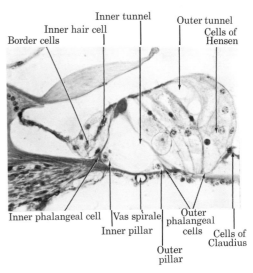

Fig. 329. Section of the human organ of Corti. (From the collection of Dr. Dean M. Lierle.) Photomicrograph.

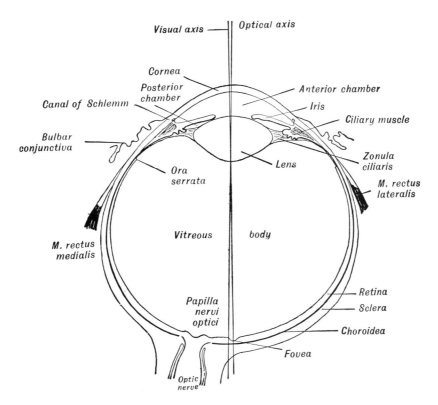

Fig. 330. Diagram of horizontal section through the right eye of man. (From Bloom and Fawcett. *A Textbook of Histology,* 8th ed., W. B. Saunders Company.)

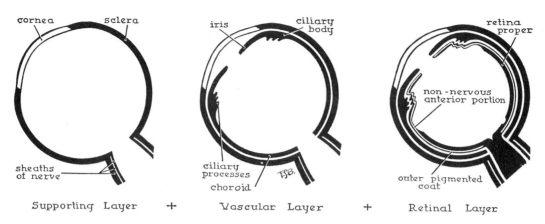

Fig. 331. (Left) Diagram of the supporting coat of the eye. (Middle) Diagram showing the vascular coat of the eye inserted on the inside of the supporting coat. (Right) Diagram showing the retinal coat of the eye on the inside of the outer two coats. (From Ham and Leeson. *Histology,* 4th ed., J. B. Lippincott Co.)

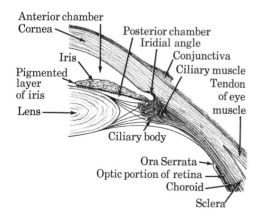

Fig. 332. Portion of a meridional section of the eye, showing the iridial angle.

For purposes of clarity and accuracy, the structure of the walls of the two segments of the eyeball will be considered separately.

WALL OF THE POSTERIOR SEGMENT. The wall of the posterior segment consists of three coats or layers—the sclera, which is an outer fibrous layer, the choroid or middle layer, and the retina or inner layer (Fig. 331).

The *sclera* is the outer, dense fibrous, opaque layer that encloses the posterior segment of the eye. It is continuous with the cornea of the anterior segment. Along its anterolateral surface it affords attachment for the ocular muscles. Posteriorly, the fibers of the optic nerve perforate the scleral coat. This small perforated area is called the *lamina cribrosa.*

The *choroid* is the pigmented, vascular, middle layer. The anterior extension of the choroid forms the ciliary body and the iris. At its junction with the ciliary body, the iris leaves the wall of the eyeball and projects inward, at the side of and in front of the lens (Figs. 331 and 332). In the ciliary body is the ciliary muscle (muscle of accommodation). By its contraction or relaxation the ciliary muscle exerts a pull on the suspensory ligament of the lens capsule and thus effects changes in the curvature of the lens. The iris is a thin fold of the ciliary body. It is the "colored" part of the eye that covers most of the lens except for a circular area in the center called the *pupil.* The actions of smooth muscle fibers in the iris increase or decrease the diameter of the pupil.

The *retina* is the innermost layer of the posterior segment. It consists of a visual or optic portion and a thin, non-visual or non-optic portion. The change from the visual to the non-visual retina occurs suddenly and is marked by a decrease in the thickness of the layer. The point at which this change occurs is called the *ora serrata* and is very close to the posterior limit of the ciliary body (Figs. 330 and 332).

The visual retina is a thick, soft, fragile layer composed almost entirely of nerve elements. It contains specialized cells, the *rods* and the *cones* (Fig. 333), which are the receptor cells for visual stimuli. Also present are ganglion cells whose fibers form the optic nerve. The supportive structures of the retina are modified neuroglia elements. Actually, the retina is subdivided into ten layers (Fig. 333). The layer nearest the choroid is a layer of pigmented epithelial cells. The next is the layer of rods and cones; they are covered by the remaining eight layers, through which stimuli (light waves) must penetrate to activate the rods and cones. The distribution of rods and cones is not uniform throughout the retina. In the back portion of the eye, just lateral to the posterior pole, there is a thickened, yellowish, oval area called the *macula lutea,* in the center of which is a small depression containing only cones. This small depression, called the *fovea centralis,* is the area of most acute vision. (See Fig. 330, p. 299). Laterally, the number of cones is decreased and the number of rods is increased. Rods are effective for vision where the light is much reduced as at dusk or at night or in a darkened room.

The nerve fibers that form the optic nerve converge toward a small area in the posterior segment of the eye, a short distance to the nasal side of the posterior pole. (See Fig. 330, p. 299.) Here the fibers perforate the wall of the eyeball and emerge as the optic nerve. On the retina, where the fibers converge to form the head of the optic nerve, they form a small, slightly elevated, white, circular area called the *optic disc.* Since it contains no rods or cones, only fibers, the optic disc is the blind spot of the eye.

For details of the microscopic structure of the retina, the student should consult a medical textbook of Histology.

WALL OF THE ANTERIOR SEGMENT. The *cornea* forms the wall of the anterior segment of the eye. (See Fig. 330, p. 299.) It is a continuation of the sclera, but differs from it in that it is transparent and nonvascular, and serves as one of the refractive media of the eye. It consists of a specialized, transparent, dense fibrous connective tissue layer. Its outer (anterior) surface is covered by a mucous membrane (a stratified squamous, non-keratinizing epithelium). The corneal epithelium is actually a part of the conjunctiva that lines the eyelids, which is reflected over the anterior exposed portion of the eye. The inner (posterior) surface of the cornea is covered by a thin layer of mesothelial cells. Both of the epithelial layers rest on and are joined to the cornea by thin, structureless membranes.

REFRACTING MEDIA OF THE EYEBALL. These media include the cornea, the aqueous humor, the lens, and the vitreous humor.

The *cornea* is described above.

The *aqueous humor* is a thin, watery fluid, similar to blood serum in composition, that fills the space between the cornea and the lens of the eye. It is constantly being formed and drained away. It is formed by the capillaries of the ciliary processes primarily, and to lesser degree by capillaries of the iris. It is absorbed from the anterior chamber by way of the trabecular spaces (spaces of Fontana) and then drains into the canal of Schlemm, a venous space near the iridial angle of the eye.

The *lens* is a slightly yellow, transparent, biconvex body located immediately behind the iris and in front of the vitreous humor. The anterior surface of the lens is very slightly convex; the posterior surface is strongly convex. The edge where the two surfaces come together is rounded and is called the *equator.* The midpoint of the anterior surface is called the *anterior pole;* and the midpoint of the

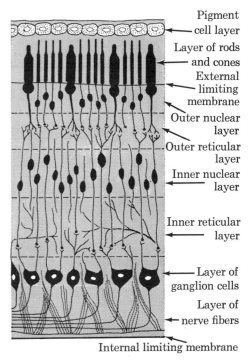

Pigment cell layer
Layer of rods and cones
External limiting membrane
Outer nuclear layer
Outer reticular layer
Inner nuclear layer

Inner reticular layer

Layer of ganglion cells
Layer of nerve fibers
Internal limiting membrane

Fig. 333. Drawing of a portion of the retina of the eye.

posterior surface is called the *posterior pole.* The axis of the lens is an imaginary line drawn between the two poles. The lens is enclosed in a transparent elastic *capsule* and is held in place by the fine fibers of the *suspensory ligament* which extends from the equatorial area of the lens to the ciliary body. Contraction of the smooth muscle of the ciliary body lessens the pull on the suspensory ligament, permitting the lens to become thicker and adapt itself for focusing on near objects. With aging, the lens becomes less elastic and focusing on near objects is no longer possible—corrective lenses are worn to compensate for the failure of the lens to respond for near vision.

The *vitreous humor* (*vitreous body*) is a thick, gelatinous, transparent material that fills the posterior part or segment of the eye behind the lens. A thin, cuticular membrane, the *hyaloid membrane,* separates the vitreous body from the surface of the retina.

BLOOD SUPPLY.   The eyeball is supplied by ocular branches of the ophthalmic artery. The supraorbital artery supplies the rectus superior, levator palpebrae, and obliquus superior muscles. The ciliary arteries supply the levator palpebrae, rectus superior, obliquus superior, rectus lateralis, rectus medialis, rectus inferior, and obliquus inferior muscles.

NERVE SUPPLY.   The eyeball is innervated by the oculomotor nerve which supplies the levator palpebrae superioris, obliquus inferior, rectus superior, rectus inferior, and rectus medialis; the trochlear nerve which supplies the obliquus superior; and the abducens nerve which supplies the rectus lateralis.

ACCESSORY STRUCTURES OF THE EYEBALL

The Eyelids

The eyelids are two thin folds of skin that cover the front of the eye, and when closed, serve to protect it. The upper lid (Fig. 334) is larger and more movable than the lower lid. The outer surface of each eyelid is skin. Beneath the skin is a delicate loose areolar connective tissue layer which is practically devoid of fat. Beneath this subcutaneous tissue is the palpebral portion of the orbicularis oculi muscle, the sphincter muscle that closes the lids (Fig. 334). Beneath the bundles of the striated muscle fibers lies the tarsal plate, a thin, curved, elongated, firm plate of dense connective tissue that gives support and form to the eyelid. The levator palpebrae superioris muscle attaches to the anterior surface of the tarsal plate of the upper lid; its function is to raise the lid. The glandular secreting elements of the elongated sebaceous glands, the Meibomian glands, are located in the tarsal plates. Their ducts empty along the free margin of the lid near its posterior border. The next and final structure of the eyelids is the mucous membrane, the conjunctiva which lines the inner surface of the lids. Along the free margin, the conjunctiva merges with the skin of the outer surface of the lids. Above, along the attached margin of the lids, the conjunctiva is reflected onto and covers the anterior surface of the eyeball. Along the free margin of each lid are three or four rows of coarse curved hairs, the eyelashes. The eyelids can be drawn together over the eyeball and serve to protect it. The involuntary opening and closing of the lids spreads the lacrimal gland secretion (tears) over the eyeball, keeping it moist and at the same time removing dust and other particulate matter from the surface of the eyeball.

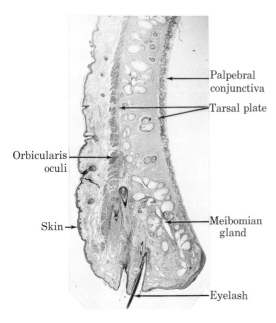

Palpebral conjunctiva

Tarsal plate

Orbicularis oculi

Skin

Meibomian gland

Eyelash

Fig. 334.   Upper eyelid. Photomicrograph.

The Lacrimal Apparatus

Included in the lacrimal apparatus are the lacrimal glands, lacrimal ducts, lacrimal sac, and the nasolacrimal duct (Fig. 335).

THE LACRIMAL GLAND. This is a small compound gland that secretes a thin, watery serous fluid, with a salty taste, the tears. It is oval in shape, about the size of an almond, and lies in the lacrimal fossa of the orbital plate of the frontal bone. Small excretory ducts six to twelve convey the secretion from the gland. The orifices of these ducts open along the lateral margin of the upper eyelid. The tears keep the mucous membrane or conjunctiva of the eye moist, and on occasions flood the surface of the eyeball to wash off irritating particles of matter or chemical substances that may have gotten into the eye.

THE LACRIMAL DUCTS (FIG. 335). A system of lacrimal ducts conveys excess tears from the eyes and empties into the nasal cavity. Each duct system starts as two small epithelial lined ducts, the superior and inferior lacrimal ducts, each of which begins at a small opening called the *punctum,* atop a small *lacrimal papilla* on the free margin of each lid near its medial end. These ducts at first diverge, then each makes a sharp turn to converge and join, forming a very short common duct that empties into the lacrimal sac.

THE LACRIMAL SAC (FIG. 335). This sac is the upper, dilated, blind end of the nasolacrimal duct. It is lodged in the lacrimal groove at the junction of the maxillary and lacrimal bones in the anteromedial wall of the orbit. It is an epithelial-lined structure, roughly 1.25 centimeters long; below, it is continuous with the nasolacrimal duct.

THE NASOLACRIMAL DUCT (FIG. 335). This is an epithelial-lined membranous canal, roughly 1.9 centimeters long, that extends from the lacrimal sac (with which it is continuous) to its termination in the inferior meatus of the nasal cavity. It lies within a bony nasolacrimal canal formed by the maxilla, the lacrimal bone, and the inferior nasal concha. This system of tubular structures drains, by way of the nose, any excess tears that are secreted by the lacrimal glands. This explains why a "drippy nose" and tears usually go together.

The Fascia (Capsule of Tenon) and the Conjunctiva of the Eyeball

The *fascia bulbi* (*capsule of Tenon*) is a thin fascial membrane that encloses the posterior segment of the eyeball. Posteriorly, it merges with the sheath of the optic nerve and the adjacent sclera; anteriorly, it blends with the conjunctiva and together they attach to the eyeball in the ciliary region. Where the orbital muscles perforate the fascia, it is reflected back onto the muscles as *tubular fascial sheaths.* Below the eyeball, the fascias thicken to form the "hammock-like" *suspensory ligament* of the eye. The *conjunctiva* is the mucous membrane layer that lines the inner surfaces of the eyelids (the palpebral conjunctiva) and is reflected over the anterior segment of the eyeball (the bulbar conjunctiva). At the medial angle of the eye, the palpebral portion forms a vertical semilunar fold called the *plica semilunaris.* The angular space formed by the reflection of the conjunctiva from the lids onto the surface of the eyeball is known as the *fornix, superior* or *inferior,* depending on whether the reference is to the upper or lower lid.

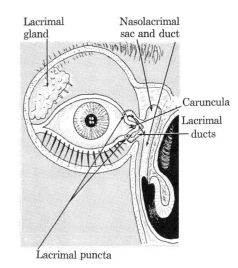

Fig. 335. Lacrymal apparatus of the right eye.

Muscles of the Eye (Ocular Muscles) (Fig. 336)

Levator palpebrae superioris	Raises the upper eyelid
Rectus superior	
Rectus inferior	
Rectus medialis	Move the eyeball within its orbital socket
Rectus lateralis	
Obliquus superior	
Obliquus inferior	

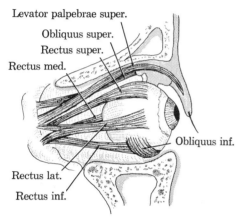

Levator palpebrae super.
Obliquus super.
Rectus super.
Rectus med.
Obliquus inf.
Rectus lat.
Rectus inf.

Fig. 336. Muscles of the eye viewed from the lateral side.

In the posterior part of the bony orbit is an opening, the optic foramen, that transmits the optic nerve and the ophthalmic artery. Encircling the optic foramen and the medial end of the superior orbital fissure, which is just lateral to the foramen, is a ring of dense fibrous connective tissue called the *annulus tendineus communis.* Four of the ocular muscles (the four recti muscles) arise directly from the annulus. The remaining orbital muscles arise from adjacent bony surfaces.

The *levator palpebrae superioris* is a flat, triangular muscle that extends forward above the rectus superior, to the eyelid, where it inserts by three thin, leaf-like fibrous laminae, into the derma of the skin, the tarsal plate and the fibrous connective tissue beneath the conjunctiva of the upper lid. This muscle raises the upper eyelid. Excessive elevation of the lid is prevented by a transverse ligamentous band of fibers attached to the sides of the orbit and to the upper surface of the levator. This structure acts to check the action of the levator muscle.

The *recti muscles (superior, medialis, inferior,* and *lateralis)* extend forward from their origins on the annulus, and insert into the sclera of the eyeball a short distance behind the cornea. Acting alone, each muscle would turn the eye toward the side of the contracting muscle, i.e., the medial rectus would turn the eye medially, et cetera. If the two medial recti contract together, the orbits turn medialward and the person looks "crosseyed." To "look to the right" the right lateral rectus and the left medial rectus contract together.

The *obliquus superior,* from its origin near the margin of the optic foramen above and to the medial side of the superior rectus, extends forward and ends in a long cord-like tendon. At the upper medial margin of the orbit the tendon extends through a fibrocartilaginous ring (trochlea) that acts as a pulley and is attached to the frontal bone. The tendon is then directed backward, laterally, and downward to insert into the sclera of the lateral quadrant of the eye, behind the equator.

The *obliquus inferior* is a narrow muscle that has its origin from the orbital surface of the maxilla, lateral to the lacrimal groove. The muscle extends diagonally backward, upward and around the lateral surface of the eyeball to insert into the sclera opposite the obliquus superior and lateral to the rectus superior.

Contraction of the oblique muscles causes the eye to rotate on its ocular axis. The superior oblique rotates the eye medially, directing it downward and laterally; the inferior oblique rotates the eye laterally, moving it upward and laterally.

THE ORGAN OF TASTE

The organ of taste consists of small clusters of modified epithelial cells called *taste buds.*

LOCATION. Taste buds are found most commonly in the epithelium of the vallate papillae of the tongue, and to a lesser extent in the epithelium on the adjacent wall of the furrow, in the epithelium covering the upper surface and the sides of the tongue, on and between the fungiform papillae, on the under surface of the soft palate, and on the laryngeal surface of the epiglottis.

SHAPE. Taste buds have been described as resembling a Japanese lantern in shape. Each taste bud communicates with the surface by way of a small pit-like opening in the surface epithelium, called the *gustatory pore.*

STRUCTURE (FIG. 337). A taste bud is made up of two kinds of cells—the *outer sustentacular* or *supportive cells* that enclose and support the *inner neuroepithelial cells,* the *taste cells* (*gustatory cells*) that are epithelial cells modified for the reception of gustatory sensations. The sustentacular cells are shaped like barrel staves, and extend from the central part of the base of the taste bud to the margin of the gustatory pore. The gustatory cells are long, slender, spindle-shaped cells. From the free end of each cell a stiff hair-like process projects into the gustatory pore. Fine nerve fibrils enter the base of the taste bud and terminate in small club-shaped enlargements that contact the gustatory cells.

NERVES OF TASTE. The chorda tympani conducts taste impulses from the anterior two thirds of the tongue. The glossopharyngeal conveys taste sensations for the posterior third of the tongue. The vagus carries fibers for taste from the taste buds of the epiglottis.

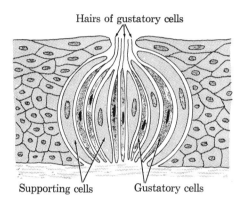

Fig. 337. Taste bud.

THE OLFACTORY ORGAN

The olfactory organ is really not an organ in the sense that the eye or the ear is an organ. Rather, the receptor cells for the sense of smell are part of a modified, specialized epithelium, the *olfactory epithelium,* that forms a small portion of the nasal mucosa.

LOCATION. The olfactory epithelium covers the roof and the upper part of the walls of the nasal cavity.

DESCRIPTION. The olfactory region appears yellowish-brown in color and is readily distinguished from the reddish-colored respiratory epithelium which lines the greater part of the nasal cavities.

STRUCTURE. It consists of a fairly thick, pseudostratified columnar type of epithelium with three types of cellular components—*sustentacular* or *supportive cells, olfactory cells,* and *basal cells.* The sustentacular cells are numerous. The superficial or upper part of each cell is broad, elongated, and cylindrical. This portion contains the nucleus, pigment, and longitudinal rows of granules. The basal portion of each cell is long, slender, and forked. These forked processes serve to anchor adjacent sustentacular cells together and to the underlying stroma of connective tissue. The basal cells lie between the basal processes of the sustentacular cells and are pyramidal in shape.

The olfactory cells, scattered between the sustentacular cells, are actually bipolar ganglion cells (first order neurons). Each cell consists of an enlarged basal portion containing the nucleus. From this enlarged portion a slender protoplasmic process extends to the free surface of the epithelium where it ends in a number of fine, hair-like filaments, the *olfactory hairs*. From the base of the "cell body" a delicate process, the axon, extends in the opposite direction. Processes of neighboring olfactory cells join to form bundles of fibers that pass through perforations in the cribriform plate of the ethmoid bone and, as the olfactory nerve, extend to the olfactory bulb where they synapse with the second order neurons.

The basal cells are small stellate-shaped cells. Their processes anastomose with processes of adjacent basal and sustentacular cells to form a supportive protoplasmic network.

Pseudostratified columnar epithelium.

INDEX

(Boldface numbers indicate major discussions.)

307